JOURNEY FOR HEALTH

THEO KOUFAS, PH.D.

with Bernard Shapiro, M.Ed.

D1157286

NATIONAL HEALTH INSTITUTE, INC.
Lakeland, Florida

NOTE TO THE READER

IT IS IMPORTANT TO SEEK THE ADVICE AND GUIDANCE OF A QUALIFIED PHYSICIAN IF THERE IS ANY REASON TO SUSPECT YOU HAVE ANY DEGENERATIVE DISEASES OR SERIOUS HEALTH PROBLEMS.

Any useage of names or nouns of existing products or persons used in *Journey For Health*, should not be recognized as an endorsement from these products or persons.

Published by National Health Institute, Inc.
        P.O. Box 935
        Highland City, Florida 33846

Printed by Daniels Publishing Co.
Cover by Ramona Severn
Cover Photograph by Jeff Blanton
Typesetting by Sheila Huffman-Dailey
Illustrations by Jeff Erickson

TO MY CHILDREN

Michael, George, Brett, Thea, Natasha

and to all the children of the Universe.

I wish you good health, happiness and prosperity.

The children of today are the future dreams of tomorrow.

A WORD ON THE AUTHORS

THEO
KOUFAS, PH.D.

The author is a clinical nutritionist and holds a Doctorate of Philosophy in Nutrition. He is a staff member and counselor for the Family Chiropractic Health Center in Lakeland, Florida, advisor and consultant to Nutri-Bio-Genetics, Inc., president of the National Health Institute, Inc., and he is on the advisory board of the American Institute of Health and Nutrition, Inc.

For the past five years he has lectured, counseled and advised people from all over the United States in the proper balancing of foods. He has designed individual diets for preventing disease and nutritional programs for regaining health. Those who have sought his counseling and advice are doctors, dentists, chiropractic physicians, dietians, nurses, lawyers, a mezzo-soprano singer, teachers, salespersons, executives, engineers, secretaries, housewives and mothers.

He has spent many hours in his kitchen preparing and testing over five hundred recipes found in *"Journey For Health."* He is most noted for his weight loss program, "The Autobahn Diet," a program designed to lose weight safely and naturally by balancing your foods. The diet includes the use of whole cereal grains, fresh fruits and vegetables, seafood and poultry, seeds and nuts, and a host of delicious sweet desserts.

He is the author of *"A Guide To Better Own Your Own Health," "The Food Connection,"* and now *"Journey For Health."*

BERNARD
SHAPIRO

Bernard Shapiro is a graduate of Temple University, B.A., M.Ed. He was the chairman of the foreign language department at Glasboro, New Jersey for a few years.

In 1970 he relocated to Florida, becoming a corporate pilot for a land company with interests throughout the caribbean. This afforded him a first hand opportunity to compare and contrast the dietary themes and relative "wellness" of the so-called lesser developed countries of the Caribbean and South America.

He also lived in Santiago, Chile for three years and became an enthusiastic practitioner of Yoga.

ACKNOWLEDGEMENTS

My deepest appreciation to:
Sensi Sakurazawa, for bringing forth "SHOKUYO."

Special thanks to:
Michio Kushi, for "one grain, ten thousand grains."

To my special friend and loving wife, Cheryl:
I am truly blessed to have found this lady to share my life and dreams. She worked by my side through long days and nights, assisting me in the preparation of recipes, typing and retyping the manuscript and she is a constant source of inspiration to me.

My heart warmed thanks to the following friends who's help made this JOURNEY FOR HEALTH possible:
Nobby Belanger
George Koufas, Senior
Bonita Richards
Margaret Ruppart
Jeanne Semmelroth
David Short
Joel Wollner

I am grateful to all those friends and patients who's individual needs inspired and stimulated the writing of JOURNEY FOR HEALTH!

TK

"THE DOCTOR OF THE FUTURE

WILL GIVE NO MEDICINE

BUT WILL INTEREST HIS PATIENTS

IN THE CARE OF THE HUMAN FRAME,

IN DIET, AND IN THE CAUSE AND

PREVENTION OF DISEASE."

THOMAS A. EDISON

TABLE OF CONTENTS

Your Trip Ticket

WELCOME CENTER

INTERSTATE 1

EXITS

1   **THE DRIVING FORCE** 17
         FOOD CONTROLS THOUGHT

2   **VITAMINS AND MINERALS** 23
         THE PATH OF CONFUSION

3   **DEGENERATIVE DISEASES** 29
         AVOIDING THE ROCKY ROAD

4   **EXPANSION - CONTRACTION** 35
         THE TWO ←→ WAY STREET

5   **HIGH AND LOW RISK FOODS** 41
         LET'S TAKE THE LOW ROAD
         SALT 43

6   **CHANGING LANES NATURALLY** 45
         THE CROSSROADS OF ALTERNATIVES

7   **7 MILE POSTS OF IMPORTANCE** 49
         STOP! LOOK! EAT!
         MOUNTAIN ARK TRADING CO. 50
         YOUR ORGANIC FILLING STATION

8   **THE ROAD MAP** 53
         THE FOUR DIETARY STAGES 55
         TWO WEEKS OF MENU PLANNING 59
         HOLIDAY MENUS 66
         STARTER LIST OF NATURAL FOODS 67
         PASSPORT TO HEALTH 68
         UTENSILS - *The Fork in the Road* 69
         REFINED FOODS SUBSTITUTION LIST 71
         FOOD CHART - *Balancing the Engine* 72

INTERSTATE 2

EXITS

9   **AVOID THE WIDE ROAD** 75
         BEWARE . . . BAD CURVES OF OVEREATING

     THE AUTOBAHN DIET 81

         LOSE WEIGHT SAFELY AND NATURALLY
         AUTOBAHN - *Two Weeks of Suggested Menu Planning* 87

10   **MISO AND TAMARI** 95
THE OCTANE BOOSTERS!
FAT -- BEWARE -- DANGER AHEAD! 97
SOUP STOCK, AND SOUPS. 98

11   **GRAIN GROUP** 117
THE STARS OF THE SHOW!
BROWN RICE - *BEST OF THE GRAIN GROUP* 121
MILLET 131
BUCKWHEAT - *For Heavy Duty Hauling* 136
BARLEY. 138
WHEAT, BULGHUR, CRACKED WHEAT. 141
RYE 144
OATS 146
CORN 148

12   **BREAKFAST** 153
THE HIGH POWER STARTERS!
THE EGG 161

13   **LUNCH** 163
THE MID-DAY CRUISE

14   **NOODLES** 175
GRAINS IN THEIR MODIFIED CLASS

15   **BEAN POWER** 179
WHEN BETTER BODIES ARE BUILT,
BEANS WILL BUILD THEM

16   **SPROUTS AND SPROUTING** 187
THE ASSEMBLY LINE

17   **TOFU - TEMPEH -** *Have it Your Way* 189
THE CONVERTIBLE BEAN

18   **VEGETABLES** 197
THE POWER ACCESSORIES

19   **SALADS** 215
AUTOMATIC TRANSMISSIONS
TO SMOOTH YOUR ROAD

20   **SEA VEGETABLES** .221
THE HIGH DETERGENT POWER

21   **SEAFOOD AND POULTRY**. 229
OPTIONAL EQUIPMENT

22   **SAUCES - SPREADS - SALAD DRESSINGS - SANDWICH MIXES**. 239
POLISH, SHINE AND GLAMORIZE

23   **CONDIMENTS** 251
PIN STRIPPING - *The Crowning Touch*

24   **CREATIVE DESSERTS AND BASIC BREADS**. 255
FROM MODEL "T" TO THUNDERBIRD
SNACK LIST 276
THE PIT STOP

25   **BEVERAGES** 277
THERMOSTATIC CONTROL

26   **PICKLING** 283
THE WHOLESOME ADDITIVE
GLOSSARY 287
BIBLIOGRAPHY 291
INDEX 293

Foreward

by DR. MABBETT K. RECKORD, III, D.C.

Good day and welcome, my friends, to the new age of *BALANCE* and beneficial nutrition. There was no great heralding of trumpets or sounding of loud drums to announce the arrival of A JOURNEY FOR HEALTH. You have probably noticed some people who are simply struggling for survival, while others are calm, serene and embued with the true essence of life. Why has it come to be that way? This book has come at a time when 1 out of 2 Americans die of heart disease, 1 out of 4 of cancer, and fully 30% of the population suffers from the ill effects of severe obesity. It is time for you to take a good hard look at what you eat and how you are affected by the foods you eat.

As a practicing physician, I see many patients whose ailments consist of nothing more than having a body that has become nutritionally weak. They are unable to cope with and handle the stress and strain of our high pressure society. These people are not only the high pressure executives, the salesman trying to make his quota, and the man on the street, but also the common laborer, as well as the person who recently waited on you at the fast food counter. Poor nutrition affects everyone, even physicians and health advocates, like Mr. Pritikin, known for his diet, and Mr. Fixx, known for his jogging and exercise program. Their solutions to health are too narrow and sometimes extreme.

The person who practices a *BALANCED* nutritional program is the one who immediately commands the attention of everyone with whom they come into contact. You can see the sparkle in their eyes, the smoothness of their skin, and feel the vitality and energy they radiate. They are usually slender without being skinny. Their energy and vitality comes from the selection of high quality foods that are prepared with *BALANCE* in mind.

Dr. Theo Koufas, PhD, has dedicated his life to the goal of establishing methods and diets to benefit mankind. During the past several years, I have watched him take the basic, sound principles of nutrition, *BALANCE* and spice them with philosophies of seasonal selections, together with the preparation of foods, and adopt them to our American Culture. I have watched him use the *BALANCE* of foods to cause far reaching beneficial effects on human behavior and health. Through this book, *BALANCED* eating will become an exciting journey. By following the recipes in this book, your well being, as well as the well being of your children, will undergo a smooth, easy, and exciting transformation to better health.

I can relate from first hand experience the beneficial qualities of this nutritional program. Not only has my family benefited from *BALANCED* eating, but so have many of my patients. By introducing whole cereal grains into the diet, together with basic *BALANCED* eating, remarkable changes do occur.

My story is a good example. Just over five years ago I married Luann. We were a typical newly wed couple. Our daily diets consisted of scrambled eggs, pizza, and spaghetti. Like a typical American couple, neither of us could cook nor gave a thought to our nutritional needs. Our previous dietary habits were so poor that the result was congestion and stagnation throughout our bodies. This was brought about by the heavy consumption of cheese and dairy products we had consumed over the years. In addition, this poor dietary habit was a cause for my wife's infertility. This was a deep blow to us, as we desperately wanted to raise a family.

The turning point in our lives was the day Luann convinced me to accompany her to a nutritional seminar in Lakeland, Florida which was being conducted by Dr. Theo. After hearing him speak, we immediately made an appointment for consultation. After listening to us explain our dietary habits, he made some very basic and easy to follow dietary recommendations, which we coupled with *BALANCED* eating. The beauty of his program is its flexibility. The program allowed our bodies to work again, but best of all, Luann was able to conceive. Our daughter Ashley is now 18 months old and in the best of health. It is my firm belief that Ashley's birth could never have taken place had we not followed Dr. Theo's dietary recommendation. The small effort we made towards learning *BALANCED* eating was well rewarded. Ours is a sample story of success.

Since that time, I have referred several of my patients for consultation. One of my patients is a federal employee who had suffered from a mild form of skin cancer his entire life. This form of cancer breaks out all over his body, resulting in constant visits to the surgeon to have lesions burned or surgically removed. I referred him to the program. After two months of *BALANCED* eating his condition was brought under control. The dietary recommendations freed him from the pain and discomfort that made his daily existence nothing more than a constant effort. He has since achieved a black belt in martial arts and looks and feels the finest he has in his entire life. One of the key elements in both of our successes was that of family participation in the experience of *BALANCED* eating.

Another case in point, that I can personally relate to you, is that of my father-in-law, who was beset by cancer from head to toe. He ran the gamit from lung and head surgery to radiation and chemotherapy treatments, until he reached the point that his broken and debilitated body could take no more. This is not to say that *BALANCED* eating is a cancer cure all, but a *BALANCED* diet was able to provide my father-in-law with a calm, serene, and painless last eight months of his life. This was something he was unable to experience for years, because of the pain and torture which are the side effects of conventional cancer treatment.

A further example of *BALANCED* eating, as a treatment of cancer, is that of Dr. Anthony J. Sattilaro, M.D., President of Methodist Hospital, Philadelphia, Pennsylvania, and author of *Recalled by Life.* His body was ravaged by cancer, and has successfuly recovered through adherence to *BALANCED* eating. His story is told in his book.

The point of the preceeding case histories is that *BALANCED* eating is a blueprint which enables you to take charge of your own body and health. Most Americans are guilty of offering themselves blindly to the work of the "healing physician," who, unfortunately, does not always solve your health problems. Mother nature has provided our bodies with self-healing mechanisms, which modern medicine and technology cannot reproduce. These self healing mechanisms are often disrupted or hindered through the use of prescription drugs or medications.

A JOURNEY FOR HEALTH will explain how the body should function properly; how this process is disrupted by the ingestion of over-doses of dairy products; how lethal doses of toxins are introduced by heavy meat consumption; how the kidneys are over worked and improperly utilized through the daily consumption of eight to twelve glasses of liquids or juices; and how the body ingests empty calories from the average yearly consumption of one hundred forty seven pounds of sugar.

It becomes readily apparent that a little *BALANCE* is required in order to reach the level of harmony for which society is desperately searching.

JOURNEY FOR HEALTH is a force that can dramatically alter your way of living. However, like all new adventures, it can be an experience of the magnitude of whatever you make of it: painful and frustrating, or fun and rewarding. There is no doubt in my mind that the benefits far outweigh any unpleasantness. It is going to take a willingness to experiment with these foods and these principles of *BALANCE* to discover which direction is best for you.

Like all cooks, we had no choice but to laugh hysterically at some of the failures we had created in our kitchen. The point is: take a chance; dare to take a step forward towards good health. Declare today that you want control of your health and your body, now. Once you take that first step forward to a journey for health, you will be amazed at how rapidly it all falls into place.

ENJOY!!!

WELCOME CENTER

Welcome on your **JOURNEY FOR HEALTH**, the book you have waited for so patiently. The BOOK of the 90's!! Congratulations! We are glad that you have accepted our invitation and have made the decision to journey with us. You have taken the first step and will be joining a select and unique group of people who have made a choice to be masters of their own health by changing some old eating habits. Please hold on to your invitation, at the end of this trip, you may choose to turn it in for your **PASSPORT TO HEALTH!** (See Exit 8)

Are you tired, confused, and frustrated with all the books promising you the ultimate in diets and the fountain of youth? Of course you are! Yet, I know you want to eat better and to feel good about what you are doing for yourself and your family.

The purpose and mission of *Journey For Health* is to help you become aware of the natural alternatives available to you for better health through cooking with sound nutritional principles.

At this point I would like to introduce your tour guide and attendant, Cheryl. She will be asking you some pertinent questions and together you will find the answers along the way. Stay alert for the latest updated health bulletins.

Good day Ladies and Gentlemen, and a special Good Day to all you beautiful boys and girls to whom we dedicate this journey. Please follow me. The first thing we will do on this hot summer day is check your thermostat and, if needed, fill you up with some unleaded tea or some freshly squeezed juice. If you wish to join us, you may get out of your easy chair and go quickly to your refrigerator. You may choose your favorite beverage and snack. Hopefully, after taking this journey, you will stop clogging your engines with junk foods. Please hurry back, there is not much time. Every single second someone out there will die of heart disease.

WOW! That was close. I am glad to see that you all made it back. Please buckle up and fasten your seat belts, you are about to begin your journey.

Drivers, Start your engines! Well, that is to be expected. We knew that we would lose a few of you there. No, Miss. I'm sorry, no tow trucks available! No, Sir. We are fresh out of mechanical hearts!

FLASH, NEWS BULLETIN . . . .
Americans currently affected with heart disease: 42,330,000!

Please follow the blue signs leading to the car wash. We will be cleaning your vehicle both inside and out. Many of you have already made some dietary changes in your life. Some of you have made those changes many times and are still searching for the right road. This is understandable since there are literally hundreds of books and diets available from which you may choose, all promising you the pot of gold at the end of the rainbow. You and I know that you have taken many detours along the way, some leading to the "pot around the waist," but not of gold.

FLASH, NEWS BULLETIN . . . .
Americans currently affected with birth defects: 12,750.00, mental retardation: 4,640,000!

Would you intentionally feed your children any of the products found under your kitchen sink? Of course not! All those products contain poisons, additives, acids, corrosives and chemicals. All are non-food. Do you read the labels on your store bought foods? Are you feeding yourself and your family the contents of packages and cans which list ingredients you can't even pronounce, let alone know what they are? *Journey For Health* will guide you through this dilemma by helping you learn how to choose and prepare nutritious, whole foods without the worry of ingesting carcinogens, dyes, additives, preservatives, chemicals and toxins.

FLASH, NEWS BULLETIN . . . .
Americans currently affected with cancer: 4,640,000!

Ladies and Gentlemen, can I have your attention please? We have arrived at the car wash. You will now shift into neutral gear, please remain in your seats with seat belts fastened. Do not open your doors and windows until the vehicle comes to a complete stop. Do any of you or your family members have high stress jobs and never find time to eat properly, which all contributes to hypertension?

FLASH, NEWS BULLETIN . . . .
Americans currently affected with high blood pressure: 37,000,000!

While we are all in line waiting our turn to have our vehicles cleaned, I would like to share with you my personal Journey for Health.

At 39 years old, I believe myself to be a healthy, vibrant wife, mother and total woman. Not so, a few years ago. At age 21, I was in a car that was struck by a moving train. Since I was not Superman, I was not able to leap tall buildings, and, in this case, stop a speeding locomotive. It took eighteen months of surgeries, therapies and lots of love from my mother and father to get me back on my feet. For fourteen years after the accident I was plagued with severe migrain headaches, Bell's Palsy, allergies, aches and pains in my legs and hips and in general ill health. I experienced 4 miscarriages, further complicated by my Rh negative factor. I was medically told that I would never have children. My future looked like a permanent attachment to doctors, medicines, hospitals and a hysterectomy.

FLASH, NEWS BULLETIN . . . . . . :
Americans currently affected with hysterectomies: 800,000

What a pleasant future! At some point, I began reading all the books that were available on nutrition, vitamins, herbs, diets, etc. I read and tried them all. Some of the programs gave me temporary relief, then it was back to the old medicine cabinet. I was a busy, successful, career woman. I owned my own wholesale manufacturing company in Columbus, Ohio and worked 12 - 14 hours a day. I was a slave to the microwave oven, fast foods and fad diets. I never really thought that my eating habits or the food that I was consuming were contributing to my ill health. After all, I had been in an accident, was taking medications and up to 50 different vitamins and minerals a day.

Then I met Dr. Theo, and I began to prepare and eat the foods that were whole, natural and balanced. I threw away the vitamins and medicines, saving me $150 - $200 a month, and within 3 weeks something started to happen. I kept waiting for the migrain headaches, which I "normally" had at least once a week. What a relief! None came and to my surprise, I could breathe in the morning, and I was not experiencing allergy and sinus attacks. Still a skeptic, I was too proud to admit that my eating habits had been wrong. After all, everyone else ate the way I did: canned, frozen. microwave foods. Since the new diet was working, I continued on. As the story goes, I married, and a year and half later, I gave birth to Natasha Nicole Alexandria. What a joy the past 3 years have been, **NO** medicines, **NO** pains and aches, just a peaceful, calm, healthy life and now a beautiful healthy baby girl. I had 9 months of pregnancy with no sickness and I was in labor for only 2½ hours, had natural child birth, and my medical doctor released me from the hospital the same day. I have breast fed my daughter for 9 months. Now I prepare all of Natasha's foods from whole grains, fresh fruits and vegetables and she loves them. Theo and I share the responsibilities in the kitchen and, in addition to our regular meals, we love making our own homemade breads, cookies, pies and cakes. We even grind whole wheatberries to make the whole wheat flour we use in our recipes.

I hear you . . . Ladies and Gentlemen. You all work, right? So do I, helping my husband 8 - 10 hours a day in his practice and traveling with him on his lecturing tours. I take care of the house, laundry, the baby and business and still prepare all the foods. I devote no more than an extra hour a day in the kitchen. I believe that I have found my pot of gold.

FLASH, NEWS BULLETIN. . . . . . .
Americans currently affected with allergies: 35,400,000!

As your windshield dries and your vision clears, you will see directly in front of you the beginning of the rainbow. Are you ready to take responsibility for the quality of life and health for you and your loved ones? Of course you are! I cannot guarantee that you will ever reach the pot of gold, as I am not driving and maintaining your vehicle. I can only point out all the important signs, give you the proper tools, hand you the road maps and show you how to use them to reach your final destination.

FLASH, NEWS BULLETIN . . . .
Americans affected with strokes: 1,830,000!

How many books have you picked up that promise you in 7 short days, you will **cook** like Betty Crocker, **look** like Charlie's Angels and **feel** like James Bond. All of them, right? We can only promise that in 7 short days you may **look** like Betty Crocker, **cook** like Lassie, and **feel** like Mr. Rodgers.

Ladies and Gentlemen, we will be making a brief pit stop. Feel free to turn your motors off, stretch, and take a few refreshing breaths of air. No, I'm sorry Little Jamie, you can't have it your way. There are no golden arches or flame broiled here. But let me offer you some homemade oatmeal raisin cookies or perhaps a piece of freshly baked apple, peach or blueberry pie. Yes, folks, it's time to get back to the basics. A little more time may be needed in the kitchen, perhaps an hour a day, but isn't it worth it?

FLASH, NEWS BULLETIN . . . .
Americans currently affected with diabetes: 11,000,000!

Ladies, **CAN WE TALK?** How many times have you wanted to tell your spouse, I have a headache, or, just pull the nightie down when your done honey! Do you and your spouse lack initiative and sex drive? Has the spark to your engines become sluggish? Do you have a hard time turning on your motor? If you have answered yes to any of the questions that I have posed, and you desire a sexy, healthy, happier, slimmer you, then the journey that follows will help you find the answers.

FLASH, NEWS BULLETIN . . . .
Americans currently affected with arthritis: 31,600,000!

Let us review your trip ticket. In the first phase of your journey, Dr. Theo, will be guiding you through many historical landmarks and adventures. He will be explaining to you how foods control your thoughts. He will be guiding you through the path of confusion on the subject of vitamins and minerals. He will be helping you over the rocky road of degenerative diseases, leading you to the two way street of expansion and contraction and down the low road of high risk foods. You will be receiving directional signals on how to change lanes naturally, then you will **STOP, LOOK AND EAT** at the Seven Mile Posts of Importance. You can fill up at the organic filling station, choose the direction that suits your own personal needs and environment from four different road maps of dietary stages. You will have your tires and engines balanced, pick up a 28 day menu, your starter list of natural foods and utensils.

For those of you who are having trouble putting the seat belt around your waist and wish to rid yourselves of the spare tire, the next phase of the journey will be of extreme importance to you and will show you how to avoid the wide road, the bad curves of over-eating.

FLASH, NEWS BULLETIN . . . .
Americans currently suffering from obesity: 40,000,000!

Place yourself on the exciting and safe **AUTOBAHN DIET.** Meet many people who have traveled down the Autobahn road and have their **PASSPORT TO HEALTH.** Oh, just a minute, here are a few of those people now.

ART DARLING
LAKELAND, FLORIDA

I was a victim of a myth. A myth that men start to put on weight after they hit 40 years of age. It happened to me. I was requiring more sleep, losing my drive and adding pounds at an uncomfortable pace. Various diet tricks did little good. Consumption of a variety of expensive vitamins did not help either.

After my wife started her new eating habits, as outlined by Dr. Theo, to correct a medical problem, I determined to join her more as support than for any personal gain. Much to my delight, I have shed 35 pounds, kept it off for over a year, and regained the level of energy I had 10 years ago.

The best medicine is the right food. Dr. Theo has helped our family find those foods and showed us how to properly prepare them. His book is on the kitchen counter and is used daily in our food preparation. Our food bill has also declined. Many of the most nutritious foods are some of the most inexpensive. I recommend the Autobahn Diet to all my friends.

JANEL THOMASSON
SAFETY HARBOR, FLORIDA

Excuses! Excuses! Excuses! I have used many excuses over the years as to why I was overweight. My mother fed me too well, too much pressure on the job, etc., etc. One could go on forever making excuses. The modern day American way of eating and fast food did not help my problem either.

I was very lucky that the fad diets I tried, (and believe me I tried them all), did not kill me. But there comes a point in one's life that you must take responsibility and "own" your own health. You must also take the time to find out what your body requires. I was very fortunate to find out about the AUTOBAHN DIET.

I had a consultation with Dr. Theo and together we went over my needs. I am the national sales manager for a large toy manufacturer and have a schedule that takes me all over the United States. Through the Autobahn Diet I lost 30 pounds in 7 weeks. Most dramatically everyone wanted to know how I was losing weight and how I could still have the energy to run circles around everyone. The Autobahn Diet has given me the knowledge to eat for nutritional value rather than habit.

I highly recommend the Autobahn Diet to everyone seeking a sound, BALANCED nutritional program to lose weight, increase energy levels and maintain good health.

At the time of my consultation, I was at least 20 pounds overweight, feeling tired and generally not happy with my eating habits. In the past, I tried various diets and other devices in attempts to lose weight and "feel better about myself"; these all failed. When I initially consulted your office regarding my needs, I informed you that I needed some type of dietary change which would not leave me starving or hungry for food and would not give me any significant energy drop.

My life style is such that as an attorney, I require a lot of energy during the day and from a recreational standpoint, I am involved with Tae Kwon Do requiring a great deal of physical energy. It is a definite requirement of mine that whatever dietary change is made would not involve any significant energy drop. To my delight, the Autobahn Diet allowed me to drop almost 22 pounds in 3 weeks and not suffer any energy loss. I also found, to my delight, that the change in my diet allowed me to feel satisfied after each meal and not suffer any type of hunger problems between meals. At this point, my family has seen such a positive change in my appearance and energy level, that they are also making a change in their diets so that they may derive the same benefits.

I would highly recommend the Autobahn Diet to everyone.

The **AUTOBAHN DIET** can and will help you lose weight safely and naturally, give you long lasting energy, allow you to cope and handle stress, reduce your food and medical costs and give you renewed interest and vitality in life.

Step into our kitchen, where you will find that all the foods are wholesome and nutritious. Medical studies and yes, even modern science, are now encouraging the consumption of whole foods to prevent heart disease, cancer and other degenerative diseases. You will be learning how to prepare whole, balanced foods from soups, whole grains, fresh fruits and vegetables, meats, breads and desserts. Over 500 exciting, delicious recipes that are easy to prepare.

FLASH, NEWS BULLETIN . . . .
Americans currently affected with alcoholism: 14,272,000; epilepsy: 2,135,000; cerebral palsy: 750,000; Parkinson's disease: 1,500,000; multiple sclerosis: 500,000. These figures do not include the population that is affected with sexually transmitted diseases and drug addiction.

Do you remember when the price of coffee and sugar got so out of hand? It wasn't until you, the American Public, got together and boycotted the purchase of those products, that the prices came down quickly. **NOW IS THE TIME**, let your voices be heard, start saying **NO**, to the major food industry and see how fast they change their attitude and products to meet your family's health needs.

LET'S GO AMERICA! You are still the greatest! You have the ability to overcome all adversities. Is this not America the beautiful? **LET'S GET STARTED!** You are all packed and ready to go. Have fun, knowing that your journey will be safe and that your life will be a healthy one.

Exit 1
THE DRIVING FORCE

You are about to embark upon an adventure that will lead you to better health and greater happiness: **A Journey for Health.**

Before we begin this exciting new journey of prevention and renewed life, let us first look at some interesting facts and statistics.

Hippocrates, the father of modern medicine, in *Epidemics,* Book I, states many factors to be considered by physicians when diagnosing and treating their patients. First on the list, "What food is given to him (the patient) and who gives it?" Next, conditions of the climate and local environment, the patient's customs, mode of life, pursuits, age, speech, mannerisms, thoughts, sleeping patterns, dreams, and last - but not least - "the notorious physical symptoms."

In his book, *Nutriment,* Hippocrates also declares, "let food be thy medicine and medicine thy food." The Hippocratic Oath, which is still subscribed to by medical doctors states in part: "I will apply dietetic measures for the benefit of the sick according to my ability and judgement."

You will be reading later about how your perceptions and judgement may be altered by various factors, such as chemicals, additives, preservatives, drugs, and dyes. Almost **every-one** is affected by these factors. There are few exceptions; neither butcher, baker, candlestick maker, doctor, lawyer, nor Indian chief are immune.

Returning to the Oath, "I will keep them from harm and injustice. I will never give a deadly drug to anybody, if asked for it, nor will I make suggestions to this effect . . .". Barley cereal grain, along with whole cooked grains, were his favorite remedies. "Smooth, consistent, soothing, slippery, and fairly soft, thirst quenching and easily got rid of; doesn't produce constipation or rumbling or swell up the stomach."

It has been at least 40 years since modern medicine mounted its campaign against cancer and other degenerative diseases, and still 80% of the Americans who died in 1980 were killed either by cancer, cardio-vascular problems, stroke, diabetes, cirrhosis of the liver, or arteriosclerosis. Scientific and medical researchers have pioneered such techniques as radiation therapy, chemotherapy, laser therapy, surgery, hormone therapy, and many, many others. The results, at best, are a temporary relief of the symptom; they have not been successful in **preventing** the diseases.

My purpose in preparing this cookbook and guide to better health is **not** to denigrate our researching scientists nor the medical profession, but to propose an alternative; an alternative which proposes that you can regain and maintain your health and prevent illness and disease by properly balancing your foods.

When you follow the Path of Prevention, you will inevitably ride the road of good health. Those who choose only to follow the **other** path - that garden path of modern medicine and scientific fact-finding methods whose promise has long-been to cure all disease may be short changing themselves. Modern medicine has led us to a body disease relationship that is okay as far as it goes, but leaves out the option of the other dimensions.

It would be so simple if the scientific community would just tell Americans that the body and its proper maintenance is the **individual's responsibility**.

I realize that what I am suggesting may seem a little different at first, but the effort **you** make in accepting responsibility for **your own** health will be made worthwhile within the first seven days of practice. Your body is remarkable and the healing powers inherent within you are astounding!

All of us, for some time now, have been taking our food supply and nourishment for granted with little or no regard to the physiological or psychological effects that foods play in our daily lives. It has been much easier to go to the doctor and have him take responsibility since we "knew no better." **NOW** is the time to assume the responsibility for your own health. You can no longer sit back and look to research. The magic pill simply does not exist.

Add to modern medicine's inability to find cures for these degenerative diseases the dilemma of the cost of medical treatment, which has increased astronomically in the past 10 years. In 1965, the average family of four spent $1950.00 per year for medical services. In 1979 that figure rose to $3500.00. At present, the increased medical costs will reach well over $7000.00 per family in 1985. I recently had a patient referred to me for consultation who, in less than one year, spent over $100,000.00 for treatment of cancer. Radiation, surgery, and the most "modern" techniques were employed in the treatment only to have the cancer recur. It is plain to see that medical spending is out of control with no end in sight. Any success to be found in your **JOURNEY FOR HEALTH IS TRULY UP TO YOU!**

Man cultivates, extracts, and consumes the animals and vegetables from the universe in which he lives. He drinks the waters of the Earth. But he has the power to be selective in his food intake.

FOOD CONTROLS THOUGHT

Eating in a more natural way will bring about a renewed life based upon achieving a **BALANCE** between yourself and your environment. By breathing, we take in air through our respiratory system. Simultaneously, our receptors take in various forms of vibratory nourishment through the largest organ in our body, our skin. Through our sense of touch, we deal with and interpret vibrations which have manifested themselves in solid matter. Our taste organ, the tongue, selectively distinguishes between a wide array of vibrational signals called sweet, sour, bitter, salty, and pungent. Our sense of smell further interprets, identifies, and adds data to the brain. It extracts and absorbs this data from elements surrounding the Awakened Being. Our sense of hearing receives frequencies transmitted through the atmosphere which may be high or low, loud or soft, and which have a wide range of variation. Likewise your eyes, the visual receptors, interpret light waves and translate them into colors, shapes, planes and angles, perceiving the entire spectrum of physical phenomena.

Yet you are being subjected to far more influences than your limited sensory organs can identify. Magnificent as those organs are, we know that there are sounds beyond the range of human awareness. We feel smug in our ability to assess solid matter from empty space, until the physicist tells us that solid matter is really a mass of spiraling atoms. When we come to the realization that something **more** than what we formerly thought existed **does in fact exist**, then we have added to our very own reality. We have, by acknowledging a new idea, facet, or vibration, in essence, **CREATED IT.**

Thoughts become new things which in turn become reality. The child who can name the basic colors adds a new color - perhaps pink - and makes an association. She now perceives the new color and can verbalize it. In her verbal perception she makes the interaction. For her, "pink" then becomes a reality. The research on **our** Journey for Health, has taken us back through many cultural and ancient civilizations, and has led us to study many beliefs related to the physical, spiritual and nutritional needs of the body. All have some validity. You will, as you journey with us, come across some unusual cultural ideologies. Accept them merely as fuel for thought.

We may or may not be aware that we are continually consuming radiation and cosmic waves coming at us from near and far. Nevertheless, these waves do exist. They make contact through the surface of the body - the skin - and some of them transmute into electro-magnetic fields which circulate through our system. They in turn charge cells, glands, and the body's organs. Their charge enables us to move, assimilate, digest, discharge wastes and toxins, breathe, and think. The ancient Indians referred to these waves and electro magnetic fields as a force of energy coming to the body and entering at specific points they called, "Chakras." They believed this charge of energy comes from a celestial force which enters our bodies through the region at the top of our heads, continually moving in a downward direction, while the forces of the earth enters our bodies through the genital region and travels upward. Both forces are running as one channel traveling vertically through the center of our physical bodies and both forces charge the five major areas in between the **seven** major charging places in the body. Ancient Indians called these seven points "Chakras." The **spiracle** region at the top of the head and the genital region are, respectively, the entrance and exit points of this energy flow. The five remaining Chakras in between are:

1. The midbrain area, where the energy charge is distributed to millions of brain cells.
2. The throat region, where energy flow activates saliva, vibrates the uvula and the tongue, in addition to activating the thyroid and parathyroid glands.
3. The heart, including the action of the heart muscles and rhythmic motion of expansion and contraction throughout the circulatory system.
4. The stomach area, through which energy passes to such organs as the liver, spleen, pancreas, and kidneys.
5. The center of the intestinal area, where the energy charge is distributed to the bladder and regulates the entire operation of both small and large intestines, including digestion, decomposition, and absorption of food and water, and finally passes on to the genitalia, where the energy exits.

If these waves cannot flow undisturbed throughout our system, we may become blocked, causing stagnation to occur, then energy cannot flow smoothly and begins to back up causing pain and soreness.

The quantity and quality of our food and drink, along with our breathing activity, **controls** the function of our energy. This takes place internally as our energy cells are vitalized and charged electro-magnetically by our **bloodstream**. Hence, if we wish to change our consciousness, or develop greater physical coordination, or improve our psychological outlook, we must learn how to consume our food and drink within the environment in which we live. All spiritual, religious, and social disciplines begin with this basic understanding. For example, in the practice of meditation there are many different techniques. Some place emphasis on activating the Chakras of the mid-brain. Zen meditation puts its emphasis on the "hara," which is located at the center of the intestinal area. Christian monasteries practice dietary discipline by eating unleavened bread along with vegetables. Buddhism, as well, practices a cuisine for spiritual advancement.

Among Jewish traditions the practice of "Kasruth" mandates many dietary restrictions. Even before the time of Abraham, the main food of the Jewish people was wheat and other cereal grains. In the book of Leviticus, Moses' dietary teachings and disciplines appeared, showing that unleavened bread and "matzohs" were used for special occasions. Orthodox Jews today observe Kosher laws in which grains, beans, and vegetables are their staple foods. Special cooking is required for meat, poultry, and other animal foods in order to avoid their toxic effects.

Great philosophers and thinkers all practiced their dietary disciplines which were generally based upon natural ways of eating. This is **not something new** but something **for-**

gotten by a society which is laden with chronic physical disorders including cancer, cardiovascular disease, multiple sclerosis, arthritis, allergies, epilepsy, insecurity, fear, sexual inadequacies, and many other degenerative diseases. Have we forgotten something in our search for power, money and technology? Are we responsible for our physiological and psychological condition, or are we just pawns governed by an arbitrary and unknown force predetermining our fate ? "YOU are what YOU eat" - myth or reality? Whether we are healthy and happy - or sick and miserable - on this earth **depends upon ourselves** and no one else. We are masters of our fate and are in full control of our personal destiny. Sickness and death, frustration and suffering, all are created within ourselves.

You can **PROPERLY BALANCE** your diet by choosing and controlling the types of foods; how you combine those foods, how you prepare those foods, selecting foods according to the season and climate in which they are grown, **determines the quality of your own life**.

There are four billion people on planet Earth, yet no two are exactly the same. There are four billion differences being expressed in personal contact and behavior, as well as on a physical and emotional level. One person may be slower in his actions and another faster in his emotions. Some persons are more sentimental, others are more intellectual. One man is more conservative, another more progressive. Everyone has his own unique characteristics. Everyone has his own personal habits. All are different. There are no two alike. When you begin to harmonize your existence with nature and your natural environment, your body and mind realize their optimal level of oneness. The **key** to your well-being is found within your **daily food choices**.

Like a television set which has inferior parts and is therefore unable to receive and project images and sounds coming from a distant station, if your blood becomes stagnant, you are unable to perceive and respond to the waves and vibrations coming to you.

Between organic food and vibrational food, there is an antagonistic yet complementary relationship about which we are now becoming aware. This relationship concerns itself with the quantity and quality of harmony between the two. The more you consume large quantities of food, the less you can assimilate vibrational food. In addition, the more you eat **animal food**, the more material and self-centered you become. The overconsumption of animal food tends to limit your perception and **alter your awareness**. The eating of excessive animal foods tends to cause a more contractive way of thinking, or a narrow and short-sighted view.

The other extreme is rigid vegetarianism. If this practice is based on an emotional concept, or the fear of committing an offense by eating animal flesh, the eating of raw and uncooked foods **exclusively** can create the ultimate expansion and be manifested in scattered ideas and paranoid behavior. We need a correct **BALANCE** between these opposing views. We must consume a wider portion of vegetable quality foods along with some good quality animal foods. This will broaden your mental and psychological attitudes. Foods help us to create our own version of the changing world of people and situations around us. **BALANCE** in your diet leads to harmony between you and the world you live in.

If your consciousness is clouded, it may be due to the change of environmental vibrations, but it may also be due to what you are consuming in your body. We can understand this when we see how some people react nervously and emotionally, yet others maintain a normal response under the same circumstances. This can be explained by the physiological variations that occur through what we consume daily. Different foods cause the blood to form in different ways. However small the difference may be, a slice of cheese, a pineapple, a teaspoon of sugar, a cup of coffee, can delicately change the quality and volume of your blood. When the quality of your blood changes, the quality of the cells in the body as a whole changes. This includes your brain and nervous system, which change automatically, along with the transformation of physiological and psychological functions. Food influences **all** our behavior and our expressions, including our physical movements and habits. Your sensory perception, your emotional response, intellectual conceptions, and your general philosophical view of life are altered as well.

Man is truly a universal eater, being capable of eating many varieties of food. But we also added to our diet artificially processed, synthesized, chemicalized, industrialized and mass produced foods. Modern man has changed the quality of his foods, along with the quality of his blood, in various degrees. Let us not forget the **FROZEN-FRESH** foods, fast-food operations and the ultimate in convenience . . . the micro-wave oven. It is my belief that this so-called advancement in technology will prove, in years to come, to be a most devastating culprit, contributing to all the degenerative diseases.

We eat everything: cereal grain, legumes, beans, seeds, nuts, fruits, vegetables, and many other things. We consume plants in the form of ferns, asparagus, and fungi such as mushrooms, along with a variety of sea vegetables. We even eat the most primitive form of plant life, molds and yeast. Modern man eats of the animal species in the forms of beef, ham, lamb and their by-products milk, cheese, and other dairy foods. We consume birds, chickens, turkey, and duck, frogs and snails, fish from the oceans and rivers, and invertebrates such as shellfish and squid.

We also eat the most primordial life forms: bacteria, enzymes and various forms of virus, in and within all sorts of fermented foods. We consume water and air, especially oxygen, and eliminate part of our used portion of food in the form of carbon dioxide. The intake of air is proportional to the quantity and quality of what we eat. For example, heavy consumption of animal foods inhibits your breathing, and you are forced to inhale much harder. On the other hand, the more vegetable quality food you take in, the more harmonious your breathing becomes, along with achieving a lower blood pressure level. Your respiratory quotient indicates, that if you eat animal food in large volumes, which consists of much protein and fat, the result is rapid and rough breathing. This inadvertently influences your body-mind reaction.

Those who learn the key to good health, and practice a natural way of nutrition, focus their attention upon the principles of **BALANCE**. Like all other beings, man is a transformation of his food.

While some tastes are inherited, many others are acquired early in life. According to an article that appeared in the *Orlando Sentinel Star* on July 23, 1981, children's taste buds are just as developed as those in adults. Dr. Albert Farbman, professor of anatomy at Northwestern University says, "The taste buds are fully functional anatomically before birth, from about the seventh month of gestation." Dr. Leann Lipps Birch, in the other hand states, "Eating habits are basically learned."

If it appears that these two authorities are not in agreement, it would be wise to remember that this "**learning**" may also occur in the embryonic period.

It is common to hear people refer to a child's eating habits and say, "Oh well, he can't help it, it's hereditary." This comment is used by fond parents to excuse and justify everything from overeating to not liking vegetables or to craving sweets.

The distinction between "learned" and "hereditary" here is important. The label "hereditary", which means an inherited tendency, could have been learned differently through **CHANGING THE QUALITY OF BLOOD** during the embryonic period. But this would have meant a different pattern of eating, and some effort on the part of the mother. Prior to conception, the father, also, could have changed the quality of his cells through dietary means . But it is much simpler to throw in the familiar excuse for not making the effort and rationalize that "there's no accounting for taste", or "that's just hereditary." We so easily avoid responsibility.

The food programming that a child gets is also a result of our parental practice of rewards and punishment. We are all too familiar with the parent who says, "If you are good today, I'll let you have an ice cream/candy bar." Surveys say 50% - 60% of parents in this

21

country use these techniques.

Dr. Leann Lipps Birch, associate professor of Human Development at the University of Illinois, Champaign-Urbana, says another kind of reward practice also backfires. "It's what I call instrumental eating. A parent says, 'Eat your carrots then you can go outside and play.' It works reasonably well to increase consumption but paradoxically, it tends to reduce preference." As a result, once the authority figure is removed and the child is free to choose on his own, he is LESS LIKELY to select that food.

By far the best method of programming your children's food preferences is **to change your own eating habits**, and before their birth is the best time to do it. Since exposure is **one** of the basic explanations of preference and so-called "heredity" another, both can be effectively used to encourage **BALANCED** tastes in a child by working on the quality of one's own blood cells before birth, and one's own eating patterns thereafter.

Dr. Derrick Lonsdale, head of the biochemical genetics section of the Cleveland Clinic for Children, warns us against the "junk food phenomenon" and it's associated "marginal malnutrition." Many young people fall victim to this syndrome. Abrasive teen behavior such as hyperactivity, neuroses, personality changes, nervousness, headaches, sleeplessness, chest pain, vomiting and "just plain rude behavior" may be the unrecognized manifestation of partial malnutrition.

He is particularly concerned with the snack items and candy that young persons consume. He states, "Everybody is telling them there is no danger attached to this fast energy. There is a danger. Scientifically, we have reason to believe that this approach to diet is changing the balance of neurological transmission, which is the hallmark of the function of the brain and central nervous system. Soft drink consumption has doubled in the United States between 1960 and 1975. Increasing from an average yearly intake of 13.6 gallons a person to 27.6 gallons a person, the average person drinks approximately 295 12 oz. cans of soda pop containing 21.5 pounds of sugar."

He goes on to say, "I'm referring particularly to what dieticians and nutritionists call naked or empty calories; high in carbohydrate foods which do not contain any vitamin or mineral supportive qualities at all . . ." They are getting a discrepancy between the calories they take and the vitamins and minerals that should support them in order to carry out the oxidating process. The process is very much the same as an internal combustion engine. You say you are all choked up. You cannot "start your motor" in the morning. The energy crisis is within your body. Your oil needs changing? If you stop and read the labels in your local supermarket, notice how the foods are canned, processed, chemicalized, contain dyes, have ingredients that may contain carcinogens, food coloring, cyclamates and many ingredients too difficult to pronounce let alone know what they are. As you read this, a bell should be ringing, telling you that this might be part of the problem. Is it a lack of thinking on our part? Can we think clearly when we are being slowly poisoned? Once we learn to **BALANCE** our natural foods and adjust our way of eating to the seasons, we will have a **BALANCED** body as well as a **BALANCED** mind. You cannot separate the two. One nourishes the other.

Labeling junk food as a factor in many of the cases, Dr. Lonsdale published a paper for the American Journal of Clinical Nutrition. He described twenty patients with "marginal malnutrition, exhibiting behavior such as one who puts his fist through a glass window." Are not these same teenagers who now consume fantastic amounts of cola, candy, chemical foods, cakes, cookies and other junk food, the most likely prospects to grow up and swell our statistics on mental illness? Today there are a staggering **38 million** in this nation alone possessed of some form of mental illness. We are told by the National Institute of Health that fully 15% of our citizens suffer from serious mental health problems, and that those rates are increasing by 5% a year.

It is gratifying to see that no matter what words are used to describe the issue, there is growing awareness that **GOOD NUTRITION** means **BALANCE**. No other phrase so simply sums it up.

22

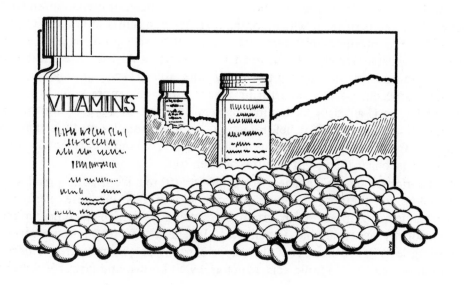

Exit 2
VITAMINS AND MINERALS

The Path Of Confusion

What about vitamins and minerals?

Man is presently sustaining his life with incomplete foods and artificial vitamins. We have never duplicated the perfection that nature provides in **whole foods**, any more than we have been able to create a perfect diamond. Our attempts have produced a product that may fool the eye and please the palate, but it does not have the **quality** necessary to prevent disease. Good health, like a diamond, is more than a temporary absence of disease. It must shine brightly enough to nourish body and mind. A worried person is not healthy; health is a product of the state of your mind, "As man thinketh so he is." Our bodies have lost their natural ability to manufacture vitamins and minerals because of the over-consumption of sugar and the introduction of chemical and synthetic foods to our modern diet.

There is infinite wisdom in the naturally occuring balance of vitamins to be found in whole foods. "Whole" means unprocessed. When you eat whole foods, you have whole nourishment. Mankind has taken his vitamins in this way for centuries. When we try to break down this natural **BALANCE** into separate chemicals and consume our vitamins in artificial supplemental form, the effect produced on our metabolism may be chaotic.

In our health food and drug stores, B-complex vitamins are commonly sold for various conditions of human health. This practice is a direct result of our refined grains, a large quantity of white bread, and bleached, enriched flours. These products do not supply vitamins naturally within your foods.

Journey for Health suggests that by eating whole foods you will be able to maintain a good balance of nutrition in your blood, body fluids, and body cells, and re-establish the body's ability to **manufacture its own** vitamins and enzymes. Except for the marmot and the monkey, animals can manufacture their own vitamin C. You can see why *George Ohsawa,* a Japanese philosopher, felt that we would be able to produce our own vitamin C if we would stop eating large amounts of fruit, which contain excessive amounts of vitamin C.

The Eskimo produces his own vitamin C. Of course he does not eat many fruits since none are available locally. A currently held belief that fruits are the best source of vitamin C is erroneous since many green leafy vegetables, especially kale, collard greens, brussel sprouts, broccoli, parsley, and turnip greens supply far more vitamin C, and they do not lose their vitamin C as easily. Vitamin C is very sensitive to oxygen, and the cutting and juicing of fruit destroys much of it before eating. Another popular myth is that cooking will destroy vitamin C and other nutrients as well. Actually, vitamin C is not easily destroyed unless cooking lasts longer than eight minutes at over 200° F.

It is curious that the Japanese have never suffered from widespread scurvy, a vitamin C deficiency, yet they eat an abundance of cooked foods. Japanese scientists even claim that certain tea leaves contain a pro-vitamin C substance which **becomes** vitamin C **after** heating. Additionally, we find that Bancha tea, Japanese twig tea, contains more vitamin C than the leading leafy green kale. It is also superior to most commercial teas because it does not contain tannic acid. It is tannic acid which is a well-known and powerful **inhibitor** of iron absorption.

There are generally two categories of vitamins: fat soluble, such as A, D, E, and K; and water soluble, including B1, B2, B12, C, Niacin, and Folic acid. When good quality whole grains and vegetables comprise the major part of your daily food intake, there will be a natural and **BALANCED** absorption; No need to worry or be preoccupied with analyzing the amount required. This is the **BALANCED**, centered approach; to eat so that one can live free from analytical, introverted concern. Organic supplements taken while making the **JOURNEY FOR HEALTH** may be a wise choice until the body has adapted to whole natural foods.

If we were to read all that has been written about the inter-relationship of vitamins with other elements in the body, and the processes which affect them in various ways, we would become very apprehensive. For example, one of the most important vitamins in the B-complex is vitamin B-1. A serious shortage can produce loss of appetite, indigestion, colitis, heart trouble, numbness of the fingers or arms, etc. This vitamin cannot be stored in the body. It must be constantly replenished. Dr. McCollum writes that "B-1 is not destroyed by normal cooking if the PH is less than seven" (an acid condition). The situation however, is similar to that of vitamin C. Destroying B-1 by cooking doesn't change the value of the food much, because B-1 will be **destroyed by digestion due to the alkaline condition in your intestines.** Herman Aihara notes, however, that vitamin B-1 can be produced from the cellulose of vegetable foods in the large intestines, with the help of beneficial bacteria. The same is true of vitamin B-6 and B-12. Can you see the wonderful mechanism and constitution of nature in this process? We **can** produce our own vitamin B-1. In addition, the vitamin B-1 contained in the foods you eat, even though destroyed by cooking, still helps in this production even after its decomposition.

Another confusing example to ponder, if you still wish to be analytical, is that of vitamin A. According to modern nutritional theories, animals cannot produce the A vitamins, nor can vegetables synthesize them. Scientists believe that carotene, which plants **do** synthesize, turns to vitamin A in the animal body. They know that exposure to heat and air tends to destroy vitamin A and carotene. But if there is heat only and no air the vitamin is not affected. Now, vitamin A is known to be stored in the liver. Isn't this strange? Vitamin A is not stable in the heat and alkaline conditions, so how can the liver store such high amounts? We know that vitamin A deficiency can cause things like night blindness, poor tooth development, hair and skin abnormalities, and even influence reproductive functions. We also know that too much vitamin A can have a toxic, even fatal effect. Since this vitamin is stored for long periods in the body, its accumulative effects can produce vitamin A poisoning. However, aside from taking this vitamin in supplements, (which frequently contain as much as 100 times the recommended allowances) or in the eating of excessive amounts of animal liver, your chance of this overdosage is not great. A diet that has been centered around whole grains and vegetables will include carrots, squash, broccoli, various beans, apples and corn. These foods do not contain the extremely high amounts of vitamin A present in some other foods, such as liver and spinach. Therefore, they constitute a more balanced source for your real needs. Since vitamin A is able to be dissolved in oil, but not water, a method of preparation of the above vegetables would be light sauteing in vegetable quality, cold pressed oil. (Sesame or corn oil)

Consider the history of one of the first known vitamin deficiency diseases, scurvy, suffered by the Canadian Indians. As reported by Bigger in 1924, they had experienced this disease every winter until they found a cure by eating pine needles. Notice that the remedy was existing in nature as a **locally grown** whole food available to them in their own environment.

Another example of a vitamin deficiency disease is Beri-beri, caused by a lack of vitamin B-1, occuring as a result of the refining of brown rice, again illustrating the disasterous results of man's trying to improve upon whole foods.

Previously mentioned was a long list of symptoms resulting from a diet deficient in this vitamin. In 1897, Eijkman experimentally produced this disease in chickens by giving them only white rice. At that time, he was unable to explain why the feeding of brown rice prevented the disease. Then in 1911, the Polish chemist Casmir Funk succeeded in extracting a crystalline substance from rice polishing which cured Beri-beri. This substance is now called vitamin B-1 or thiamine. Today, there is much use of this separate substance in pill or injection form. At first these pills worked very quickly; however, since the B vitamin must be replenished in our bodies daily, (remember they are water-soluble) it is much better to consume this vitamin in the form of whole foods. It is readily available in the outer layers of whole grains, and your body is **designed** to break down whole food to obtain the elements it needs. Many people, however, are incapable of digesting the B vitamins, because their intestines lack the beneficial bacteria which make digestion possible. This has been brought about by the over-consumption of chemicals, food additives, alcohol, and disaccharide sugars. To correct this and bring about balance, if prior eating habits were faulty, it is advisable to eat any of the following products daily: 1. Miso soup   2. Whole Wheat sourdough bread   3. Rice bran   4. Homemade pickles   5. Tamari (soy sauce). They will all help to strengthen the intestines and provide the necessary flora, as well as supplying the missing B vitamins. Please note, that rice bran is that nutritious outer part of the grain which is **thrown away** in order to reduce brown rice to white rice. Oh, Uncle Ben, what have you done to our people in the name of convenience?

In *"Man The Unknown,"* Alexis Carrel says, "Man is literally made from the dust of the earth. For this reason, his physiological and mental activities are profoundly influenced by the geological constitution of the country where he lives, by the nature of the animals and the plants that he eats, and the Ph level of the soil his food is grown in."

VITAMIN D:

Now we come to the biggest myth of all, the one called "vitamin" D. Most people are not aware that there are over twenty chemicals in the group generally referred to as vitamin D. They are all in a chemical class known **not** as vitamins but **steroids**. Steroids include adrenal hormones, and the important difference between the two is that hormones ARE produced naturally in plants and animals.

These D chemicals all differ in minor respects chemically, but in biological activity their differences are enormous. Only one of these chemical analogues is native to the human body and compatible to its biological needs. It is referred to as vitamin D-3, and it occurs in conjunction with vitamin A and cholesterol in the yolks of eggs, the cream of milk, fish oils, and sesame seed oil. Vitamin D-3 is also created when the oils in your skin are exposed to the ultraviolet rays of sunlight.

The main function of vitamin D is to enable you to build and maintain strong bones. Shortly after the turn of the century, when discoveries of dietary deficiency diseases were becoming well known, it was reasoned that since cod-liver oil was a specific cure for rickets in children, (rickets being a disease that produces bowed legs and sunken chests due to improper bone formation), that rickets must be due to a vitamin D deficiency. Actually, rickets has never been induced in laboratory animals by the feeding of a diet deficient in vitamin D. Instead, it was always induced by imbalanced diets with regard to their calcium and phosphorus intake.

Rickets was, more correctly, an air-pollution disease, (and perhaps the first one known to man) since sunlight is necessary for the body to make its own vitamin D-3. This was essential due to the very limited occurence of D-3 in the human diet, and in industrial nations smog and air pollution were creating more and more instances of rickets.

Originally, the successful treating of this disease by cod-liver oil was also accompanied by the use of direct ultra-violet radiation of milk. During the period when milk was being enriched by the natural hormone, the so-called vitamin D-3, there were no cases of toxicity in infants due to vitamin D sensitivity. All that was soon to change.

During the 1950's, medical science was to observe the emergency of a new illness of infancy characterized by very high levels of blood calcium and accompanied by increased cholesterol levels in the blood. They called this new illness "idiopathic hypercalcemia." One interesting thing about it was, that it might go undetected during infancy, only to be manifested as mental retardation in later life.

Remember too, that during the 1930' and 1940's, coronary heart disease also began its upward swing as the nation's #1 cause of death. There are readily verifiable facts that show that the elimination of the childhood disease rickets coincides with the increase of coronary diseases.

To begin to see the culprit here, we must know one more important fact. Toward the end of the 1920's, some brilliant nutritionists urged fortification of foods with vitamin D. Reasoning, of course, that we should permanently wipe out the problem of rickets. Then politics and economics came into play. It was found that instead of the expensive process of exposing the **milk itself** to ultra-violet radiation, one could expose **yeast cells** to ultra-violet light. They would multiply quickly and be very easy to grow. This was the method, which is extremely expansive, and not in **BALANCE**, used to reproduce the vitamin D fortifier used. This particular chemical is called D-2. It was much cheaper to manufacture D-2 than the naturally occurring D-3. Many researchers warned about the use of D-2 instead of D-3, but they largely went unheeded. In fact, by the time of the Korean conflict, chronic poisoning had become so common, (due to the "fortification" of the soldiers' C-rations) that 80% - 90% of young men killed in battle showed, on autopsy, cardiovasular degeneration, having calcium and cholesterol deposits in their arteries.

Now, a number of animal experiments have clearly shown that even relatively small amounts of vitamin D-2 can increase cholesterol and produce calcification. As previously mentioned, the emergence of hypercalcification in infants seems to correlate with the change in the form and method of supplying vitamin D. Dr. Helen Taussig, of John Hopkins Hospital, is one noted authority who suggested a causal relationship between excesses of vitamin D and heart disease.

To further understand the very important relationship of vitamin D and cholesterol, one should know that vitamin D-3 is the **natural** calcifying hormone (called calciferol). Evidence in biochemical literature indicates that D-3 may be a fundamental hormone **regulating** cholesterol metabolism, as well as calcium hemostasis, and vitamin D-2 often **interferes** with this natural hormonal mechanism. In addition, despite the widespread use of D-2 fortified foods, which include milk, some beer, candy, bread, margarine, and cereals, there has been **no reduction of any known adult illness.**

Unfortunately, despite a memoradum sent by the F.D.A. over twelve years ago which requested a restriction of vitamin D to 400 I.U. as the recommended daily intake, it is still possible to purchase D supplements in stores without a prescription, and many multi-vitamin supplements sold commercially contain as much as 2,000 I.U. of D-2. At present the F.D.A. is again acting on a proposal to limit the over-the-counter supplements, but at the same time a counter-proposal is being considered to make mandatory the fortification **of all milk with vitamin D-2!** This is very dangerous, because vitamin D is much more toxic in milk than in an oil base. In fact, where 10 - 15 drops of vitamin D in oil were needed to cure rickets, only 1 drop was necessary if it was incorporated in milk. In fact, there are already cities where it is impossible to obtain milk without vitamin D-2 "fortification."

If, as many researchers believe, vitamin D-3 is also a regulating hormone for calcium levels in the body, (and this would explain its increased effectiveness in milk) then we might begin to see a relationship between the current uses of vitamin D-2 as a substitute for D-3 and the unnatural deposits of calcium in various parts of the body. Many physicians know that most major diseases have a tendency to occur in conjunction with one another and, in a sensitized human, any inherent weakness in a body organ may result in calcium deposits in the weakened tissue. This may lead to the formation of kidney stones and gall stones.

The American diet is already rich in calcium. Calcium in its native form is generally bound to organic phosphorus compounds and, unless the bonding is broken, passes into waste without being absorbed. Our national practice of "enriching" foods with calcium, and particularly with an inorganic form, which is absorbed more readily, is a large contributor to the damaging results to public health.

One last culprit in our search to understand the pieces to the puzzle is the depletion of magnesium from our diets. In refined foods, from 50% - 100% of the native magnesium is destroyed and **a magnesium deficiency accentuates** the toxicity of vitamin D-2.

A balanced view shows that we consume excessive amounts of vitamin D-2 and calcium in unnatural forms. Yet we suffer from deficiencies in magnesium. These, and other man-created imbalances, are destroying your immunity system, as it attempts to maintain the equilibrium required for GOOD HEALTH.

Nature provided clues to her wisdom for us to observe. Notice how inhabitants of very sunny countries are provided with darker skin pigmentation to limit and regulate their vitamin D hormone. On the other hand, in polar regions where less sunlight is available, inhabitants are light skinned and can thus maximize sunlight absorption. Nature also provided the Eskimo and far north inhabitants with a large supply of fish and fish oils in their diets to supply even more vitamin D-3.

If we want to help nature in her war against sickness, we will avoid **regular daily** consumption of **dairy** and other foods **which contain vitamin D fortification.** War on nature is no different than war on nations. If we learn this now, it may not be too late. Diary products should be consumed in moderation.

When you focus your attention on eating whole cereal grains, beans, locally grown vegetables, seeds, nuts, and moderate amounts of fruits and animal foods, you will achieve a natural **BALANCE** within your body.

Testimony

DR. ELIZABETH HUNTLEY, PH.D.
LOS ANGELES, CALIFORNIA

I met Dr. Koufas when I had my practice as a nutritional consultant in Largo, Florida. I have observed in my years of practice, that vitamin and other nutritional supplements were not the answer to health, increased vitality and weight control. I was still searching for a complete health program.

The Autobahn Diet provided what I was looking for, a balanced dietary program based on wholesome foods. A program for my patients. This program creates a natural balance in the body that allows the body's natural regulatory system to bring about good health and proper weight control. I believe that fad diets may bring about quick weight loss, but this is achieved by throwing the body's metabolism into an imbalance, thus destroying the control systems.

I use the Autobahn program myself and have lost 13 pounds, and refer my patients to Dr. Koufas. I make extensive use of his book in my practice. This book is actually much more than a cookbook, it is a guide to help you on your journey for a healthy life.

Exit 3
DEGENERATIVE DISEASE

Avoiding The Rocky Road

There are generally four different types of sugar: glucose, sucrose, fructose, and lactose. Carbohydrates are generally known as sugars. When speaking of sugar we should be more specific.

The first and most beneficial form of sugar, from a **BALANCED** point of view is glucose. Glucose is found in grains, beans, and many vegetables.

For smooth, undisturbed body-mind activity, you should take in carbohydrates in your daily food in the form of glucose. A POLYSACCHARIDE GLUCOSE, which is a complex sugar, decomposes gradually in your system, and in turn allows your metabolism and your activity to maintain its level of energy much longer. By consuming glucose, your excess sugar is stored in the liver. When the body needs more sugar, the liver secretes it in small, even dosages. This results in a more calming and soothing effect on your body-mind interaction.

The Dietary Goals for the United States , and the Surgeon General's **Report on Health Promotion,** have also recommended re-establishing complex carbohydrates as the basis of our diet. For example, in the rice plant, each grain is composed primarily of starch, in the form of polysaccharide glucose. (you may call this "a complex carbohydrate") Proteins, minerals, and fats contained in rice are built around this basic substance. Once the digestion process has broken the grains down to their basic form; carbohydrates to glucose, proteins to amino acids, and fats into fatty acids and glycerol, they pass through the villi of the small intestines into the bloodstream.

This is not the case with sucrose, double sugars, or disaccharides, which are found in the sugars of cane and sugar beets, nor with the lactose, which is found in milk and milk products, and is also a disaccharide.

Fructose, a simple sugar or monosaccharide, is found in fruits and honey. Sucrose, lactose, and fructose are extremely unbalanced forms of sugar and enter the bloodstream almost immediately after being eaten. They produce undesireable effects, not only to our physical, but to our psychological condition, and are directly related to numerous degenerative diseases. They have been known to contribute to the abnormal symptoms of schizophrenia, and favor heart disease, cancer, diabetes, hypoglycemia, obesity and the list goes on.

Consider, that out of the ten leading causes of death in this country, six of them, heart disease, cancer, stroke, diabetes, cirrhosis of the liver, and arteriosclerosis, are degenerative diseases. In 1980, approximately 80% of all deaths in this country were from one of those causes. This is a very clear indication that our modern day population is not as healthy as we would like to believe, despite the increasing availability of medical technology.

It is sometimes believed that this degenerative disease epidemic is simply due to our lengthened life span. Some claim that the conquest of infectious diseases and consequent lowering of infant and child deaths actually allow more people to grow older, and that a society with more elderly citizens naturally means more deaths due to degenerative diseases. This is not so. In fact, a growing proportion of younger people are suffering from chronic disease. More **children** under the age of fifteen are lost through the terminal process of cancer than by any other cause, with the exception of accidents.

Degenerative diseases **are not** senior citizen diseases, nor are they an inevitable result of longer life spans or lowered infant mortality rates. It is truly an **epidemic** of all peoples **at all ages** in almost all countries today. According to the Senate Nutrition Committee, cardio-vascular disorders are the leading cause of death in the United States. One out of every two Americans suffers from heart disease.

HYPERTENSION:

According to the American Heart Association, 37 million people suffer from high blood pressure. This is one of the leading risk factors in the development of cardio-vascular illness.

DIABETES:

According to the report, **Nutrition Research Alternatives**, prepared by the United States Congress Office of Technology Assessment, over 11 million people in our country suffer from diabetes. If the incidence of this disease continues to increase at the present rate, we can expect 20% of the population, which is over 40 million people, to develop diabetes.

OBESITY:

One-third of American's population is overweight to such a degree, that their life expectancy is lowered. Overweight persons often have high blood pressure, high cholesterol, and high blood sugar levels. Obesity has also been linked to the development of heart disease, hypertension, atherosclerosis, diabetes, and liver disease.

According to the American Heart Association, each 10% reduction in weight for men aged 33-35 years would result in a 20% decrease in the possibility of developing heart disease. On the other hand, each 10% increase in weight would produce a 30% increase in the incidence of heart disease.

DENTAL DISEASE:

Tooth decay affects over 90% of the population under the age of 17 years. Also, 45% of the population suffers from periodontal disease, the leading cause of tooth loss in people over the age of 15 years.

MENTAL ILLNESS:

In 1950, mental illness affected 1 out of 20. Today that figure is 1 out of 5. About 15% of the American population, or approximately 38 million people, suffer from some type of mental disorder, according to the National Institute of Health. This rate is increasing by approximately 5% a year, or about 1,500,000 people.

CANCER:

Since 1967, over 7 billion dollars have been spent on cancer research. In 1950, the cancer rate was 1 out of 15. Today the figure is 1 out of 4. That represents 25% of our population. At this rate, 50% of our country will have cancer by the year 2000. In 1980, it was estimated that 425,000 people died of this disease, approximately 1,100 every day, or 1 every 78 seconds.

Epidemiological links between cancer and diet: Incidence of cancer dropped 60% in Holland during German occupation, after the Germans requisitioned most of the cheese, butter, milk, eggs, and meat. The Dutch were forced to live on home grown vegetables, bread and other basic staples. After the war, with the return of normal conditions, the cancer rate jumped back to its pre-war levels.

Changes occurred in the cancer incidence among Japanese migrants to the United States following the adoption of a high fat and high protein diet. The rates of colon and breast cancer in Japan are relatively low, while stomach cancer is relatively high. Just the opposite is true in the United States. Japanese diet consists largely of white rice, vinegar, and sugar. However, within three generations, Japanese immigrants in this country shifted from the cancer incidence pattern in Japan, to those common in the United States. This correlates with the change, from the standard Japanese way of eating, to the modern American diet.

There is a world wide correlation between high meat and fat intake and the high incidence of breast and colon cancer. In countries where the intake of meat and animal fat is high, such as Scotland, Canada, and the United States, the mortality rates from colon and breast cancer are also high. Countries such as Japan, and Chile, where meat consumption is low, have a correspondingly low incidence of these diseases.

Further evidence from specific population groups within the United States reinforces this connection. Such groups as the Seven Day Adventists, and Mormons, who generally follow a semi-vegetarian regimen, with a limited fat meat intake, have a much lower rate of some forms of cancer, especially breast and colon. Certain African populations who, like the Japanese, have a low fat, high fiber regimen, have been found to have correspondingly low incidence of colon cancer. It is interesting to note that the Chinese have a high rate of throat and esophagus cancer. Their diet consists of high consumption of MSG, oil, fat, sugar, spices, and chemicals.

As a growing number of people are discovering, a diet based on the more **BALANCED** foods can readily be adopted as a preventive measure for maintaining overall health, as well as for the improvement of a wide variety of chronic physical and mental disorders. Included are cancer, cardio-vascular disease, diabetes, multiple sclerosis, arthritis, allergies, epilepsy, kidney stones, anemia, insecurity, fear, sexual disharmony and emotional imbalance. A **ROAD** to prevention and cure is to **replace** high fat cholesterol rich foods, as well as simple carbohydrates. Refined sugar must be replaced with the more inherently **BALANCED** and complex carbohydrates found in grains and fresh vegetables.

The foods that appear in the chart on page 72 that are in the centrally **BALANCED** group; whole cereal grains, locally grown vegetables, beans, sea vegetables, seasonal fruits, fish and poultry and occasional use of organic beef, are consumed on a regular basis and in moderation. Foods found in the extreme categories are not eaten on a daily basis.

These common sense dietary principles are very much in line with the findings reported by the **U.S. SENATE'S SELECT COMMITTEE ON NUTRITION AND HUMAN NEEDS**, prepared in December, 1977. In this publication entitled, "**DIETARY GOALS FOR THE UNITED STATES**," they state, "The eating patterns of this century represent as critical a public health concern as any now before us. We (the government) must acknowledge and recognize that the public is confused about what to eat and to maximize health." The following is a statement by the Chairman of Select Committee, Senator George McGovern, I should note from the onset that this is the first comprehensive statement by any branch of the Federal Government on risk factors in the American diet.

"The simple fact is that our diets have changed radically within the last 50 years, with great and often very harmful effects on our health. These dietary changes represent as great a threat to public health as smoking. Too much fat, too much sugar, and too much salt can be linked directly to heart disease, cancer, obesity, strokes, among other killer diseases." In all, six of the ten leading causes of death in the United States have been linked to our modern diet.

"Those of us within the Government have an obligation to acknowledge this. The public wants some guidance; wants to know the truth, and hopefully, today we can lay the cornerstone for the building of better health for all Americans, through better nutrition."

Dr. D.M. Hegsted, Professor of Nutrition at Harvard School of Public Health, stated in the report, "Heart disease, cancer, diabetes, and hypertension are the diseases that kill us. They are epidemic in our population. We cannot afford to temporize. We have an obligation to inform the public of the current state of knowledge and to assist the public in making the correct food choices. To do less is to avoid our responsibility."

Dr. Beverly Winikoff of the Rockefeller Foundation stated, ". . . 'personal dietary preferences' are not immutable but interact with other forces in the environment and are influenced by them. People learn the patterns of their diet not only from the family and socio-cultural background, but from what is available in the marketplace and what is promoted both formally through advertising, and informally through general availability in schools, restaurants, supermarkets, work places, airports and so forth. **Americans lack the understanding of the consequences of nutrition-related diseases.** There is a widespread and unfounded confidence in the ability of medical science to cure or mitigate the effects of such diseases once they occur. Appropriate public education must emphasize the unfortunate but clear limitations of current medical practice in curing the common killing diseases. Once hypertension, diabetes, arteriosclerosis or heart disease are manifest, there is, in reality, very little that medical science can do to return a patient to normal physiological function. As awareness of this limitation increases, the importance of prevention will become all the more obvious."

Modern science tends to over-estimate the volume of calories needed for the average person. Today's nutritionists suggest caloric requirements between 1200 and 3000 calories daily. Variables include your age, sex, and personal activities. What they often neglect to explain is that a calorie is the unit used to measure heat energy in physics. One calorie is the amount of energy needed to raise the temperature of one gram of water one degree centigrade. Nutritional scientists measure the amount of energy contained in foods. Large calories are also called kilocalories or kilogram calories and equal 1,000 of the physics calories. They use a capital C which denotes that they are referring to kilocalorie or large Calorie.

Different foods produce different amounts of heat when they burn. Scientists burn samples of food in an instrument called a calorimeter and measure the heat given off. But even modern theorists disagree on whether this method of calculating calories actually shows the real need of humans for a given number of calories to produce a certain activity of the body, unless, of course, we have already been cloned and are now robots.

This is why, in our study of **BALANCING** mind and body, no particular attention need be given to the subject of calories "per se." Rather, we must take into consideration that some foods convert into calories with a much greater **speed** than other foods. A good example is sugar. Sugar processed from sugar cane will produce calories rapidly, **but the caloric discharge soon stops.** On the other hand, glucose (a complex or polysaccharide sugar which is contained in whole cereal grains), transmutes more slowly into calories and lasts longer. It is clear that the energy supplied from the latter is more constant and smooth, and that a diet centered around whole grains and vegetables, with occasional use of animal products, is far superior to that of a diet centered around meat and sugar.

- -

The goals presented in the body of the report suggest the following changes in food selection and preparation: . . ."

1. Increase consumption of fresh fruits, vegetables, and whole grains.
2. Decrease consumption of meat and increase consumption of poultry and fish.

3. Decrease consumption of foods high in fat and partially substitute polyunsaturated fat for saturated fat.
4. Substitute non-fat for whole milk.
5. Decrease consumption of butterfat, eggs, and other high cholesterol sources.
6. Decrease consumption of sugar and foods high in sugar content.
7. Decrease consumption of salt and foods high in salt content."

Testimonies

DARREL ERICKSON
CLEARWATER, FLORIDA

I am happy to have this opportunity to share with you the wonderful and exciting things that have happened to me since I was placed on the Autobahn Diet.

Over the past 10 years, I have had 5 major heart attacks and have been told by my doctors that I needed bypass surgery. I was not sold on the idea of this operation and looked for an alternative program. Prior to going on the Autobahn diet, I couldn't walk to my mailbox, which is only a couple hundred feet away, without experiencing angina (heart pains). I needed to lose weight and had not been successful in doing so with any other program.

I started on the diet and within several weeks I started to lose weight and could walk a mile with no chest pains whatsoever. I not only can take my walks now without pain but I also lost 25 pounds. I have a lot more energy and feel so good. I feel 20 years younger. I have to laugh when I go to my medical doctor for a checkup. He checks my weight, heartbeat, blood pressure, etc., shakes his head and can't understand why I seem to be getting better instead of worse like most other heart patients. He advised me to continue to do whatever I am doing.

I have been on the Autobahn program for 1½ years. I have been able to maintain the weight loss, look and feel great and of course would recommend the Autobahn Diet very highly for anyone with a similar condition as mine.

SAM GREGG
LAKELAND, FLORIDA

I am the owner and operator of a local florist shop. My business keeps me working from early morning till late into the night. I had been diagnosed as having congestive heart failure, diabetes and further complicated by being overweight.

After going for consultation, I was placed on the AUTOBAHN DIET. I immediately started to feel better and had renewed energy. Within 5 weeks I lost 20 pounds and my doctor decreased my insulin from 30 units a day to 15 units.

During my recent physical and examination with my doctor, he stated that my heart condition was greatly improved and stronger. Most importantly is that I have been able to maintain my weight, eat what I want and feel better than I ever have before.

I am always telling people about the AUTOBAHN DIET and how easy it was for me to lose weight and feel better.

Testimony

ROBERT BONFIELD
ATLANTA, GEORGIA

When I first went for consultation in February 1984, I was 225 pounds, 60 to 70 pounds overweight. I had erratic and high blood pressure, elevated blood sugar to the tune of 45 units of insulin a day and clogged arteries in the lower portion of my body.

At that time, I was 59 years old and had been a salesman for 30 years. I worked long hours, driving 50 to 150 miles a day. Since I had been advised by medical doctors to lose the excess weight in preparation for surgery in the lower portion of my body, I decided to take some time off from my work and try to get my health straightened out.

At that time, I met Dr. Theo. He placed me on the Autobahn Diet. After a short time I was able to cut the dosage of insulin and a short while later, stopped it all together.

Within a few weeks my blood pressure dropped to a very good range for my age. Over a four month period the excess weight melted off and I dropped to a weight of 170 pounds. A total weight loss of 55 pounds!

My wife was also experiencing some health problems. She also consulted with Dr. Theo and started on the Autobahn Diet. She received many health benefits, most visibly was the fading of the numerous brown spots on her legs. She also lost excess weight, from 140 pounds to 118 pounds, a total of 22 pounds.

I have long since returned to work and I am presently productive again.

The Autobahn Diet, strictly adhered to, has done more for the health of my body than any medication ever did.

SODIUM   POTASSIUM

Exit 4
EXPANSION AND CONTRACTION

The Two Way Street

Expansion and contraction play a vital role in our daily lives. The achievement of maintaining an even balance between these two factors will create for you perfect harmony; an imbalance will cause discontent.

Expansion and contraction are seen as opposites. Man and Woman are as different from each other as is day from night; they are opposites, yet they complement each other. We all know, they can be antagonistic to each other, too. Joined together, man and woman form a perfect union. From the moment man meets woman, they produce a magnetic force that has the power to spark the spirit which may yield the miracle of life. (birth)

Natures' energy forces are continuously moving independently through men and women's bodies. When men and women come together in sexual union, their magnetic poles unite and become intensified. The male's reproductive sperm cell is very expansive. It comes together with the female reproductive cell, the ovum, which is very contracted. At this time, the fertilized egg develops towards the embryonic state, lasting for a period of approximately 280 days, during which time the embryo grows. There is an increase of 3 billion times in size and weight from the beginning of pregnancy to the delivery and birth. Upon completion of the biological growing process, a single-celled fertilized egg has become a multi-cellular, highly evolved human being.

Our digestive system is more contracted or compact, since it is located in a more inward or central position. The nervous system, being located at the periphery, is more **outward** or expanded.

All of natures' phenomena are alternately pulsating between expansion and contraction.

They are both complementary and antagonistic. We will be referring to these forces as having either **expanded** or **contracted** tendencies. Although these tendencies may be seen as "opposites," it is important to remember that all antagonisms are also complementary. All things generate energy back and forth, from one to the other. As a small example, look at the basic mechanics of a battery. It has a positive and negative charge. One pole can not exist without the other.

Many great philosophers and thinkers have observed and applied the theory of expansion and contraction, though they may have labeled their systems of thought with other terms. George Wilhelm, in his interpretation of the dialectic development, postulated that human affairs developed in a spirallic form from a phase of unity which he termed "thesis," through a period of density or "anti-thesis," and on to a higher plane of reintegration or "synthesis." Frederich Hegel's principle of dialectics was later studied by Karl Marx, Friedrich Engels and their associates, and formed the basis of their philosophical speculation in the area of politics, economics, and science.

Albert Einstein was among many other scientific thinkers of the twentieth century who sensed the dynamics of antagonism that occurs between this visable world of matter and the invisible world of energy. Based upon that, he formulated his universal principle of relativity, in which he states that energy is constantly changing into matter and matter is continuously changing into energy (expansion - contraction). Infinite space is the ultimate expansion, and infinitesimal matter becomes the greatest contraction.

Yet another thinker, Arnold Toynbee, based his study of history on two alternating movements which he expressed as **"challenge"** and **"response"** in one of the early chapters of his many volumes, *Study of History*. Of the many symbols in which different observers in different societies have expressed the juxtaposition posed by the static condition, and a dynamic activity, in the harmony of nature and the entire universe, expansion and contraction are the most divergent.

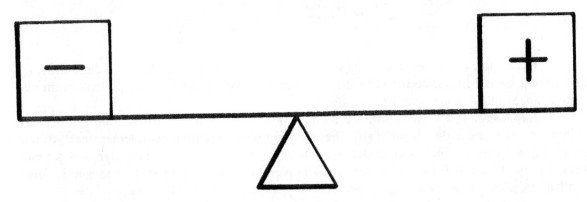

In the world of electricity and the field of magnetism, one sees expansion and contraction in the flow of current and charges between plus (+) and minus (-) poles. The equilibrium of blood is maintained between red blood cells and white blood cells, as well as a balance between potassium and sodium. When we have the correct **BALANCE**, we also have a healthy body. Normal **BALANCE** is slightly alkaline and is expressed as ph 7.3. Chemical compositions, including the DNA molecules and many others, are structured between alternating expansion and contraction, as are time and space, mass and energy, north pole, south pole, centripetal and centrifugal force. All physical phenomena, and all elements, are charged with the complementary ←→ antagonistic relationship.

A Japanese philosopher, George Ohsawa, dedicated his entire life to the health and the happiness of mankind. He used his same principle of expansion and contraction. In his teachings, however, he referred to it as "yin" and "yang." For fifty years he comprehensively interpreted the areas of medicine, food, philosophy and psychology through this relationship. During his lifetime he was successful in reviewing almost the entire scope of the order of nature, and was capable of applying pathological treatment of disease through the changing of the diet. These principles have been utilized in advancing my understanding of biological, physiological and spiritual phenomena, as well as natural and social movements. Our challenge is to **apply the BALANCING principles** of life's forces, be they called yin ←→ yang, challenge ←→ response or contraction ←→ expansion.

Some foods are at the extreme of expansion and others are at the extreme of contraction. Some contain a more even **BALANCE** of both factors. For example, when sugar is placed on the tongue it expands; when salt is used the tongue contracts. Achieving a more **BALANCED** condition between these forces is our goal.

In general, we can classify food according to expansion and contraction, or by the chemical terms of potassium and sodium. For instance, when you eat something very acidic you have heartburn. You normally take something alkaline to **BALANCE** it. Perhaps you take Alka-Seltzer. Acid forming foods are rich in potassium, whereas alkaline foods are rich in sodium. Remember, from foods we are given life. Through the proper **BALANCING** of selected natural foods and nutrients, we learn how to nourish our bodies and minds and remain in harmony with our environment.

EXPANSION CENTRIFUGAL UPWARD MOTION ACIDITY POTASSIUM SUGAR FRUIT

Expansive things are those which are passive and receptive. They are such things as space, the moon, cold, water. To illustrate this, you could place a bottle of water in the freezer and see how the volume would increase due to the interaction of water and cold. That which is physically light is considered expanded. The colors blue, purple and green however, keep their distance or seem to recede. They are expansive.

CONTRACTION CENTRIPETAL DOWNWARD MOTION ALKALINITY SODIUM SALT CEREALS

Contraction is active, creative and energetic. Such things as the sun, fire, salt, pressure and time are contracted. That which is heavy is contracted. The colors red, orange and yellow are contracted and tend to stand out.

Since the subject is expansion and contraction, let's put the knowledge of these factors into practical use. A vegetable contains two major sections. A compacted root and a more expanded stem or leaf. For example, we will look at a carrot. The root portion grows in a downward direction (contracted) towards the center of the earth and this is governed more by the centripetal force. Yet the opposite force can be seen coming out of the earth, pushing upward towards the sky. The leafy carrot top (expansion) is governed by centrifugal force. To create **BALANCE** we should eat **both** sections of the vegetable.

The color of a plant is also a guide to whether or not it has expansive or contractive qualities. At the extreme stage of **expansion** is ultra violet and violet. At the extreme stage of **contraction** is infra-red. Close to the center of the spectrum and near harmony are green, only slightly expansive, and yellow, only slightly contracted. For example, a purple eggplant is very expansive, an orange carrot, very contracted.

Moving from slightly contracted yellow into the more contracted zone, brown is the next color, then orange, red, and finally infra-red.

Moving from slightly expansive green into the more expansive zone, blue is next, then black, purple, violet and finally untra-violet.

Since our discussion of expansion and contraction is based on relative values, consider the areas of density, weather, climate, and speed of growth when you wish to determine the quality of a vegetable. Softer, faster growing vegetables, growing in a hot summer climate, are productive of the most expansive type of plant. For example, it only takes a few days for mushrooms and asparagus to reach their full size. Conversely, the harder, slower growing vegetables grown or harvested in the winter or cold climates would produce the most contracted plants. It takes 8 - 10 weeks for a carrot to grow. Summer and winter squash constitute an example with which you may test your understanding of this principle. They are both contracted vegetables when compared to the green, tall, watery stems of a celery plant. Yet summer squash is more expanded than its counterpart, the winter squash. Summer squash is yellow, softer, and contains more water. Winter squash is orange, harder and contains less water.

All vegetable forms of life in this universe have their own unique size, color, shape, and liquid content. For example, a vertical plant growing above the ground is classified as expanded, while the opposite, an elongated plant growing below the ground, is considered a contracted plant. A plant which grows in a horizontal direction **below** the ground, like a potato, however, is classed as an **expanded** plant. A plant growing **above** the ground, but in a horizontal direction would be considered a **contracted** plant.

Consider a comparative view of other foods within the spectrum of expansion and contraction. A sampling of some commonly ingested elements, in the order of **most expansive** to **least expansive**, would be; synthetic drugs, natural drugs, sugar, oil, yeast, honey, fruit, cream, yogurt, water, nuts, sea vegetables, land vegetables, beans and **grains**. From the **least contracted** going to the **most contracted** are; **grains**, fish, shellfish, tamari, miso, goat cheese, rocquefort, edam, crude salt, fowl, red meat, and refined salt.

All root vegetables may be eaten daily, with the exception of potatoes. Potatoes, like tomatoes and spinach, have too much oxalic acid for daily use. Oxalic acid is partially responsible for decreasing the calcium supply to your bone structure and depositing it in the soft tissue organs. Later, this could produce kidney and gall stones. We should not fear the above mentioned fruits and vegetables, but they should be enjoyed in moderation.

The body produces its own oxalic acid, so food high in this very strong organic acid tips the scales and creates an imbalance in the human organism. In the fruit family, incidentally, you will find a very high amount of oxalic acid in grapes. A practice of moderate fruit usage, combined with the knowledge of expansion and contraction, will automatically guide you away from these choices. Grapes, according to classification by color, as previously discussed, are expansive. You may eat and enjoy these previously mentioned foods, but consume them in moderation. Always keep **BALANCE** in mind.

Each **part** of a plant has its own particular value. When composing a meal, one should be careful to keep in mind the quality and quantity of the various elements. By doing so, one learns how to achieve **BALANCE**. For example, some people always prefer to eat only part of a vegetable and either discard or leave the rest, not realizing that the secondary part of the vegetable complements the primary. **Both** parts of the vegetable are needed to achieve **BALANCE** and complete nutrition. Some people even prefer to eat only one or two kinds of vegetables the year round, forgetting about the added nutritional value that they could derive from other plants.

Your brain fuctions like a marvelous computer, taking in and processing all the data from your sense organs. Just as a camera lens must be ground with precision to give a faithful reproduction of reality, so your body/mind must be nurtured with the proper **BALANCE** of nutritive components to produce responses that reflect the true understanding of the changing situations around you. If the lens of a camera is focused on distance, the foreground will be blurred. If the focus is moved to near, the foreground will be sharp and clear but the horizon and distant objects will not be discernable. If your camera has an "automatic" focus, it will select the median range and everything will be seen at optimum clarity, and in **BALANCED** proportion.

This same focusing principle is illustrated in the example of myopia, near-sightedness. The human eye fuctions much like an organic camera, and it too requires some fine **BALANCING** in order to give faithful interpretations. Persons with myopia see things unclearly; their vision is blurred. There are two causes for myopia. One is a swelling of the lens itself, which is due to a vertical **contraction** of the eyeball. This is caused by excessive intake of contracted foods, such as animal food and salt. The second condition causing myopia is **expansion** of the eyeball which draws back the position of the retina. This is caused by the excessive intake of expanded foods such as sugar, fruit juices, soft drinks, alcohol, drugs, and chemicals. Myopia may be caused by either extreme in eating, since either expansion of one part of the eye or contraction of another part of the eye can have the same effect on the focus. In both cases, the image of the object viewed focuses not on the retina, but in front of the retina. Both causes can be corrected with proper **BALANCING** of your food, and correct vision will be restored.

In your daily lives too, a **BALANCED** perspective will be the one most workable and favorable for you. It will require **BALANCED** EATING.

All illnesses are caused by an imbalance of acidity and alkalinity. Should you find that your illness is caused by acidity, or expansion, you should eliminate the cause which produces that condition. You must bring your system back into **BALANCE**. Likewise, when the symptoms manifested are more of an alkaline state, contracted, you should eliminate those foods which have caused that condition. Sometimes we find that an illness is caused by both extremes. Your approach then is basically the same; to bring the body to the center -- the **BALANCING** point, the middle road. This can easily be done by comparing the foods you usually eat to the ones listed in the chart on page 72. The foods listed in the center of the chart are the **stabilizing foods** and contain a good **BALANCE** of acidity and alkalinity. Towards the sides of the pages, foods become more extreme in their composition, until the ones in the outer edge columns are most extreme. If you are making the major part of your diet from the center list, you will probably not be experiencing signs of illness. However, you will find that you can make a fair diagnosis of whether your condition comes from one extreme or the other, OR BOTH, by an analysis of this chart; then you can easily make the appropriate dietary changes.

There are a few adjustments to be made, if the illness is **acute**, which may change several aspects of your daily living. For diseases which are caused from an overly acidic condition, it is adviseable to keep the humidity level low, to expose the body to more sunshine, and to be physically active. The exception is in cases where there is severe pain, fatigue, or exhaustion. If that indeed is the case, then more rest is required. When you live in a colder climate, or when illness arises in predominately winter months, it may be adviseable to relocate to a warmer, sunnier region. For example, a person living in Minnesota who is suffering from leukemia can benefit by a move to sunny Florida. The strong effects of the sun on the already overly-expanded system will help to counteract the over-acidic blood condition. Red blood cells are contracted while white blood cells are expanded. **It is always adviseable to seek the advice of your physician.**

For diseases which are caused by an alkaline condition, it is adviseable to keep the atmospheric conditions surrounding those persons slightly moist, with less circulation of air, and to be less active physically and more active mentally. When illness arises in the summer months, or when living in a warmer region, it is adviseable to move to a colder or more northern region. A person suffering from cancer of the liver, who lives in Florida, would benefit from a move to Maine or a similar climate.

When diseases arise from eating caused by **both** extremes of acidity and alkilinity, it is adviseable to maintain an average amount of physical exercise. At this point, the selection and preparation of the types of food we choose are extremely important. In order to restore our physical and psychological health, we must go to the source and cause of our illness. We are not treating the body symptomatically, shifting and moving your pain and discomfort from one place to another, nor numbing your body with narcotics. Our main concern goes much deeper, to the **cause**. It is always to be found in the dietary and living habits of the human being.

The importance of cooking cannot be emphasized enough. In the cook's hands lies the control of the source of life itself, the well-spring of power. Ralph Waldo Emerson once said, "Health is the first condition of happiness." Whether a home is happy or not depends on the health of its inhabitants. Food provides the physical foundation from which man's body, mind, and spirit can grow and develop.

Although all the foods we choose are non-chemicalized, non-artifical and **natural**, this in itself may not be enough. If your cooking methods are not proper, then the results will not be beneficial to your health. There are many ways we can inadvertently diminish the beneficial effects of food. Overcooking, undercooking, excessive or insufficient amounts of water, the use of too much oil, too many spices, as well as the use of improper cooking utensils are common errors. All are subjects we will cover in detail.

Testimonies

DR. EVANGELO V. FOTINOPOULOS
LAKELAND, FLORIDA

I first met Dr. Theo in the fall of 1981. I had been on many diet plans and programs throughout my adult life and I have lost and gained many pounds. Dr. Theo told me that the Autobahn diet could help me not only lose weight but regain my health. Being a doctor, I was admittedly skeptical at first.

I started out weighing 355 pounds and I thought I was okay! In a matter of eight months, I went from 355 pounds down to 250 pounds, a total weight loss of 105 pounds! I am never hungry and always feel energetic. My congestion is gone and I no longer have shortness of breath. Best of all I am not tired all the time.

On a recent trip to visit my family, I was asleep in the guest room. In the middle of the night my mother came into the bedroom to check to see if I was still breathing. She told me the next day that she did not hear me snoring and she was concerned. My wife is also much happier now that I do not snore and the walls do not rattle at night.

I still have a way to go to reach my goal of 197 pounds, but I am well on my way. I also know now that it is possible, pleasurable and easy with the Autobahn Diet.

BARBARA J. HOPPER
COLUMBUS, OHIO

I work full time as a dental nurse. I am 43 years old, and before I found the AUTOBAHN DIET, I was always run down, tired, had no energy, my skin tone was frail looking and my hair was dry and brittle.

After being on the diet for a short time, about two weeks, I had more energy, my complexion cleared up, my face had a healthy pink color and I lost over 10 pounds. People actually tell me that I look ten years younger and I really feel like I am. I also notice that a lot of the aches and pains that I was experiencing have left and I am able to serve my patients all day and go home not feeling tired.

I enjoy the easy whole food recipes and the natural tasting foods. Before the AUTOBAHN DIET, I was constantly trying new fad diets and all types of health programs, **all** of them left me hungry, tired and disappointed.

I would recommend the AUTOBAHN DIET highly, especially to those people who have tried everything else and have had no success.

Exit 5
HIGH AND LOW RISK FOODS

Let's Take The Low Road

In the early 1900's, Americans derived about 40% of their caloric energy from more complex carbohydrates; cereal grains, vegetables and fruits. This percentage has now declined to less than 18% of the caloric intake. Whole, unrefined grains and grain products are practically non-existent in our modern diet. At the same time, the consumption of fats and simple sugars has risen so that these items now comprise at least 60% of your diet. There have been several specific and deleterious changes in the American diet during the last hundred years:

1. COMPLEX CARBOHYDRATES: (Whole cereal grains, beans, vegetables and fruits) Until the turn of the century these were the main dietary and agricultural staples of the majority of the world's population. In the U.S., the consumption of these complex carbohydrates has steadily declined since 1910. Much of this change has occurred within the last 38 years. Compared with 1947, the 1976 per person, per year, consumption of cereal grains and products fell by 31 pounds. The consumption of vegetables fell by 18.3 pounds, and the consumption of fruit by 19.5 pounds.
2. SUGAR: From 1889 to 1961 the ratio of complex to simple carbohydrates ingested dropped more than three and a half times. In 1980, the average person ate 140 pounds of refined sugar per year compared to less than 40 pounds per person in 1875, an increase of well over 300%. A large portion of sugar consumed in this country is eaten in the form of processed foods and beverages, including: soft drinks, canned foods, bread, candy, cake, ice cream, breakfast cereals and many others. Soft drink consumption doubled in the U.S. between 1960 to 1975, increasing from an average yearly per person intake of 13.6 gallons to 27.6 gallons. In 1983, the average person drank over 400, 12 oz. cans of soda totaling 29.5 pounds of sugar.

The erroneous concept of the four basic food groups advocates the consumption of high fat items such as meat, eggs, milk and dairy products. There is little or no regard for the quality of carbohydrates consumed. The **PREVENTATIVE** approach classifies foods into **TWO** groups; **LOW RISK ROAD** : (Complex carbohydrates), Whole cereal grains; brown rice, barley, millet, oats, buckwheat, corn, rye and whole wheat, beans, fresh locally grown vegetables, along with some sea vegetables, locally grown seasonal fruits, seeds, nuts, plus low fat items such as fresh fish, shellfish and poultry. **HIGH RISK ROAD:** (higher fat items) such as red meat, butter, eggs, milk, refined sugar, artificial and highly processed foods, additives and preservatives, alcohol and table salt.

I will be discussing the nutritive value of foods and their place in a **BALANCED**, healthful diet. From this you can decide what foods are best suited for you. You will learn more about their relationship to your particular state of health.

Red meat, for example, provides an abundant amount of calories which stimulate your body by providing quick energy. This kind of energy does not last long. Moreover, to maintain the energy given by meat, you must eat meat CONSTANTLY. It is addictive. On the other hand, cereal grains and vegetables provide energy that is much less explosive. When you eat them, your body is allowed to assimilate the nutrients into the blood at a slower and more even pace. This in turn gives you energy that is less violent and of a much more enduring nature. The energy supplied by grains and vegetables is less dramatic than that of red meat, and allows you to go on doing your work. There is no feeling of heaviness, no need for rest and recuperation.

Building your body principally with cereal grains and vegetables, along with the proper proportions of meat, is more natural than building it with only animal food. In the former process, plants become blood then flesh. When we eat meat, the process is reversed, the flesh becomes blood. Because this process is quick, we receive great energy. However, this energy represents a process of **decomposition** rather than a building process. Those who eat red meat heavily are often subject to sudden attacks of fever. The meat, once it is broken down to be assimilated and rejected, gives energy but doesn't build good quality bones and tissue. The process is too fast, the need to eliminate too strong. Thus, what does not follow the natural building process is continually rejected. This is the body's attempt to burn away "dead" matter. Fever results when toxins are not eliminated fast enough and generally comes from excessive animal protein. In this sense, fever can be considered a kind of discharge. A fever indicates that the animal protein has become poison to the system. At first the protein is not poisonous, but whatever is not quickly burned to become energy is stored in the body and ultimately becomes toxic. At this stage, bacteria and viruses may be present. This storage of protein can eventually lead to diseases such as uremia, and produce numerous ill effects in the body organs and blood.

A calf has a strong body and eats only grass. A cow, which has a huge skeleton, eats only grass and builds that skeleton from grass alone. One **thousand** pounds of grass eaten by a calf might produce, say, one pound of meat. But if that calf were to eat only one **hundred** pounds of grain, it would produce the **same** amount of flesh, one pound, for grain is a more concentrated form of energy than grass. In other words, this is the process; grass or grain makes meat. Grass is expansive, changing to contraction. Meat then, is an extremely concentrated from of energy, for huge amounts of either grass or grains are necessary to produce a small amount of it.

Americans usually eat a great deal of red meat, (concentrated, heavy) and as a result, the body craves huge amounts of sugar (dispersive, light) to create a **BALANCE**. Americans often suffer from blood stagnation as a result of their excessive consumption of both red meat and sugar. Dark circles under the eyes are a visable sign of blood stagnation.

There is a practical and safe way to expel animal food toxins. It is not enough simply to stop eating so much red meat; many toxins will remain stored in the body. One can take **radish to expel fish toxins, mushrooms for egg and fowl toxins, lettuce for cheese toxins, and onions and scallions** (raw or cooked) **for beef and lamb toxins.**

For these and the reasons discussed earlier, we do not recommend the **daily** consumption of red meat, beef, lamb, pork, and only occasional use of fowl, such as turkey, chicken, wild pigeon, dove, pheasant, duck, etc. The latter can be consumed sparingly as a concession to satisfy your sensory desires. It is suggested that ALL meat be organically fed, with no chemicals, dyes, hormones, steroids, and colorings added. Only 15% of any given meal should consist of meat.

There is a **biological** reason for selecting these recommendations for the percentages of meat, fish and fowl. Let us look at the evolutionary constitution of man through the mouth, specifically the teeth. We have twenty molars, which are just perfect for grinding and chewing grains and other fibrous foods. We also have eight front incisors which are designed for cutting vegetables. **Your mouth only contains four teeth** for tearing animal flesh, the canines. Through this analysis of the structure of your teeth, it can be concluded that the homo sapiens have evolved mainly as a result of a diet consisting of a ratio of five parts whole cereal grains to two parts vegetable and one part animal food. In addition, when studying the digestive system, you will learn that the process is extremely long and not suitable for animal foods, which decompose very rapidly, and ferment in the intestines before being eliminated.

It is important for you to know and understand the relationship of foods, especially **THE HIGH RISK ROAD**, along with the effects they have on the bodily functions as a whole. From carbohydrates to degenerative diseases, to overconsumption of liquids and salts, an abusive process goes on continuously, **unless** we take the **BALANCED approach**. Everything is here for us to enjoy, but in moderation, not in excess.

A generation ago it became fashionable among medical professionals to advise their patients to drink plenty of fluids to flush the **kidneys**. Perhaps this well-intentioned advice has resulted in a general attitude among our populace that overconsumption of liquids benefits this poor, overworked little organ. This would explain why today we have a new medical invention called the kidney dialysis machine. In actuality, the kidney is not very large, only about the size of your ear. It is filled with thousands of tiny porous vessels called nephrons. The nephrons filter the bloodstream and convert waste products into urine. The kidney filters approximately one hundred quarts of liquid daily, subsequently removing about 1 - 1½ quarts of toxins and waste products and discharging them through the urine. The remainder of the useful liquids and hormones are returned to the bloodstream.

When too much liquid is consumed and frequent urination takes place, not only water and wastes pass out, but vital hormones and minerals as well. On the average, males should urinate three to four times daily, and females three times. The female bladder is larger and therefore holds more urine.

When too much meat, or salt, or hard cheese is consumed, the kidneys will not function effectively and cannot filter the large amounts of toxins. This results in a large percentage of wastes returning to the blood stream. When this occurs, it causes the kidney to contract. This in turn causes the heart to beat more rapidly, and then the blood pressure rises causing hypertension. (high blood pressure) Your blood pressure must rise in order to aid the kidney in the pushing down of liquid. While the kidney function is to excrete wastes through urination, the skin does the same through perspiration. Sweat and urine are similar in their composition. **Skin** disease invariably is a result of the inability of the kidney to filter its wastes effectively, forcing the wastes to go to the skin to be released. Water disease, swollen thighs, skin eruptions and skin disease in general all stem from kidney problems.

For those who eat less meat, and consequently use less salt, there is not as much thirst. Therefore, there is not as much liquid consumed. This results in less work for the kidneys to do, since urinations will also be far less for those persons.

For this reason, our suggestions on the use of liquids and beverages will be limited, since far less liquid will be desired by the person who eats with the knowledge of **BALANCING** the extreme contraction and expansion factors. Extremes in temperature are also best moderated. Therefore, we take our beverages warm or cool, rather than icy or hot. Extreme temperatures produce a "shock" to the system which can inhibit digestion and cause headaches by quick changes in internal pressures generated by the sudden effect.

SALT

There is much to be said about salt, both for and against. A common belief is that the heavy consumption of refined salt is one of the major factors causing heart disease.Excessive use of commercial salt can lead to water retention, constipation. high blood pressure, kidney trouble and heart disease, along with fatigue and sudden outbursts of anger.

Too much salt causes you to consume large quantities of water. This overloads and burdens the kidneys, as well as the large intestines. When this occurs, the heart and lungs decrease in activity from their normal pace, which in turn causes the stomach to become overactive. One symptom of the overconsumption of salt is dark brown urine.

If you are underactive or bedridden, you should limit your intake of salt to a bare minimum, or none at all. If your daily activity is moderate, such as a secretary or office worker, then a moderate amount of salt can be used.

Perhaps those who are against salt are correct. When looking at our nation, with all of its modern technology and conveniences, man is becoming less active and therefore needs less salt.

The excessive use of drugs, sweets, and fruits, expands our minds while inhibiting our ability to concentrate and focus our attention on our daily lives. The constant ingestion of these expansive foods removes salt too rapidly from our bodies, at which point we usually find ourselves with a strong craving for salty foods.

Salt does provide us with energy. If we are not receiving enough salt we suffer from a lack of energy. This also may result in the loss of sexual desire, as well as leaving us vulnerable to many colds and cramps in the legs.

The truth of the matter is, that we could avoid these problems simply by **BALANCING** the salt we consume with a little oil, along with good physical exercise.

In general, infants and babies require little or no salt until age one, or until they are walking. Then, caution and good judgement should be used when giving your children what is needed for their growth.

Maintaining proper salt **BALANCE** is a very important matter, but should not be feared to the point of making a healthy family tremble. Salt is used to make our foods tastier, and provide a **BALANCE**. If we sprinkle a grain of salt on an unripened strawberry, we bring out the sweetness of the berry. If we use too much salt it may turn bitter, or perhaps give it a flavor similar to vinegar.

The salt I use is non-iodized, and unrefined; it is mineral rich, sun dried, and unprocessed sea salt. I combine the roasted sea salt with unhulled sesame seeds, (which contain a little oil) combine and grind them together in a suribachi bowl, a clay, serrated, edged bowl, that can be purchased at your local health food store or direct from the Mountain Ark Trading Co. (See The Organic Filling Station). This makes our condiment, "sesame salt." This sesame salt may be sprinkled lightly on grains, vegetables and foods, without the fear of heart disease and other associated diseases. Sesame salt is high in calcium, iron, vitamins A and B. It also makes an excellent anti-acid, used in place of an Alka-Seltzer. Try a teaspoon if you are having problems with an upset stomach, or you feel faint. (See the condiment section of this book for the directions and preparation of this valuable condiment.)

CATHY DARLING
LAKELAND, FLORIDA

I have always been interested in nutrition but never realized the real power in foods until I started eating the AUTOBAHN WAY. Within a month, I started to lose weight and have lost a total of 30 pounds to date. Plus, I no longer suffer painful migrain headaches, which plagued me for 22 years.

My family says that my disposition and interest in life's activities have improved; and my level of energy has zoomed so that I can accomplish all the things necessary as a wife, mother, volunteer and part time secretary.

My family and I enjoy better health now, but we are saddened to see our friends' health deteriorate because they eat so nutritionally poor. I do whole heartedly recommend the Autobahn Diet.

Exit 6
CHANGING LANES NATURALLY

The Crossroads Of Alternatives

Intake of whole grains and other vegetable products results not only in recovery and rejuvenation, but also in an improvement of memory and judgement. Consequently, we gain an expanded awareness of freedom and thinking. It overcomes not only physical but also mental, moral, and spiritual illnesses. Many people in our modern society have already regained their health by learning to **BALANCE** their daily foods and prepare simple and delicious dishes. A fringe benefit is that you can save 35% to 50% of your food costs when you observe eating in a more natural way. You may save money through this **BALANCED** approach to eating and at the same time, restore your health and improve the quality of your life.

Due to the increasing awareness of the importance of food, America is now experiencing a phenomena unique to history. Diets of all types are flooding the market. We have the raw food diet, the grapefruit diet, the Cambridge diet, the Weight Watchers diet, the steak and salad diet, the Scarsdale diet, the Pritikin diet, the Beverly Hills diet, and the water diet. Every individual tries to find a method of eating compatible with his makeup, and everyone who succeeds is happy, although not necessarily healthy.

Eating should be orderly. Some people proceed to eat whatever food presents itself. It is not always advisable to do this. Instead, we should discipline ourselves to adhere to some order. It is preferable for people in delicate health (with a weak stomach or generally weak digestive system) to begin with hot soup followed by a portion of grain which is consumed gradually throughout the meal. Then a small portion of animal food, vegetables, and finally fruit, pastry or a beverage. Any kind of sweet food taken at the beginning of a meal inhibits the digestive system. Cold beverages do the same. Sweets or candy taken prior to eating will shut down the digestive system for about 15 - 20 minutes. Therefore, it is wise to consume them at the end of the meal.

Eat something solid or hot first, and always chew well. Chewing activates the secretion of digestive juices, allowing the food to be assimilated easily, causing no indigestion or heartburn.

Saliva is an alkaline liquid. Its main function is digesting and decomposing carbohydrates. There is an important enzyme, called pythalin, which is produced only in saliva. This particular enzyme acts upon food to accomplish the initial breakdown of food so that it can later be acted upon by other enzymes during the digestive process. If food is not chewed sufficiently, this enzyme will not be given the opportunity to act, and the food will not be broken down by other enzymes. Hence, many nutrients in the food will not be released nor absorbed by the blood, and never be assimilated at the cellular level. The very purpose of eating is defeated. Further, undigested food putrifies and becomes over-acidic, causing heartburn, indigestion, belching and other distresses. It also tends to adhere to the intestinal lining where it gradually builds a wall, inhibiting absorption of nutrients from properly digested food. This build up also causes intestinal rigidity and its associated problems.

It is important to chew all food thoroughly. In the act of chewing you not only show you care for the food that you are eating, but also for your body as well. It is recommended that you chew each mouthful at least 25 - 35 times, and in some cases up to 100 times. So chew well; you will live a healthier and longer life.

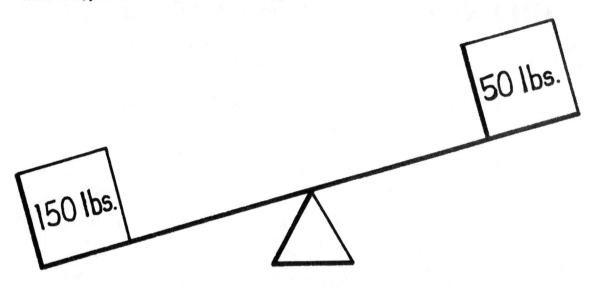

Let us visualize a see-saw. It **BALANCES** at its center point. Each end moves correspondingly to the weight and force exerted at the opposite end. For example, a 50 pound boy cannot **BALANCE** a 150 pound man. The imbalance of weight creates uneven motion at the extremes. The center is the point of least conflict. People do not get thrown off a see-saw sitting in the middle. Disease does not occur when you are in **BALANCE**.

When you begin to eat more naturally, you will heighten your natural sensitivity. Your sense of touch will begin to respond to the unnaturalness of synthetics in the clothes you wear. It is recommended that you use vegetable quality materials such as cotton, silk and jute. Natural materials permit the skin to breathe and allow heat and moisture to pass from the skin unhampered. Since the **discharging of heat is the final process of our ingestion of food, this release of energy must not be restricted**. When you have decreased the amount of calories, fats, and liquids in your diet, you will find that your clothing does not retain odor and will last longer. Have you ever noticed how unpleasant a synthetic nylon or polyester blouse or shirt smells when ironing it? The concentration of toxins released by the body has been trapped next to the skin and it permeates the fabric. What do you suppose this constant contact does to the body?

In addition to eating more natural wholesome foods, the hygenic needs of the body are also best supplied by organic, not chemical aids. Brushing teeth is best accomplished with the use of natural vegetable chlorophyl paste or powder, sea salt, or natural clays. There are several commercially made products from these natural ingredients available.

In caring for our skin, instead of using products which contain chemicals, perfumes, and synthetic additives, a more naturally processed soap can be used, including those clay based, or of natural plant materials. You also can use natural sesame or olive oil or any lotion containing those oils, however, products with artificial vitamins added are not advised.

Along with the use of more natural products and natural eating, it is adviseable to avoid over-utilization of technological "advances" which can leave you with a negative effect. Such things as micro-wave ovens, televisions, and excessive electric and electronic appliances can produce atmospheric charges. On a subtle level these may influence your nerves and cause you to be irritable.

We hear a lot today about "sound pollution," but there are other subliminal forces below the conscious level which continually bombard us with radiation and vibrational frequencies, to which our increasingly sensitive bodies respond.

This is not to suggest that you deprive yourself of modern conveniences, but to bring to awareness the unseen stimuli which can be avoided in the pursuit of creating a stress-free life. Therefore, it is not adviseable to eat while watching television.

In biblical times "truth" was based on quite a different system of values than those we use as our standard today. A dream reported by a trusted person who considered it to be a "revelation" might carry with it the impact of public acceptance. If people believed the dreamer, it would be recorded in the written records of the day.

Today, "truth" is accepted by most people if the information is:

1. Stated by a respected name. (most particularly if a doctor said it.)
2. Verified by so-called scientific studies and . . .
3. Able to be repeated in laboratory finds, etc. . . .

We **think** our methods for establishing truth are better than those based on revelation or intuition. Actually our methods are mere cultural habits in our mode of thinking and **are highly influenced by the evolution of our diet.** We have a more artificial or "chemically reproduced" diet today, and our version of "fact" is based on the same unnatural view of data which is frequently taken out of context and assumed to prove that which it does not.

Intuition today is regarded as not much more than simple superstition. Unfortunately, few people acknowledge the intuitive portion (or right hemisphere) of the brain.

Logic is King! Fast food is its' enhancer. Sensitivity has been regarded as bourgeois sentimentality and "visions" are seen with grave suspicion on the part of many.

The concept of body and mind **BALANCE** through natural eating is not new. The same principles have been applied by civilizations existing for thousands of years, in most parts of the world. By contrast, scientific studies on food and nutrition in our modern age have begun only within the last two decades. Modern science is strong on details but weak on essential fundamentals. It can propose theories, beginning with a planet filled with homogenous gas, develop an evolutionary sequence of events, but cannot explain how the gas got here to begin with.

I doubt very seriously if science will ever reach a stage of perfection. Modern science is too analytical. It often overlooks the dynamic relationship between life and environment as an organic whole.

More scientific research must be carried out concerning the composition of food. It will be interesting for doctors and nutritionists to learn each element, not only in terms of the quality contained in various foods, but also the elements' relationship with, and interdependence upon the other elements.

Testimony

DR. DENNIS D'ERAMO
LONGWOOD, FLORIDA

I am a Chiropractic Orthopaedist in private practice in the Orlando, Florida area. I first met Dr. Theo in mid-June of 1983, I was referred to him by one of my collegues in the Lakeland area.

At the time I was 25 pounds (plus or minus) overweight, somewhat hypertensive at 142/98, tired most of the time and facing a life insurance physical. Needless to say it was to my advantage to drop a little weight and decrease my blood pressure.

Dr. Theo recommended the Autobahn diet. I am pleased to say that in less than four weeks I lost very nearly 20 pounds, reduced my blood pressure to 118/76 and noted a tremendous increase in energy as well as a generalized feeling of "well being." Not only was the diet easy to follow but the food is excellent and relatively easy to prepare. I have since recommended this diet to a multitude of my patients as well as other physicians. All were extremely pleased and experienced similiar results.

The habit of injesting "non-foods" is not a difficult one to break, and I highly recommend this regimin of "good common sense eating" to anyone.

Exit 7
7 MILEPOSTS OF IMPORTANCE

Stop! Look! Eat!

Certainly you are interested in restoring your health and the health of your family and loved ones; the question is asked, how to begin? There is always the desire to start something new, quickly. My suggestion is WALK, DON'T RUN.

A patient writes: "I found myself rushing into the kitchen, reading labels and emptying out the cupboards, cleaning out the refrigerator and freezer and filling the hefty bags to the brim. When I was all through cleaning out the junk I became hungry and didn't know what to eat or how to prepare natural foods." This also may not go over too well with the rest of the family. If there is a life or death situation present, or if someone is suffering with a degenerative disease such as cancer, then "cleaning house" immediately might be the necessary approach. If this is the case, the support of the entire family is needed, "One for all and all for one," or, "A house divided against itself cannot stand." However, in most cases, the more practical approach is to make a **gradual**, orderly progression from your present diet towards the **BALANCED**, health giving program we offer. The seven mileposts will show you the way!

I believe that I have kept **BALANCE** in mind while preparing the recipes and text, using only whole, natural, unprocessed foods. The title, "Journey for Health" is a natural road and a cooking guide to help you better control your own health. Generally speaking, taking one step at a time will lead to the return of good health. That road should be a joyous one.

The steps that you might want to follow to introduce yourself to renewed life through **BALANCED** nutrition should be sure and smooth. The following suggestions are to help you along the way.

MILE POST [1] ELIMINATE the consumption of chemicals, additives, preservatives, dyes, colorings, artificial flavorings, etc. This can be done by reading the labels and checking the ingredients in the foods that you are currently buying and serving your family. If you do not recognize the ingredients and the additives used in the product, ask yourself this question, "Is there a natural alternative?" (See Refined Foods Substitution List, Exit 8)

MILE POST [2] Gradually introduce whole natural foods to your diet, such as grains, beans, fresh vegetables, fresh fruit, and fresh seafood and poultry. ELIMINATE canned and frozen foods.

MILE POST [3] Perhaps the most important step is not to deprive yourself or your family of anything **until you have replaced it** with a natural alternative. Example, replace all sugars (raw, brown, powdered, white turbinado, carob, dextrose, etc.) with a polysaccharide sugar. Use a natural sweetner made from whole cereal grains such as barley or rice syrups or a combination of barley and corn syrup, with occasional use of honey and maple sugar. I have provided many dessert recipes for your sweet tooth and enjoyment. You may also use your favorite recipes and substitute using, for example, whole wheat flour instead of white, fresh fruit instead of canned and frozen, grain syrups instead of white and brown sugars.

MILE POST 4 Set the example for your child and family. Do not punish or condemn them for eating "junk" foods. You may want to ask yourself where they got the habit. Remember **sugar is very addictive** for both the child and parent. If you take the time to prepare natural snacks and goodies for your family, they will indeed eat them. Bake a fresh apple pie and place it on the table next to **your** favorite candy bar giving them a choice. Their sense of smell will guide them in the right direction.

MILE POST 5 Replace red meat with fresh seafood and organic poultry, always keeping **BALANCE** in mind when serving a meat dish. The ratio should be 1 part meat to 3 - 4 parts of fresh vegetables. Your family may surprise you and enjoy the **BALANCED** meal you prepare. Remember that eating is a habit; do not be afraid to break old habits and try new, healthful eating patterns.

MILE POST 6 By preparing **BALANCED** meals and incorporating whole foods such as cereal grains, fresh vegetables, fresh fruits and a moderate amount of fresh seafood and organic poultry, you will find that you and your family will be satisfied and the cravings for "junk" foods will be eliminated. Remember that eating incomplete and "junk" foods causes a craving to eat more incomplete foods, never satisfying a chemically related habit.

MILE POST 7 Make the time to make the change. You and your family are worth it. Have a weekly conference and discuss the week's activities. (work, school, play, etc.) Then plan a **BALANCED** menu around that schedule. Everyone should make suggestions, (Natural ones, of course) as to what the menu and meals should include. Planning in this manner will gain the full support of the family, save money at the grocery and farmers market, eliminate impulse buying and, most important, ELIMINATE impulsive junk food eating.

I have also prepared for you a chart showing those foods which are more **BALANCED** and those which lie at the extreme opposite of **BALANCE**. I have prepared a 28 day menu, along with a Holiday menu to be used as a guide. It is suggested that you use these menus as **guides** and that you allow your intuition to guide you in planning a menu and meals for you and your family.

I have further prepared for your convenience a shopping guide and utensils list, as well as a refined foods substitution list. This will aid you when you start the adventure of shopping for **BALANCED** foods at your health food store or grocery.

 *YOUR ORGANIC FILLING STATION*

You may choose to purchase your foods as we do, without leaving our home, direct from MOUNTAIN ARK TRADING COMPANY. It all amounts to a convenient and fast way to shop for the finest quality natural foods available in the country today.

In the summer of 1982, four families – three from Boston, and one from Houston – moved to Fayetteville, a picturesque town in the hills of northwest Arkansas. Their purpose: to start a community founded on the principles of natural living, essential to a healthy and happy life. They hoped their community would serve as an educational focus for the rest of the country.

Each of the four families had different talents and vocations, but all four shared a concern for the conditions in our country, and all shared the belief that natural living offered a clear road to good health. They realized that their efforts to establish a centered community must begin with a source of the highest quality, heathful and delicious foods.

Thus, Mountain Ark Trading Company was born, providing the highest quality, natural foods, by mail order nationwide. Frank Head and Joel Wollner, both of whom had extensive business experience, particularly in the natural foods business, formed the nucleus of the company. Bill Tims, a practicing naturopath, and Tom Monte, a noted author on natural health, rounded out the Board of Directors. Collectively, these four families have more than 40 years experience in the natural health field.

Mountain Ark provides a variety of services for its 15,000 customers nationwide. In addition to its mail order service, it publishes a GUIDE TO WHOLE FOODS, a monthly newsletter on natural cooking, sponsors educational seminars, and cooperates with healing centers around the country. A call to the Mountain Ark toll-free order desk is often filled with information and cooking tips in addition to fast and efficient service.

Mountain Ark emphasizes high quality. It has assembled a network of farmers and food-crafters from all over the country who grow and produce foods by the highest standards humanly possible. These standard-bearers of excellence provide Mountain Ark with an incredible array of whole grains, beans, sea vegetables, soybean foods, whole grain flours and bakery goods, pastas, hard-to-find specialty foods and durable kitchen equipment. Mountain Ark believes that these high quality products should be available to all, at competitive prices, along with excellent service. Once an order is placed, it is shipped right out via United Parcel Service (UPS) and reaches the customer's front door within a few days. Call Mountain Ark toll-free at 1-800-643-8909 to place an order or request a FREE CATALOGUE.

Testimony

DR. MARGARET CARMAN
ATLANTA, GEORGIA

I have been thin my entire life, however family and friends always commented about the "excess" baggage on my thighs and hips. Weighing 130 pounds and being six feet tall, losing weight obviously was not my goal.

However, the cellulite which had accumulated around my thighs and hips was a constant source of embarrassment to my self esteem and a constant reminder that I needed to find a method to rid myself of the "cellulite."

I am a 27 year old Chiropractic Physician and have an extremely busy and hectic schedule. I am also not overly fond of strenuous exercise. I have read every article and book available on the subject of losing accumulated cellulite. None had worked for me.

In just three short weeks, after changing my dietary and nutritional habits to the AUTOBAHN DIET, I lost 10 pounds and **all the cellulite**. My entire body felt lighter and more toned. I have never felt better in my entire life. All was accomplished without vigorous exercise, simply by following a well **BALANCED** nutritional program.

People commented about the change in my shape, and of course, I love all the compliments. I would recommend the AUTOBAHN DIET to those people seeking a safe, healthy and sure way of losing cellulite and excessive weight.

Exit 8
THE ROAD MAP

Now the star of the show, the "GRAIN GROUP." This consists of whole cereal grains and their by-products: bread, chapati, noodles and pasta. At every meal prepare at least 30% - 40% whole cereal grains, selecting from: brown rice, millet, barley, oatmeal, fresh corn, wheatberries or some buckwheat groats. Whole wheat and rye may be enjoyed in their secondary form, such as whole wheat and rye breads, chapati, pita, noodles, macaroni, and corn grits. These secondary forms should be enjoyed in moderate amounts. Beans and seeds, since they are near to the cereal species, could also be used as part of the principal food or as a side dish to complement the principal food. For example, beans can be cooked or served together with brown rice and other grains.

These "stars" are not to be eaten all at once, but rather consumed gradually throughout the meal, along with the supporting cast.

SOUP: MISO AND TAMARI - *THE OCTANE BOOSTERS*

EVERYDAY, 1 - 2 cups of soup should be included in your daily food intake. Soup is an excellent way to begin a meal. Soup taken at the beginning of a meal prepares the digestive system for the foods that follow. Soup should consist of land vegetables, as well as sea vegetables, and may be seasoned with fermented enzymes such as miso or tamari. At other times, you may season your soups with sea salt. You may add beans and grains to your soup for variety.

FRESH VEGETABLES: *THE POWER ACCESSORIES*

EACH MEAL should include about 20% - 30% of a variety of vegetables, including leafy greens, ground, round and root vegetables. Most of them will be cooked using a variety of cooking methods such as steaming, boiling, baking and sauteing. One-third may be eaten in an uncooked form such as salads or pickles, according to environmental conditions and your taste preferences. Remember when using oils in sauteing and cooking that they should be of good quality, cold pressed vegetable oil. I suggest the use of sesame oil and corn oil. These are the least processed and refined. Also try to keep the use of oil to a minimum. Mayonnaise and commercial dressings should be avoided. There are many recipes for salad dressings in the dressing section that I know you will enjoy. With your spirit of creativity, I know you will be able to invent and create your own original dressings.

BEANS AND SEA VEGETABLES: *WHEN BETTER BODIES ARE BUILT BEANS WILL BUILD THEM*

The daily meal should contain about 10% - 15% of beans and sea vegetables. They may be cooked separately or combined with land vegetables and can be served in soups or prepared as side dishes. Choose beans such as lentils, adukis, chickpeas, (garbonzos), black beans, pintos, limas, navy, kidney, etc.

Sea vegetables such as arame, wakame, kombu, hiziki, Irish moss, dulse, nori and agar-agar can be used in a variety of cooking methods, including desserts.

SEAFOOD AND POULTRY: *OPTIONAL EQUIPMENT*

The daily meal can contain a 4 - 6 oz. portion of seafood and/or other animal food. Remember that we are building a healthy body, and the largest portion of food on our plate is whole cereal grains. Always eat plenty of fresh vegetables when having your meat dish; the ratio is 3 - 4 parts vegetables to 1 part meat.

FRUITS, SEEDS, AND NUTS: *A DELICIOUS MANEUVER*

Your first preference would be to chose from those fruits which are locally grown and in season. Fruits may be enjoyed as desserts, either fresh, cooked or in dried form. Desserts may be enjoyed and should be made with polysaccharide sugars such as barley malt or rice syrup. Try preparing them as baked or broiled fruit pies. Seeds and nuts should be enjoyed as part of your meal, they may be eaten raw or lightly toasted. They can be seasoned with sea salt or tamari. Honey and maple syrup can be used occasionally.

BEVERAGES: *THERMOSTATIC CONTROL*

Please try to avoid drinking during meals. It is better to enjoy your beverages before or after a meal. The recommended beverages are bancha twig tea, (sometimes called Kukicha tea) which contains calcium, no tannic acid and only a trace of caffein, dandelion tea and cereal grain coffees. They are now appearing in plentiful quantities in our markets and are quite good. Barley grain coffee, Durham, Heritage House, or any beverage which does not contain high amounts of caffein, and does not have an aromatic, fragrant odor may be used. Herbal and aromatic teas are not recommended for daily use. Good quality beer such as Coors and Guiness Stout may be enjoyed in small quantities. Soya milks and nut milks are excellent substitutes for cow's milk and can be used without the fear of incurring the possible dangers of disease. Well and spring water can also be used.

Foods To Be Avoided For Better Dietary BALANCE Are:

Soda, artificial drinks, coffee, dyed aromatic, stimulant teas such as mint and peppermint teas, sugar, syrups, saccharine and other artificial sweetners, all chemicalized foods such as colored, preserved, flavored, sprayed and otherwise chemically treated foods, all refined polished grains, bleached flours and their products, mass-produced industrialized foods, including canned and frozen foods, hot spices, aromatic, stimulant foods, vinegar. TRY TO AVOID the **regular** consumption of white potatoes, tomatoes, eggplant, asparagus, spinach, avocadoes, and any other tropic fruit and vegetables, as long as you are living in a non-tropical climate. Occasional use of tropical, semi-tropical fruits and their juices is O.K. The use of dairy products should be limited to occasional enjoyment, not for every day use. Their mucus-forming qualities do not enhance good health, plus the processing and additives used in these products (including so-called vitamin D-2) create a health risk.

I have prepared four separate dietary stages and have broken them down by percentages for your daily food consumption. Each diagram shows a **BALANCED** plate and the foods are proportioned accordingly.

Some people may choose to completely abandon their present eating habits and patterns, others may proceed more slowly, gradually introducing grains and vegetables in their meat based diet. Either way is satisfactory. Everyone should feel comfortable, advancing at their own pace, without feelings of rigidity or guilt.

STAGE 1 - THE STARTER WHEEL

* ELIMINATE processed and chemicalized foods from your diet, many of them may contain carcinogens.

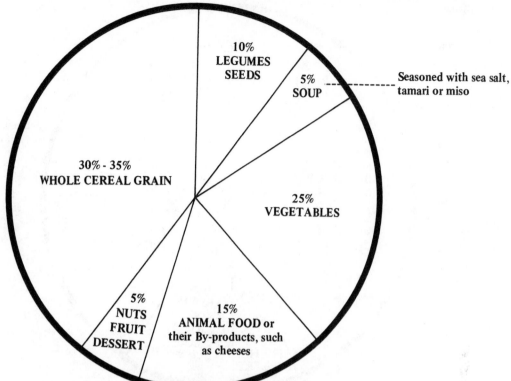

MILE MARKER 1   5% of your diet may include soup, which contains both land vegetables and sea vegetables. Soup may be seasoned with sea salt, tamari or miso.

MILE MARKER 2   30% - 35% of your diet should include whole cereal grains. These should be prepared in a variety of cooking methods and include; brown rice, barley, millet, oatmeal, corn, buckwheat groats or buckwheat noodles. Whole wheat and rye may be enjoyed in the form of bread, chapati, sprouted wheat bread or noodles and macaroni.

MILE MARKER 3   10% of your diet may include legumes, lentils, adukis, chickpeas, pintos, limas, black beans, navy beans, etc. Seeds such as, pumpkin, sesame, squash, and sunflower.

MILE MARKER 4   15% of your diet may contain a portion of white meat fish, shellfish, organic poultry or lean red meat. The fish should be fresh and locally caught. The poultry and beef should be organically fed, not injected with dyes, hormones, steroids and artificial colorings. To maintain **BALANCE** when having meat the ratio should be 1 part meat to 3 - 4 parts vegetables.

MILE MARKER 5   25% of your diet should include fresh, locally grown vegetables, organically grown when possible or they should be grown in a climate similiar to your own. 2/3 of the vegetables should be cooked using a variety of cooking methods such as steaming, boiling, baking and sauteing. 1/3 may be eaten in raw salad form.

MILE MARKER 6   5% of your diet may contain desserts. Desserts can be made with polysaccharide sugars such as rice syrup or barley malt syrup, with or without fruit and nuts. Fresh fruits used should be in season and locally grown or from a climate similar to your own. Dried fruits may be used moderately. AVOID imported tropical fruits, refined sugars, artificial sweetners and ALL products containing them.

MILE MARKER 7   All beverages should be consumed before a meal or after a meal, NOT during a meal.

STAGE II - THE WHEEL

* ELIMINATE processed and chemicalized foods from your diet, many of them may contain carcinogens.

15%
LEGUMES
SEEDS
SEA VEGETABLES

5% ----- Seasoned with tamari,
SOUP   sea salt or miso

40% - 45%
WHOLE CEREAL GRAIN

25%
VEGETABLES

5%
NUTS
FRUITS
DESSERT

10%
ANIMAL
FOOD
and their
by-products
such as cheeses

MILE MARKER 1 5% of your diet may include soup, which contains both land vegetables and sea vegetables. Soups may be seasoned with tamari, sea salt or miso.

MILE MARKER 2 40% - 45% of your diet should include whole cereal grains. These should be prepared in a variety of cooking methods and include; brown rice, millet, barley, oatmeal, corn, buckwheat groats or buckwheat noodles. Whole wheat and rye may be enjoyed in the form of bread, chapati, sprouted wheat bread or noodles and macaroni.

MILE MARKER 3 15% of your diet may include beans, sea vegetables, and seeds. Adukis, lentils, garbonzo, pintos, limas, black, etc. Pumpkin, squash, sunflower and sesame seeds. Arame, dulse, agar-agar, Irish moss, wakame and kombu may be prepared in your beans, soups or as a side dish. Beans 2 - 3 Tbs. daily, Sea Vegetables 1 Tbs., seeds 1 Tbs. and nuts 1 Tbs.

MILE MARKER 4 10% of your daily diet may include animal food such as white meat fish, shellfish and organic poultry. ELIMINATE red meat. The fish should be fresh and locally caught. The poultry should be organically fed, not injected with hormones, dyes, steroids and artificial colorings.

MILE MARKER 5 25% of your diet should include fresh, locally grown vegetables, organically grown when possible or they should be grown in a climate similiar to your own. 2/3 of the vegetables should be cooked using a variety of cooking methods such as, steaming, boiling, baking and sauteing. 1/3 may be eaten in raw salad form.

MILE MARKER 6 5% of your diet may include desserts. Desserts should be made with polysaccharide sugars such as rice syrup or barley malt syrup, with or without fruit and nuts. Fresh fruit used should be in season and locally grown or from a climate similar to your own. Dried fruits may be used moderately. AVOID imported tropical fruits, refined sugars, artificial sweetners and ALL products containing them.

MILE MARKER 7 All beverages should be consumed before a meal or after a meal, NOT during a meal.

STAGE III - THE BALANCED WHEEL

* ELIMINATE processed and chemicalized foods from your diet, many of them may contain carcinogens.

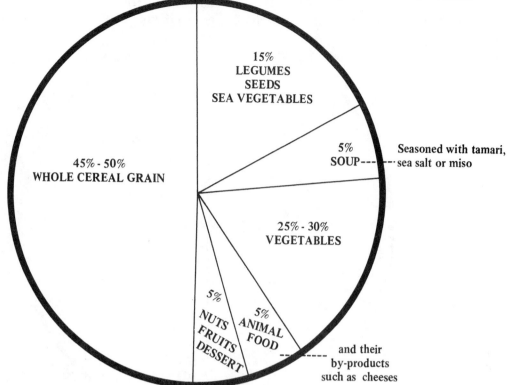

MILE MARKER 1 5% of your diet may include soup, which contains both land vegetables and sea vegetables. Soups may be seasoned with tamari, miso or sea salt.

MILE MARKER 2 45% - 50% of your daily diet should include whole cereal grains. These should be prepared in a variety of cooking methods and include; brown rice, millet, barley, oatmeal, corn, buckwheat groats or buckwheat noodles. Whole wheat and rye may be enjoyed in the form of bread, chapati, sprouted wheat bread or noodles and macaroni.

MILE MARKER 3 15% of your diet may include beans, sea vegetables, and seeds. Adukis, lentils, garbonzo, pintos, limas, black, etc. Pumpkin, squash, sunflower and sesame seeds. Arame, dulse, agar-agar, Irish moss, wakame and kombu may be prepared in your beans, soups or as a side dish. Beans 2 - 3 Tbs. daily, Sea Vegetables 1 Tbs., seeds 1 Tbs. and nuts 1 Tbs.

MILE MARKER 4 5% of your daily diet may include animal food such as white meat fish, shellfish and organic poultry. ELIMINATE red meat. The fish should be fresh and locally caught. The poultry should be organically fed, not injected with dyes, hormones, steroids and artificial colorings. This is a desireable stage and will free one from illness and provide a solid foundation for better health.

MILE MARKER 5 25% - 30% of your diet should include fresh, locally grown vegetables, organically grown when possible or they should be grown in a climate similar to your own. 2/3 of the vegetables should be cooked using a variety of cooking methods such as, steaming, boiling, baking and sauteing. 1/3 may be eaten in raw salad form.

MILE MARKER 6 5% of your diet may include desserts. Desserts should be made with polysaccharide sugars such as rice syrup or barley malt syrup, with or without fruit and nuts. At this stage it is preferred that all fruits are cooked. Use fresh fruit, in season. Dried fruits may be used moderately. AVOID imported tropical fruits, refined sugars, artificial sweetners and ALL products containing them.

57

STAGE IV - THE TURBINE WHEEL

* ELIMINATE processed and chemicalized foods from your diet, many of them may contain carcinogens.

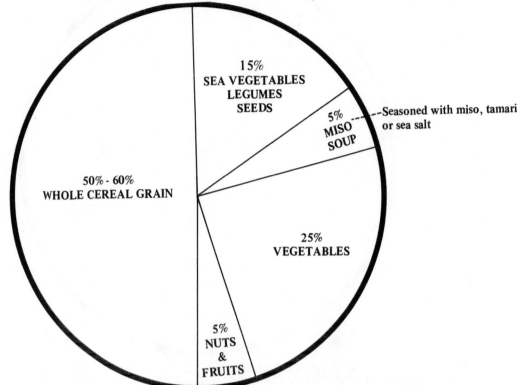

MILE MARKER 1 The meals have now become simpler. After soup, the main dish will include 50% - 60% whole cereal grains which include; brown rice, millet, barley, fresh corn, oatmeal, some buckwheat groats or buckwheat noodles. Whole wheat and rye may be enjoyed in the form of unleavened bread.

MILE MARKER 2 20% - 25% of your diet should include fresh, locally grown vegetables, organically grown when possible or they should be grown from a climate similar to your own. All the vegetables should be cooked using a variety of cooking methods such as steaming, boiling, baking and sauteing.

MILE MARKER 3 15% of your diet may include legumes such as lentils, garbonzos, black beans, adukis, pintos, navy, etc. The meal will also include a portion of sea vegetables such as arame, hiziki, dulse, wakame, kombu and Irish moss. Seeds, roasted or toasted such as pumpkin, squash, sunflower and sesame. 3 Tbs. Beans, 1 Tbs. sea vegetables and 2 Tbs. seeds.

MILE MARKER 4 5% of your meals may include a portion of either cooked or fresh fruits that are in season and that are locally grown or grown in a climate similar to your own. Roasted or toasted nuts such as almonds, filberts or walnuts, 1 Tbs.

MILE MARKER 5 Fresh seafood may be eaten once or twice a week. The sea food should be fresh and locally caught.

MILE MARKER 6 All beverages should be consumed before a meal or after a meal, NOT during a meal.

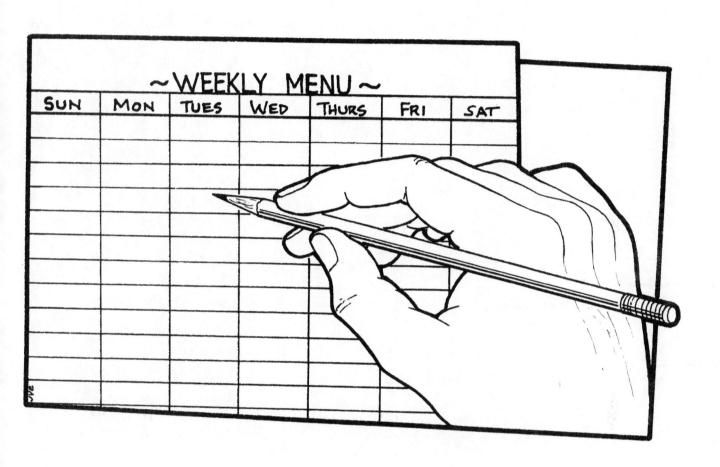

* All recipes can be found in the *Journey For Health* recipe section.

SUGGESTED MENU PLANNING

	BREAKFAST	LUNCH	SNACKS	DINNER
DAY 1	1 Fresh Orange 1 Bowl Cinnamon Oatmeal Fruit Cereal 1 Slice Whole Wheat Toast 1 Cup Grain Coffee or/ Bancha Tea	1 Bowl Straight 8 Vegetable Soup 2 Ears Fresh Corn Fruit Bean Casserole Salad with 1 oz. Cheese Tamari Lemon Dressing Steamed Broccoli Beverage	Seeds and/ or Nuts	1 Cup or Bowl Straight 8 Vegetable Soup Fruit Bean Casserole Brown Rice Delight Mashed Sweet Potatoes and Squash Steamed Greens Salad with Italian Dressing 4 - 5 Oz. Broiled Chicken Breast Beverage Strawberry Custard
DAY 2	½ Grapefruit Apple Nut Pancakes with Barley Malt Syrup 1 Cup Grain Coffee or/ Bancha Tea	1 Bowl Yokohama Barley Soup Salad Granada on a Bed of Lettuce Sliced Tomatoes and Sprouts Fresh Strawberries Beverage	Rice Cake with Apple Butter	1 Cup or Bowl Yokohama Barley Soup Ramen Noodles and Vegetables Sweet Potatoes and Nut Butter Steamed Cauliflower/Carrots/ Broccoli Applesauce Beverage
DAY 3	Stewed Dried Fruit 1 Bowl Breakfast Cereal for Quick Start 1 Slice Whole Wheat Toast 1 Cup Grain Coffee or/ Bancha Tea	1 Bowl Autobahn Miso Soup Tofu Eggsalad on Bed of Lettuce with Sprouts 1 Oz. Portion of Cheese Pickle Sliced Tomato Beverage	Carrot Sticks	1 Cup or Bowl Autobahn Miso Soup Tempura Fish and Vegetables with Tamari Ginger Sauce Salad with Autobahn Dressing Apple Pie Beverage
DAY 4	Apple Juice 1 Bowl.Daytona 500 Cereal 1 Cup Grain Coffee or/ Bancha Tea	1 Bowl Carrera Miso Soup Tofu Sloppy Joes Mixed Fresh Fruit Salad Pickle Beverage	Toasted Pumpkin Seeds	1 Cup or Bowl Carrera Miso Soup Millet Delight Steamed Collards with Orange Slices Stuffed Acorn Squash Sauteed Tofu and Vegetables Beverage

SUGGESTED MENU PLANNING CONTINUED

	BREAKFAST	LUNCH	SNACKS	DINNER

DAY 5	Stewed Apples and Apricots
	1 Bowl Three Grain Cereal
	1 Slice Whole Wheat Toast
	1 Cup Grain Coffee or/
		1 Bowl Rally Green Miso Soup
		Bugatti Bonanza Spread in
		  Whole Wheat Pita Bread
		Chopped Lettuce
		Pickle
		½ Cup Fresh Strawberries
		Beverage
			Sliced
			Apple
				1 Cup or Bowl Rally Green
				  Miso Soup
				Brown Rice
				Sweet Baked Beans
				Fish Kebab
				Salad with Summertime
				  Dressing
				Glazed Carrots
				Steamed Leafy Greens
				Peach Crisp
				Beverage

DAY 6	Apple Juice
	Blueberry Muffins
	1 Cup Grain Coffee or/
	  Bancha Tea
		1 Bowl Rally Green Miso Soup
		Sweet and Sour Fish
		Macaroni Salad
		Sliced Tomatoes
		Creamed Carrots and Onions
		Pickle
		Baked Apple
		Beverage
			Seeds and
			or
			Nuts
				1 Cup or Bowl Fast Back Soup
				Refried Beans on Chapati
				Brown Rice
				Chopped, Scallions, Tomatoes
				  and Lettuce
				Grated Cheddar Cheese
				Strawberry Pudding Freeze
				Beverage

DAY 7	½ Grapefruit
	1 Bowl Grand Prix
	  Breakfast Cereal
	1 Cup Grain Coffee or/
	  Bancha Tea
		1 Bowl Milan Minestroni Soup
		Brown Rice and Vegetable
		  Casserole
		Broccoli Parmesan
		Pickle
		Carrot Cookies
		Beverage
			Our
			Granola
				1 Cup or Bowl of 911 Miso
				  Soup
				Brown Rice and Corn
				Chicken Van
				Steamed Greens with Sweet
				  and Sour Pumpkin Dressing
				Steamed Carrots and Turnips
				Salad with Italian Dressing
				Apple Sauce Pie
				Beverage

SUGGESTED MENU PLANNING CONTINUED

	BREAKFAST	LUNCH	SNACKS	DINNER
DAY 8	1 Bowl Brown Rice Crispies with Fresh Fruit and Almond Milk Raisin Nut Muffins 1 Cup Grain Coffee or/ Bancha Tea	1 Bowl Escort Miso Soup Three Bean Salad Macaroni Salad ½ Fresh Apple Pickle Beverage	Raisins	1 Cup or Bowl Escort Miso Soup Brown Rice Delight Steamed Collards with Tofu Dressing Steamed Squash 4 - 5 Ozs. Broiled Fish with Lemon Wedge Salad with Autobahn Dressing Red/White/Blue Dessert Beverage
DAY 9	Tangerines Grain Omlette with Sliced Tomato 1 Slice Whole Wheat Toast with Apple Butter 1 Cup Grain Coffee or/ Bancha Tea	1 Bowl Recaro Mushroom Soup Millet Burgers with Lettuce and Sprouts Steamed Collards with Tofu Dressing Pickle Beverage	Brown Rice Crispies Snack	1 Cup or Bowl Recaro Mushroom Soup Brown Rice with Garbonzo Beans Sweet and Sour Carrots Hot Turnips and Steamed Turnip Greens Mashed Sweet Potatoes and Squash Blueberry Pie Beverage
DAY 10	4 Ozs. Fresh Squeezed Orange Juice Buckwheat Pancakes with Barley Malt Syrup 1 Cup Grain Coffee or/ Bancha Tea	1 Bowl Bandit Miso Soup Grain/Fruit/ and Nut Casserole Steamed Broccoli Pickle Beverage	Rice Crackers	1 Cup or Bowl Bandit Miso Soup Barley Delight Steamed Carrots, Squash, Cauliflower and Broccoli 4 - 6 Ozs. Fried Trout Salad with Brown Rice Dressing Strawberry Apple Custard

SUGGESTED MENU PLANNING CONTINUED

	BREAKFAST	LUNCH	SNACKS	DINNER
DAY 11	Stewed Peaches and Apples 1 Bowl Three Grain Cereal 1 Cup Grain Coffee or/ Bancha Tea	1 Bowl Bronco Aduki Bean Soup Power Shift Burgers Tossed Salad with Italian Dressing Tangerine Pickle Beverage	Toasted Almonds	1 Cup or Bowl Bronco Aduki Bean Soup Brown Rice and Corn Shrimp Tofu Delight Italian Style Green Beans Salad with Autobahn Dressing Apple Pie Beverage
DAY 12	Melon in Season 1 Bowl Cream of Oats 1 Slice Whole Wheat Toast 1 Cup Grain Coffee or/ Bancha Tea	1 Bowl Heel and Toe Miso Soup Bugatti Bonanza Spread on Bed of Lettuce Sliced Tomato Pickle Beverage	Seeds and or Nuts	1 Cup or Bowl Heel and Toe Miso Soup Millet Delight Broccoli Parmesan Steamed Kale, Carrots and Tofu BBQ Shiitake Mushrooms Brown Rice Pudding Beverage
DAY 13	4 Ozs. Apple Juice 1 Bowl Millet and Oats Cereal 1 Cup Grain Coffee or/ Bancha Tea	1 Bowl Mosport Miso Soup Continental Brown Rice Salad Fresh Fruit Salad Pickle Beverage	Popcorn	1 Cup or Bowl Mosport Miso Soup Baked Chicken and Brown Rice Beets Julian Steamed Leafy Greens with Daikon Radish Steamed Cauliflower Salad with Choice of Dressing Peach Compote Beverage

64

SUGGESTED MENU PLANNING CONTINUED

DAY	BREAKFAST	LUNCH	SNACKS	DINNER
14	Stewed Apricots and Peaches 1 Bowl Hot Cream of Wheat Cereal 1 Slice Whole Wheat Toast 1 Cup Grain Coffee or/ Bancha Tea	1 Bowl Rally Green Miso Soup Tofu Eggsalad Sandwich Mix on Whole Wheat Pita Bread Chopped Tomatoes Shredded Lettuce and Sprouts Pickle Beverage	Pear	1 Cup or Bowl Rally Green Miso Soup Stuffed Green Peppers with Brown Rice Fish Kebab Sauteed Carrots and Turnips Steamed Mustard Greens with Red Radish Salad with Choice of Dressing Peach Bavarian Beverage

HOLIDAY MENUS

     * It is suggested that if you are having a bit of "Holiday Cheer," always keep **BAL-ANCE** in mind and keep everything in moderation.

I.   **Holiday I.**

     Autobahn Miso soup or 911 Miso Soup
     Brown Rice Delight
     Steamed broccoli and caulifloweretts
     Whipped buttercup squash
     Organic turkey with mushroom gravy (4 - 6 oz. portions per person)
     Cranberry sauce
     Apple pie
     Bancha tea or Martinellis sparkling cider

II.   **Holiday II**

     Mosport Miso Soup
     Brown rice with fresh corn
     Sauteed mustard green (or collards) with daikon radish
     Apple sauce
     Fresh Salad with Autobahn dressing
     Chicken Van
     Buttercup squash pie or pumpkin pie
     Bancha tea or Martinellis sparkling cider

III.   **Holiday III**

     Corn Chowder
     Boiled watercress with sweet sour dressing
     Steamed cauliflower
     Glazed carrots
     Roast turkey with rice stuffing
     Apple sauce
     Apple pie or pumpkin pie
     Bancha tea or Martinellis sparkling cider

STARTER LIST OF NATURAL FOODS

Basic supplies for two people

Short grain brown rice	2 lbs.		Mugi Barley miso	8 ozs.
Pearled barley	2 lbs.		Tamari soy sauce	8 ozs.
Millet	2 lbs.		Umeboshi plums	8 ozs.
Azuki Beans	1 lbs.		Kuzu	8 ozs.
Chickpeas	1 lbs.		Sea salt	8 ozs.
Lentils	1 lbs.		Sesame oil	8 ozs.
Wakame (sea vegetable)	1 Pkg.		Apple Butter	1 jar
Kombu (sea vegetable)	1 Pkg.		Bancha Tea	4 ozs.
Soba-Buckwheat noodles	2 Pkgs.		Rice Cakes	1 Pkg.
Whole wheat noodles	2 Pkgs.		Sesame seeds	8 ozs.

Suribachi bowl with a wooden pestle

- -

Additional suggested foods:

Rolled oats	Arame (sea vegetable)	Grain Coffee
Steel cut oats	Hiziki (sea vegetable)	Nut Butters
Wheatberries	Dulse (sea vegetable)	Almonds
Sweet Brown rice	Irish Moss (sea vegetable)	Umeboshi paste
Whole wheat macaroni	Barley Malt Syrup	Brown rice vinegar
Koji	Rice Syrup (Yinney's)	Walnuts
Pinto beans	Agar-agar	Filberts
Black Beans	Umeboshi vinegar	Whole wheat flour
Lima Beans	Corn oil	Unbleached white flour
Navy Beans		

- -

FRESH FOODS (Buy only as needed);

Squashes: Butternut, buttercup, acorn, summer, spaghetti
Pumpkin
Greens: Collards, kale, mustards, turnip and dandelion
Broccoli
Carrotts
Cauliflower
Celery
Cabbage
Onions
Scallions (green onions)
Daikon radish/ or red radish
Ginger root
Lettuce
Garlic
Apple juice
Apricots
Fertilized eggs
Fruits in season: Oranges, etc.

Green Beans
Fresh corn
Mushrooms (fresh)/ or Dried Shiitake mushrooms
Tofu
Leeks
Sprouts (or seeds to sprout your own)
Apples
Peaches
Strawberries
Raisins
Brie, Camembert, Guyere, Blue, Dutch cheeses
Seafood: Fresh and locally caught, white meat fish
Poultry: Organically fed, not injected with hormones, steroids, dyes and colorings
Shellfish: Clams, oysters, shrimp
Fresh raw milk

Dear Friends:

The National Health Institute, Inc., is a group of health directed professionals. We are a wellness-oriented organization.

Now that you have made a decision and taken the first step towards a path of wellness, we would like to take this opportunity to offer to those people, who feel comfortable with it, an additional nutritional step.

We appreciate the opportunity to help you with your individual problems and conditions, and together we will seek to help you correct them.

As a growing number of people are discovering, a diet based on the more BALANCED foods can readily be adapted as a PREVENTIVE measure for maintaining overall health. Many case histories and testimonies reveal the improvement of a wide variety of chronic diseases and mental disorders by gradually shifting your diet to whole grains and natural foods, and eliminating those toxic foods which stealthily clog your arteries. Case histories and testimonies report the improvement in dealing with:

Cancer	Diabetes
Cardiovascular Diseases	Asthma
Arthritis	Glaucoma
Allergies	Ulcers
Anemia	Parkinson's Disease
Epilepsy	Endometriosis
Colitis	Obesity
High Blood Pressure	And many, many more

To this end the National Health Institute, Inc. has available a personal nutritional/ medical history questionnaire. This is a NOW type of questionnaire: how you feel and are TODAY. It is based on individuality, body language, food consumption, seasonal and climatic environment, physiognomy, and overall condition. This is not a computerized evaluation. You will receive a personally tailored, balanced, nutritional program prepared by Dr. Theo Koufas, Ph. D.

For further information regarding your specific dietary and nutritional recommendations, write to the staff of:

National Health Institute, Inc.
P.O. Box 935
Highland City, Florida 33846

Our staff is ready and available to share this exciting nutritional program with you.

To Your Continued Good Health!!!

The Staff
National Health Institute, Inc.

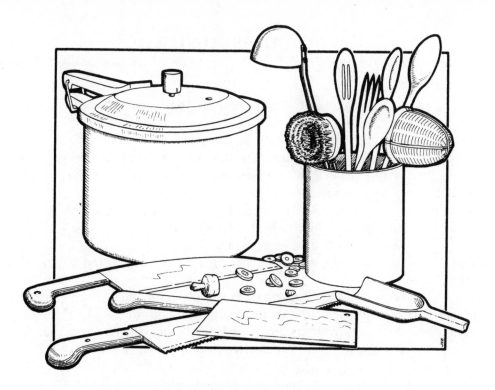

SUGGESTED UTENSILS

Flat wooden spatulas, and rice paddle: They come in all sizes and are excellent for stir frying, mixing flour and serving grain.

Colander or wire mesh strainer: Used for rinsing grains, beans, sea vegetables and rinsing cooked noodles.

Cutting board (Wood): Used for cutting vegetables, dicing nuts and will be useful in kneading dough and flour.

Crock Pot: (Non-electric), Used for making pickles.

Food Mill: Used to puree foods.

Grater: Used to grate vegetables. Vegetable juice also may be extracted. A fine toothed flat stainless steel or porcelain grater is best.

Glass Jars: In a variety of sizes, with air tight lids. Used for storing grains, beans, nuts, seeds and flour.

Knife: Used for cutting. A sharp stainless steel or carbon steel knife is recommended. A caddie knife is an excellent choice.

Pressure cooker: Used for cooking grains, beans and sometimes vegetables. Stainless steel is best.

Soup Pot: Used to prepare soups. Heavy cast-iron, enamel or stainless steel with a tight fitting lid. (Le Cruesant) We never use aluminum cookware, it produces an acid effect in the body.

Skillet: Used for sauteing and frying. Cast-iron is the best. For the best buys check flea markets and garage sales. You can pick one up for $3 - 4 and it will last a life time. Stainless steel is the next choice.

Sharpening Stone: Needed to maintain a good cutting edge on your knife.

Suribachi Bowl: Used for pureeing miso, grinding seeds, etc. It is a baked clay bowl with serrated edges inside, with baked on porcelain or enamel. It comes with a wooden pestle. We have several sizes.

Vegetable brush: Used for scrubbing vegetables. A natural bristle brush is best.

Bamboo Mat: Used to cover foods. It allows the heat to escape while air can enter. It will keep food longer and not spoil as fast.

Bamboo Tea Strainer: To strain the twigs from bancha tea.

Steamer Basket: Used to steam vegetables. (Stainless steel or bamboo.) We have several.

Pots: In various sizes, stainless steel, cast-iron are the best buys. Be sure that they have tight fitting lids. We use Le Cruesant.

Heat dispersing pad or wire trivet: Needed when pressure cooking. This is to be used at ALL times when pressure cooking. A heat dispersing pad for gas stove and a wire trivet for electric. Gas heat is the best for cooking.

Baking dishes: Glass or porcelain in various sizes for baking casseroles, vegetables and for various desserts.

Chop Sticks: I really enjoy having chop sticks to stir the food and to turn foods over when frying etc. Not to mention they are fun to eat with and will be a treat for all.

Large wooden bowl: For mixing flours and kneading the ingredients for bread. Also a dual purpose in serving salads. Stainless steel bowls may also be used.

Wooden spoons and ladles: For stirring and serving soups, etc. We find that wooden utensils of all kinds are much nicer to cook with and very pleasant on the ears.

Pie, cake and bread pans: For baking. We prefer clay but glass is acceptable.

Gas stove: Gas cooking is the optimal in cooking.

Measuring spoons and cups: Stainless steel is best.

*** We keep all our utensils and cooking pots in a convenient place so that we have easy access to them. Before starting any recipe, we suggest that you get **all** the utensils, pots and ingredients in the recipe on the counter before starting to prepare your foods. This will save you time.*

REFINED FOOD SUBSTITUTION LIST

Try preparing your favorite recipes using the following list of natural ingredients. I know you will enjoy the full richness and the rewards of good health that come with using whole natural foods instead of refined chemicals, preservatives and additives.

REPLACE	NATURAL SUBSITUTIONS
1. Refined grains and instant white rice	Whole grains: brown rice, barley, millet, oats, corn, buckwheat, rye and wheat
2. Prepackaged sugar cereals	Whole grains or cracked grains and flakes
3. All purpose bleached white flour and cake flour	Whole wheat pastry flour or whole wheat flour, or unbleached white flour
4. Sugars; Raw, brown, powdered, white tubinado, carob, dextrose, artificial sweetners	Barley malt syrup, rice syrup, honey, maple syrup, fresh fruit
5. Commercial salt	Sun dried sea salt, sesame salt, kelp, powder, wakame powder, tamari soy sauce, miso
6. Distilled vinegar, cider vinegar	Brown rice vinegar, umeboshi vinegar
7. Refined oils, fats, lard, shortening	Cold pressed, sesame oil, corn oil (light or dark), safflower oil
8. Bread crumbs, soda crackers	Whole grain flakes, wheat germ, stale bread
9. Corn starch	Arrowroot, kuzu, whole wheat flour or other whole grain flours
10. Canned and frozen vegetables	Fresh vegetables, organically grown if possible
11. Baking powder	Active dry yeast or sourdough starter
12. Canned and frozen fruits	Fresh fruits, in their growing season
13. Commercial eggs	Fertile eggs
14. Processed milk	Raw milk, oat milk, almond, rice milk, soya milk, bancha tea
15. Canned beans	Dried adukis, garbonzos, black beans, pintos, navy, limas, kidney, etc.
16. Coffee	Cereal grain coffees
17. Commercial salad dressings	Homemade dressings

CHART OF RELATIVE BALANCE

POTASSIUM KINGDOM	COOLING/REFRESHING		BALANCED	SODIUM KINGDOM	HEAT PRODUCING
Expanding Acidity	Sugar Fruit		PRINCIPAL FOODS	Contracting Alkalinity	Salt Cereals
EXTREMELY EXPANDING WEAKENING	EXPANDING CALMING, RELAXING		(Stabilizing)	CONTRACTING TENSION PRODUCING	EXTREMELY CONTRACTING TENSION PRODUCING
TO BE AVOIDED or USED AS LITTLE AS POSSIBLE	SIDE DISHES			SIDE DISHES	TO BE AVOIDED or USED AS LITTLE AS POSSIBLE

POTASSIUM KINGDOM — EXTREMELY EXPANDING, WEAKENING — TO BE AVOIDED or USED AS LITTLE AS POSSIBLE

Drugs
Chemicals
Preservatives
Artificial Sweeteners
Sugar
Honey*
Maple Syrup*
Wines
Whiskey
Brandy
Coffee
Vinegar
ALL Dairy Products:
Milk
Ice Cream
Fats-margarine
Yogurt*
Spices*
Rice Syrup*
Barley Malt Syrup*
IN SUMMER:
Fresh squeezed*
Juice, diluted
with water
FERMENTED BEVERAGES:
Beer*
Home Brew*
Coors*
Rolling Rock
Guisness Stout*
Sake*
Eggplant*
Potatoes*
Asparagus*
Spinach*
Tomatoes*

*Occasional Use

COOLING/REFRESHING — SIDE DISHES

Lima Beans
Black Beans
Soya Beans
Navy Beans
Raw vegetables
Sprouts
Parsley
Yellow Summer Squash
Onions
Leeks
Radish
Carrot
Turnip
Pumpkin
Endive
Lettuce
Kale
Collard Greens
Mustard Greens
Turnip Greens
Kohlrabi
Escarole
Burdock
Scallions
Parsnips
Dandelion
Watercress
Squash:
  Butternut
  Acorn
White Cabbage
Chinese Cabbage
Broccoli
Cauliflower
Brussel Sprouts
Celery
Beets*
String Beans*
Swiss Chard
Olives*
Garlic

Green pepper*
Mushrooms* (Dried)
Cucumbers
Pickles
Sweet Potato*
Zucchini*

BALANCED PRINCIPAL FOODS (Stabilizing)

Buckwheat
Millet
Brown Rice
Whole Wheat
Rye
Oats
Corn
Barley
Beans:
  Adukis
  Lentil
  Garbonzo
  Pinto

ALL ROOT & LEAFY GREEN VEGETABLES (IN SEASON, LOCALLY GROWN),

SEA VEGETABLES:
Hiziki
Arame
Wakame
Nori
Dulse
Agar-Agar
Irish Moss

TOP QUALITY VEG. OILS:
Sesame Dark
Sesame Light
Corn
Sunflower

GRAIN COFFEE:
Chickory
Barley
Ohsawa - YANNOH
Bambu

OTHER BEVERAGES:
Bancha Tea, Water
Rice Milk, Almond Milk,
Oatmilk, Soy Milk

SODIUM KINGDOM — CONTRACTING, TENSION PRODUCING — SIDE DISHES

Sesame Salt
Sea Salt
Tamari
Miso
FISH (Slow moving White meat only)
Sole
Flounder
Salmon
Grouper
Shrimp
Mangrove snapper*
Caviar*
Trout
Lobster
Clams
Mussel
FOWL:(Organically fed)
Turkey
Duck*
Partridge*
Pigeon*
Chicken
Frog*
Snails*
DAIRY: (AVOID as much as possible)
Roquefort
Dutch
Gruyere
Camembert
Brie

* WHAT ABOUT FRUIT? Fine, in moderation and provided the fruit is in season and locally grown or from a climate similar to your own. Tropical fruit for occasional summer use is okay.

HEAT PRODUCING — EXTREMELY CONTRACTING, TENSION PRODUCING — TO BE AVOIDED or USED AS LITTLE AS POSSIBLE

Commercial Salt
Red Meats:
  Beef
  Pork
Salted Hard Fats
Red Fleshed Fish
Eggs: (in cooking) Should be fertile
Wild Game*
Pheasant*
Goat Cheese*
Cigarettes*

*FRUIT
Strawberries
Chestnuts
Cherries
Apples
Peaches
Almonds
Walnuts
Peanuts
Raisins
Watermelons
Oranges
Apricots
Pears
Tangerines
Filberts
Blueberries
Raspberries
Pears

NATURAL FOODS THAT SUPPLY MINERALS

CALCIUM: Whole cereals, fruits, citrus fruits, nuts, legumes, cabbage, parsnips, soya milk, Bancha Tea, cow's milk. Calcium builds bones and good teeth. The National Dairy Council, from kindergarten on, has been telling us that milk provides calcium, and that we must drink milk for health. They advertise the same message on T.V. nowadays, because milk sales are falling sharply. Why? People are discovering the **truth.** Cows' and goats' milk form hard curds in the stomach which putrify and leave the body susceptible to many diseases.

Long before milk became "fashionable" in the late 19th century, we had a healthy intake of calcium by eating whole cereal grains and fresh fruit. These **still** provide the best source of calcium, and **will continue to do** so long after milk and the National Dairy Council fall from grace.

FOOD	SERVING SIZE	CALCIUM	IRON
Milk	1 Cup	288 mg.	0.1 mg.
Turnip Greens	1 Cup	252 mg.	1.5 mg.

IRON: Wholewheat, oats, lentils, dried beans, dried peas, red and white cabbage, onions, watercress, celery, beets, all greens, raisins, currants, prunes, cherries, apples, blackberries, strawberries, loganberries, English walnuts, the yolk of eggs.

MAGNESIUM: Brown rice, barley, oatmeal, whole cereals, soybeans, legumes, watercress, dandelion, turnips, radishes, cabbage, all green vegetables, chinese cabbage, celery, potatoes, string beans, cherries, blueberries, blackberries, apples, raisins, oranges, plums, prunes, figs, coconuts, nuts.

PHOSPHORUS: Whole cereals, legumes, nuts, baked potatoes, prunes, egg yolk, cottage cheese.

LIME: Legumes, soybeans, greens of all kinds, egg yolk, cottage cheese.

FLUORINE: Cauliflower, cabbage, potatoes.

SILICA: Barley, oats, oatmeal, onions, cabbage.

IODINE: Fish, bean, peas, agar-agar, all garden vegetables.

SULPHUR: Cabbage, cauliflower, onion, brussel sprouts, celery, radishes, egg yolk.

CHLORINE: Parsnips, turnips, cabbage, watercress, cauliflower, radishes, lettuce, unpeeled cucumbers, **RAW** red and white cabbage and carrots, onions.

SODIUM: Carrots, celery, cauliflower, spinach, strawberries, apples, miso, tamari.

POTASSIUM: Watercress, parsley, mustard greens, endive, been tops, cucumbers, turnips, red cabbage, parsnips, swiss chard, dandelion, potatoes, apples, plums, cherries.

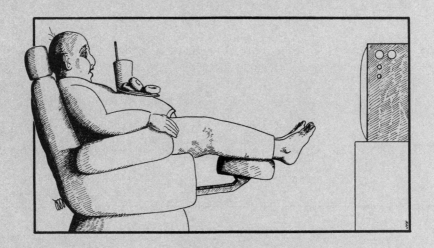

Exit 9
AVOID THE WIDE ROAD

Beware Bad Curves Of Overeating

Imagine that you are in a large, luxurious resort complex, spending a weeks vacation. The first morning there, at breakfast, they serve thick country ham, eggs fried in butter, grits and gravy, bread and butter, milk, coffee with cream and sugar. You enjoy a full, complete meal, then stand up to leave the restaurant. On your way out, you see 166 people in the dining room, slumped over their coffee; dead or dying from heart attacks or strokes.

You leave quickly, in disbelief, and head for the golf course and fresh air. Before you tee off, an ambulance arrives and takes five people away for cancer treatments. **Every minute,** another ambulance arrives to pick up five additional cancer victims. This continues every single minute. As you leave the 18th hole, you find another 166 bodies slumped over the golf carts; people dying of heart diseases.

IS THIS A BAD DREAM? No, friends. **America** is a vast, luxurious resort. Statistics just released show that more than 166 people every hour, approximately **900,000 this year** will suffer a heart attack or stroke. Every 60 seconds someone is diagnosed as having cancer. Look around you now; if you can see six people, two of them will be cancer victims. What's wrong here at **Club America?** Our diet. The fuel that runs our engines is killing us, from the inside out. Our arteries collect fat deposits, our organs store toxic impurities, **our waistlines tell us** that we are on the road to obesity, making us prime candidates for high blood pressure, diabetes, heart disease, cancer, arthritis, and other debilitative conditions.

In 1985, the National Institute of Health, Bethesda, Md., after concluding a conference of 700 nutritionists, researchers, and obesity specialists, issued a stern warning to the 34 million Americans who are overweight. They concluded that a dozen cancers, (colon, rectal, prostate and breast tumors included) are obesity related. Obesity **triples** a persons chances of contracting high blood pressure.

Once you set yourself upon the Autobahn road to health, overeating will **never again** curse you. Through the selection of natural, whole foods, properly **BALANCED** between contracted and expanded varieties, you will be among a vibrant, alert, special group of Americans. You will discover your optimal weight, attain greater vitality, and tone your entire body without vigorous exercise.

YOU WILL NOT COUNT CALORIES

You will eat all that you care to and lose weight proportionally, gaining a new, striking figure. You will not have to count calories. Calorie counting is for test tubes and nutritional scientists, not for people. A calorie burns evenly in a test tube, and different foods produce different amounts of heat. Each and every one of **YOU** are individuals with separate personalities, jobs, life styles and activities. There are no two people alike; each person will burn calories differently. The AUTOBAHN way of **BALANCING** the expanded and contracted qualities of food precludes one from ever having to count calories. **YOU WILL LOSE WEIGHT SAFELY AND NATURALLY.**

THE **BALANCED** AUTOBAHN DIET will stimulate new hair growth and keep your hair shining and fresh.It clears up pimples, brown spots, puffy eyes, and keeps the skin smooth and firm. The Autobahn Diet breaks down cellulite and tightens skin around the face, neck, and arms. Women will discover superior fingernail growth and reduced monthly menstrual cramps.

The Autobahn Diet is a blueprint for living well. It is not a fad or temporary program. There are no harmful chemicals, pills, stimulants, or exercise devices. You are safe knowing that success is based solely on eating and cooking in a NATURAL way.

You are probably asking yourself, "Why is this program any better than the multitude of diets available to me, and how do I know that it will work for me."

First of all I personally object to the word "diet." "Diet", to me denotes something that is done on a temporary basis, "here today and gone tomorrow ." Those individuals who place themselves on "fad diets" may lose a few quick pounds, but find that when they return to their normal eating patterns the weight quickly returns to them and they again find themselves in the same overweight, unhealthy condition.

The Autobahn Diet is not really a "diet" as known in the American vernacular. It was given its name because so many patients and friends wanted to be able to identify their new eating program with a name so they could share their discovery with others. For years I referred to it as just a **BALANCED** way of eating, but I knew that it was more, a program leading to healthier lives. The word "Autobahn" to me represents a free, safe and fast road to good health.

Since I am not really speaking of a "diet" but a **BALANCED** way of eating, let us pause for a moment and glance at the foods that are displayed on the front cover. I show a variety of whole, natural foods that are delicious, easy to prepare and all can be consumed for your enjoyment.

In the beginning so many people said to me, "I can't believe you can eat all this food and lose weight. If I were to eat this much food I would surely gain weight." But when you sit down to a **BALANCED** meal of whole complete foods, your body is receiving all the vitamins and nutriments it requires for good health and a slim, energetic body. You will no longer be eating NON-FOODS which produce FAT and EXCESSIVE WEIGHT!

I want to share with you why I believe and know that this **BALANCED** program called, "The Autobahn Diet" will work for you. There was a time in my life when I weighed 275 pounds and suffered with severe migrain headaches. I had attributed my overweight condition partially to my heritage, being an American born of Greek-Italian descent. Having a loving Italian mother, who naturally expressed her love through good cooking and lots of it. mom's thinking was that if you were not eating all the time, you were either in love or ill. If you happen to be thin, something was definitely wrong. According to my mom, at 275 pounds I was not fat, I just had big bones. I further justified my overweight condition like so many of us do, by telling myself that I just enjoyed eating good food. But the "good foods," although pleasing to my jaded palate, were all **UNBALANCED NON-FOODS**, thus producing a fat and unhealthy body.

Once introduced to the principles of **BALANCE** through nutrition, it was but a few short weeks and my migrain headaches were completely gone. My weight came off so fast, I could hardly keep up with it. I went from 275 pounds and a 44 inch waist to 140 pounds and a 30 inch waist in 8 short months. I have maintained that weight for well over 7 years.

One-third of America's population is overweight to such a degree that their life expectancy is dramatically lowered. Overweight people often have high blood pressure, high cholesterol levels and high blood sugar levels. In the past five years, working as a clinical nutritionist, I have become increasingly aware that 7 out of 10 patients who presented themselves were suffering from some form of degenerative disease, such as cancer, heart disease, hypertension, diabetes, liver problems; and all were OVERWEIGHT.

I believe that obesity, which is fostered by poor and **UNBALANCED** nutritional habits, is the true cause of, our growing degenerative disease population.

Many of the patients who presented themselves for consultation have tried every other diet, as well as all the pills, powders, and mystical miracles of losing weight while sleeping. Some awoke feeling hopelessly depressed, suffering with many emotional problems. The search is over and YOUR JOURNEY IS ABOUT TO BEGIN.

Your diet will be centered around whole cereal grains, fresh vegetables, and the proper amounts of meat. Your desserts will be sweet and contain sugar in the form of glucose, which is a polysaccharide sugar, and will provide you with a smooth, constant supply of energy. The amazing thing about this program is that "**YOU**" do not have to go hungry, or deprive yourself of having sweets. You will regain your health, lose weight, and maintain your figure, no longer indulging in the extremes of eating, which produce an unhealthy, restless life. You will no longer "live to eat." You will be truly free, knowing how to **BALANCE** your foods and achieve mastery of your health, both physically and spiritually. You can focus your life on any goal you wish, and know that happiness is within your grasp. We all have the ability to draw upon the energy and power source of our great universe. Your body and mind are as one, and the food that you eat controls your very thoughts.

Physicians today remove hearts, kidneys, and various other body parts, and install replacement organs or artificial devices. Just as in an automobile, worn out components are exchanged for serviceable spares. But nature intended that our bodies serve us, intact, for a long, full, healthy lifespan. Part exchanges are both unnatural and unnecessary. What the doctors' are **not** telling us is how to **maintain** the engines of life which pulsate, pump, gurgle and grind inside you.

An automobile requires oil changes, lubrication, tune-ups, and tire rotation. If you fail to do these, the car will run poorly and eventually stop.

The main "fuel line" for your body is the bloodstream. Body cells are constantly dying off and being replaced by fresh cells, which feed from and are nourished by the bloodstream. If the foods you are eating contain all the vitamins and minerals required, **and** your nourishment source is non-chemicalized, non-processed whole foods, **then** your new cells will be healthy; your organs will not fail, your arteries will not clog, your vision will not dim, your liver and kidneys will function well.

To complement your new dietary program you may want to include a few simple breathing exercises to help stimulate and cleanse your new healthy body.

Breathing properly and using the lungs to their full capacity will increase the oxygen supply to your bloodstream, brain and to your muscles. The results will be increased energy levels, improvement in body circulation, respiration and heart rate. If, for example, you find yourself yawning and feeling fatigued during the day, we suggest a brief but effective breathing exercise which takes only 5 minutes. This may be done every morning for a quick, clear start that will rev up your engine or simply give you an extra boost of energy when needed.

Although we humans can survive for many days even weeks without eating, without oxygen we would perish within moments. Every activity of the human cell is centered around the oxydation and reduction process, the exchange of oxygen and carbon dioxide. Each of the billions of cells in the body can function to maximum capacity only with a steady supply of oxygen. Breathing is the essential link between life and death. Good breathing insures good health, resistance to disease, vigor and vitality. Yet most of us do not know how to breathe well. The result is diminished capacity to perform physical exercise, irritability, nervousness and less than peak health.

Proper breathing actually begins with the exhalation process. The reason is simple; in order to correctly and completely fill the lungs, they must first be fully empty. Of course there is always a small amount of residual air that can not be expelled, but this must be reduced to the absolute minimum. Obviously the greater the volume of fresh air introduced into the lungs the more efficient will be the exchange that takes place on the alveolar surfaces of those organs. The principle is basically the same as having your air filter on your automobile cleaned by a mechanic. He removes the dust and particals by blowing fresh air into the filter, this allows the engine to run without hesitation. Breathing properly will send fresh clean air (oxygen) throughout your body and peak your metabolism.

We call this diaphramatic breathing. The most important thing is for you to be comfortable, sitting or lying down. This breathing may take a little practice but have no fear, your body already knows how to breathe properly, this is just a friendly reminder.

When you inhale and exhale you will be using your nostrils, so please keep your mouth closed. You will be taking one breath, but in three stages, smoothly and evenly.

Stage I
Emptying the lungs completely.

Stage II
Slowly allowing air to enter the lungs by lowering the diaphram; i.e., swelling the abdomen.

Stage III
Continuing to inhale while expanding the rib cage.

These three stages are done in a smooth, continuous manner, breathing only through the nose. Proper breathing will dispel fatigue and restore vigor and the will to work. Holding the lungs full of air for 10 - 15 seconds will insure the greater exchange of gases in the alveola and enhance the benefits. This breathing technique can be done at anytime during the day, while driving, shopping, cooking, or watching T.V. The cost is nothing and the benefits are enormous.

Improving your circulation and muscle tone can simply be done by using a loofabrush or wash cloth. While taking a shower, simply rub the cloth or brush all over your body, briskly, until the skin becomes pink. This allows the body's fluid to circulate smoothly. When you have finished your body massage stand under the shower and regulate the water, first hot then cool. You will feel invigorated. This should be done once daily.

When you **BALANCE** and **Nourish** the engines of life properly, you are allowing nature to be your personal "service department."

The time has come to change the direction of your waistline, from more to less. Travel with us, as many others have before you, along the AUTOBAHN WAY, a freeway leading to a slender, healthy life. The Autobahn Diet is a completely **BALANCED** nutritional program.

DR. ARTHUR C. HUSTON
COLUMBUS, OHIO

Congratulations, if you have gotten this far in reading "Journey for Health," you are about to have an opportunity to "value" a creative feeding program that may change how you live and feel each day. I would like to pause and share with you what the world "value" means to me.

When I am talking to my patients, I am always searching for what my patients' values are. In doing that I can better prescribe a treatment program that is in keeping with my patients' concerns, needs and lifestyle, rather than just treating the same problem the same way for everybody. I believe that each person is separate and unique; as I am; and of course, as YOU ARE!

If you have come to the place where this program sounds like junk, throw it away, but it still has given you the opportunity to "value" something that you feel won't work for you. If you are still curious or have become excited about the **potential** of the Autobahn Diet, then what follows may be of some help to you.

The people in my practice who seem to latch onto this program feel to me like people who have gotten to the place in life where they want to do better at being healthy and well. They want to take some reasonable discriminate steps towards better health. Most, but not all, of my patients who have opted for the Autobahn Diet are already healthy, by standard medical norms. A lot of them have just had successful physical exams.Because my patients know that we dabble in nutrition they often ask us to help them search for a new personalized feeding program.

In the beginning, the biggest resistance to this program is that it seems complicated and looks different from what they normally prepare and consume. However, I suppose my first bicycle ride or the first time I took the trip down the slope on skis looked difficult. Once you learn the program and practice it a few times, this resistance melts away.

The observed results are really quite **astonishing**. I have had reports from patients who have experienced significant, comfortable weight reduction, that their arthritis is much better, their skin appears clearer, their blood pressure is lower, their headaches are much less and other dramatic lessenings of general physical maladies.

Although the Autobahn Diet was designed exclusively to lose weight, safely and naturally, I am pleased at these reports because chronic ailments are always such a pervasive nuisance. (It's a pain to have a pain.) The most amazing thing my patients report to me is that they have such an increased perception of calmness, alertness, high energy and general well being. What is even more amazing to me is that these feelings should also be so intense within the group of healthy people, who just wanted to nutritionally "take their best shot." Instead of just **being** healthier they report **feeling** healthier.

So in closing, let me suggest that if it suits your particular "values" to try the Autobahn program, try it for a couple of weeks. Pick a friend or mate to journey with you. Patience may be a virtue, but hang in there and give it a chance.

If the above stated rewards begin to occur for you then GOOD LUCK, WELCOME ABOARD and HAVE A NICE LIFE! Or to paraphrase, "The last time I checked you only get one ticket on this merry-go-round, so you might as well pick the best horse."

CURT J. SCHULZE
LAKELAND, FLORIDA

Do you love to eat, snack and consume all you desire? I did and still do, but I am now 70 pounds lighter. I am a 45 year old, senior manufacturer methods engineer and thanks to the Autobahn Diet, I feel better and look a lot better than I have in twenty-three years.

When I came to Dr. Koufas for consultation, I was obese at 260 pounds and very depressed. I had tried numerous diet plans for twenty years, but to no avail. I would go without eating for three to five days which would end up into binges of overeating. To complicate matters, I had a brain tumor removed 7 years ago. The tumor destroyed my pituitary gland, which requires me to take hormones and steroids which ultimately increased my overweight problem.

With the Autobahn Diet, I have achieved a slim 190 pounds and a sensible, livable program of good things to eat that are healthful and nutritious. I do not have to count calories or record what I eat or how much. The best thing of all is I am happy and feeling great!

HARRY BEDFORD
MULBERRY, FLORIDA

My first introduction to the Autobahn Diet and way of eating balanced foods was in the spring of 1984. At the time of my consultation with Dr. Theo, I weighed 212 pounds, my blood pressure was 150/100 and I was taking blood pressure medication.

In a period of 3 months I reduced my weight to 180 pounds, a weight loss of 32 pounds. My waist line went from 38 inches to 34 inches. My blood pressure lowered to a safe 120/80 and the medical doctor has taken me off medication.

I would like to say this is the easiest way to lose weight that I have ever tried. I would recommend the Autobahn Diet to anyone who is seeking a safe and natural program to lose weight.

DAVID MORIARITY
TAMPA, FLORIDA

When I first went for consultation, I weighed 186 pounds, had high blood pressure, a heart condition, high sugar and other complications associated with my overweight condition.

I was placed on the AUTOBAHN DIET and within three months, I lost 40 pounds, my blood pressure returned to normal (110/58), my sugar is normal and all other symptoms and pains are completely gone.

At age 61, I walk over 10 miles a day and have more vitality and energy. I feel better than a 21 year old.

The amazing thing is with the AUTOBAHN DIET, I can eat all that I want and I am still able to maintain my current weight. The foods, especially the desserts, are easy to prepare and delicious. I have been a printer for 30 years and have seen hundreds of diet programs and have tried many of them. The Autobahn way is the most sensible diet to come along in years and has worked miracles for me.

THE AUTOBAHN DIET
Lose Weight Safely & Naturally

MISO - *THE OCTANE BOOSTER!*

FIRST GEAR Let's swing out onto the Autobahn and start our journey. Think Soup. Soup with **miso added** is enjoyed at the beginning of every meal; it helps to **prepare the digestive system for the foods that follow.** Miso is a fermented, aged soybean paste. It contains living enzymes which aid digestion and provides a nutritious balance of natural carbohydrates, essential oils, vitamins, minerals, protein and linoleic acid. Miso aids the blood in helping to promote cell and tissue building which nourishes the skin and hair. Miso contains linoleic acid and lecithin and, when taken daily in soup, will help dissolve cholesterol in the blood and soften the blood vessels. This will prevent high blood pressure, as well as arterio-sclerosis. Miso contains the proper amounts of **glucose** which will give you **long lasting energy**. Soybeans, the base of miso, contain approximately 34% protein, 31% carhohydrates and 18% fat. They have nearly twice as much protein as red meat and fish and 10 times as much as milk. In addition, soybeans are rich in calcium, phosphorus, iron, and other minerals. Miso effectively creates the proper balance needed within your metabolism to insure smooth digestion and **rapid expulsion of wastes.**

*You are to include 3 **Bowls** of soup in your daily food intake, which contain both land vegetables and a sea vegetable called "wakame". It is suggested that you season your soup using 2 **TBS.** of miso to 8 **cups** of water or soup stock. We suggest mugi miso, derived from barley. Other misos are available, for variety.*

THE POWER PAC

SECOND GEAR We have momentum. We shift now to the whole cereal grains. These are the most **BALANCED** of all foods. POWER for endurance, fullness of body and spirit, energy and stamina are contained within each sun ripened, potent capsule.

*You are to include ½ **cup** or more of whole cereal grain at each meal. Whole grains should represent at least 50% of each meal. You may prepare your grains using a variety of cooking methods. Once cooked, surplus grain may be refrigerated and later reheated. Oatmeal and raisins may be added to left over grains to make a delicious breakfast cereal. See Breakfast Section, Exit 12.*

*Select a short or medium grain brown rice, millet, barley, fresh corn, steel cut oats, oat meal or buckwheat groats. Noodles made from rice, whole wheat or buckwheat may be enjoyed 3 **times** a week.*

CHEW EACH MOUTHFUL 20 - 25 TIMES

I recommend the following Grain Combinations for the first seven days. After your initial start up, you may use any of the grain combinations listed in the book.

Monday	75% Brown Rice - 25% Millet	Page 122
Tuesday	75% Brown Rice - 25% Barley	Page 121
Wednesday	75% Brown Rice - 25% Corn	Page 122
Thursday	75% Brown Rice - 25% Garbonzo Bean	Page 122
Friday	Millet - Maserati	Page 132
Saturday	Brown Rice Delight	Page 125
Sunday	Fiesta Rice	Page 126

For **30 DAYS, ELIMINATE ALL** *flour products, including breads, saltines, crackers, and pretzels. Instead, we include a variety of delicious dessert recipes in the AUTOBAHN DIET. After 30 days, prepare homemade breads and pretzels, muffins, cakes and pies from our baking recipes.*

SLUDGE - *TO GUM UP YOUR ENGINE*

NEUTRAL GEAR

For **30 DAYS, ELIMINATE** *your consumption of dairy products, ice cream margarine, butter, cream, eggs, yogurt and milk. Replace ice cream, with Toffutti or Rice Dream, delicious non-dairy desserts. When using eggs, they will be fertile. Eggs will be consumed* **ONCE** *a week and may be used in baking. You are to include a* **1 oz.** *portion choosing from the following cheeses,* **3 TIMES** *a week: Brie, Camembert, Gruyere; other cheeses for occasional use are Blue or Roqueforte. When having cheese, keep* **BALANCE** *in mind and accompany the cheese with a portion of lettuce, sprouts or a piece of fresh fruit.*

BEAN POWER - *WHEN BETTER BODIES ARE BUILT, BEANS WILL BUILD THEM*

THIRD GEAR

Beans are an excellent source of protein, carbohydrates, iron, vitamins and minerals.

You are to include **2 - 3 TBS.** *of beans, at least once a day, in THE AUTO-BAHN DIET. Choose your beans from a selection of lentils, adukis, garbonzos, black beans, pintos, navy, lima, white, etc. You may include the beans in your soups, or you may prepare them as a side dish or even prepare beans in combinations with the grains.*

When preparing beans, it is suggested that you prepare them using a sea vegetable called "Kombu." Kombu, used in a 5" strip, helps to reduce the flatulence, and during cooking helps to keep the beans intact.

CHEW EACH MOUTHFUL 20 - 25 TIMES

OPTIONAL EQUIPMENT

FOURTH GEAR	*For* **30 DAYS ELIMINATE** *your consumption of red meat. (Beef, pork, lamb, etc.) After 30 days on the Autobahn Diet, the red meat and poultry eaten should be organically fed, not injected with hormones, steroids, dyes, antibiotics and colorings.* **ONCE** *a week enjoy a* **4 -5 oz.** *portion of poultry.* **ONCE** *a week enjoy a* **4 - 5 oz.** *portion of shellfish.* **THREE TIMES** *a week enjoy a* **4 - 6 oz.** *portion of white meat fish. Two days a week are meatless.*

Maintain a good **BALANCE** when having a meat dish. To **BALANCE** a meal containing meat include: a salad, a root vegetable, a ground and/or round vegetable and a leafy green. The ratio should always be 1 part meat to 3 - 4 parts fresh vegetables.

POWER ACCESSORIES

FIFTH GEAR	Eat more fresh, locally grown vegetables, organically grown when possible. If not locally grown, produced in a climate similar to your own. **AVOID ALL** canned and frozen vegetables.

Ideally, vegetables should comprise **35 PERCENT** *of your daily diet. Vegetables should be cooked using a variety of cooking methods such as steaming, sauteing, baking and boiling. Concentrate on using* **10 PERCENT** *root vegetables, (onions, scallions, carrots, etc.);* **10 PERCENT** *ground and round vegetables, (squashes, cabbage, broccoli, cauliflower, etc.); and* **10 PERCENT** *leafy greens, (kale, collards, mustards, etc.).* **5 PERCENT** *of your vegetables may be enjoyed in raw salad form, (Romaine lettuce, carrots, scallions, radishes, green leafy vegetables, cabbage, and sprouts). Use homemade dressings in the salad dressing section of this book.*

CHEW EACH MOUTHFUL 20 - 25 TIMES

A DELICIOUS MANEUVER

OVER-DRIVE	**ONE** *dessert may be enjoyed* **DAILY IF** *it is made with polysaccharide sugars such as barley malt syrup or rice syrup. Desserts may be made with or without fruit. Fruit used should be fresh and in season, such as: apples, cherries, strawberries, raspberries, blueberries, blackberries, pears, peaches, plums, tangerines, raisins and apricots. Dried unsulphered fruits may be used. NATURE PROVIDES THE IDEAL FOODS IN YOUR OWN CLIMATE.*

AVOID *the daily use of tropical and semi-tropical fruits and spices, unless living in those regions.*

ELIMINATE *your consumption of* **ALL** *refined sugars,* **ALL** *artificial sweetners and* **ALL** *products containing them.*

FUEL INJECTION

AVOID ALL *icy drinks, along with artificially produced beverages, coffee, cokes, sodas, diet drinks, herbal teas, aromatic teas and stimulants. Fresh fruit juices may be enjoyed in small amounts. All beverages should be taken* **before** *a meal or* **after** *a meal,* **NOT** *during a meal.*

We recommend bancha tea (twig tea) or sometimes called "kukicha tea." This tea contains only a trace of caffein and is a source of calcium. This tea also helps to **BALANCE** *an acidic or alkaline condition. For a variety, mix* **80 PERCENT** *bancha tea with* **20 PERCENT** *freshly squeezed apple, orange, grapefruit, lemon or lime juice.*

Other drinks and beverages to use are cereal grain coffee, (Heritage House, Wilson's , Durham, etc.), roasted barley tea, spring and well water.

AVOID *the use of* **ALL** *alcoholic beverages.*

Soya milk and nut milks are excellent substitutes for cow's milk and can be used without the fear of incurring the possible damages of diseases.

YOUR MAXIMUM DAILY LIQUID INTAKE IS 25 - 30 OZS. PER DAY. This does not include the liquid in your soups. Drink only when thirsty.

For **30 DAYS***, DO NOT DRINK COFFEE!! Coffee will prevent you from losing weight. Caffeine and nitrates inhibit the digestive process and prevents your metabolism from burning carbohydrates.*

SNACKS - THE PIT STOP

Enjoy **2 - 3 TBS.** *daily of toasted or raw seeds, such as squash, pumpkin, sunflower or sesame seeds.*

Enjoy **1 - 2 TBS.** *daily of toasted, or raw nuts, such as almonds, walnuts, filberts, peanuts, hickory, pecans, chestnuts.*

For **30 DAYS, AVOID** *the use of nut butters, then they are to be used occasionally. (sesame butter, peanut butter, almond butter).*

Other snacks are popcorn, rice cakes, rice crackers, apple butter, sesame sticks, granola, fresh and dried fruits.

MAINTENANCE AND PREVENTION

These nutritional recommendations for weight loss **work**. Pounds and inches will come off in the first couple of weeks. There may be a period of no apparent weight loss, but you will notice that inches are coming off the waist and hips. You have nothing to lose but WEIGHT and everything to gain, (EXCEPT WEIGHT). So for those of you who have tried every other diet, as well as every pill, give the **AUTOBAHN DIET** a **30 DAY** trial. I am sure you will not only lose the desired weight, but feel better than you have ever felt, both physically and mentally.

If you do have a strong craving for certain foods, indulge youself, **but keep the portion small.**

Walking is a good exercise, as well as swimming, tennis, etc. Start out walking a ¼ mile daily, go slow and build to a mile daily.

You hold in your hands the key to a long life of glowing health. This is not simply a DIET, the Autobahn Pathways are an introduction to a HEALTHIER way of life. Peace of mind, contentment, and a disposition which puts you at ease with the world, are benefits which go along with your new body. Your view of life and of yourself will forever be changed. It cannot be otherwise. A frail plant, lacking in sunshine and fresh water, blooms majestically and miraculously, given a sunny window box and daily sprinkling.

The AUTOBAHN PLAN will provide YOU with the secrets of food **BALANCE**, and the techniques of cooking that will allow your 20th Century, chemically soaked body, to RETURN to its natural, vibrant, wholesome state.

Be consciously aware of proper chewing. EACH MOUTHFUL SHOULD BE CHEWED 20 - 25 TIMES, *as a natural aid to digestion.* **This will insure your desired weight loss.** *You may eat as often as you like.*

Cooking oil should be used in **MINIMUM** *amounts. I recommend the use of* **sesame** *or* **corn** *oil. A good quality cold pressed oil is always preferred.*

After your meals enjoy a pickle, or a small portion of sauerkraut. This is an excellent aid to digestion. One or two teaspoons are sufficient.

AVOID *eating large quantities of food for* **2 HOURS** *before sleeping, since food at this time is difficult to digest and tends to become surplus.*

AVOID ALL *products to which additives and preservatives have been added; many of them may contain carcinogens.*

Purchase your products fresh and prepare them at home.

AUTOBAHN DIET

SUMMARY

FIRST GEAR	INCLUDES 3 BOWLS OF SOUP DAILY, SEASONED WITH MISO
SECOND GEAR	INCLUDE ½ CUP OF WHOLE CEREAL GRAIN AT EACH MEAL
NEUTRAL GEAR	AVOID SLUDGE
THIRD GEAR	INCLUDE 2- 3 TBS. OF BEANS DAILY
FOURTH GEAR	ELIMINATE RED MEAT FOR 30 DAYS - SUBSTITUTE SEAFOOD AND POULTRY
FIFTH GEAR	INCLUDE 30 PERCENT FRESH VEGETABLES AT EACH MEAL
OVERDRIVE	DESSERTS MAY BE ENJOYED DAILY
THERMOSTATIC CONTROL	MAXIMUM DAILY LIQUID INTAKE 25 - 30 OZS.
SNACKS PIT STOP	NUTS, SEEDS, POPCORN, RICE CAKES, AVOID USING NUT BUTTER FOR 30 DAYS

MAINTENANCE AND PREVENTION

OIL	COLD PRESSED - LIGHT USAGE
ADDITIVES AND PRESERVATIVES	AVOID BY READING LABELS
CHEWING	EACH MOUTHFUL 25 TIMES
DO NOT EAT	LARGE QUANTITIES 2 HOURS BEFORE SLEEPING
EXERCISE	MODERATELY

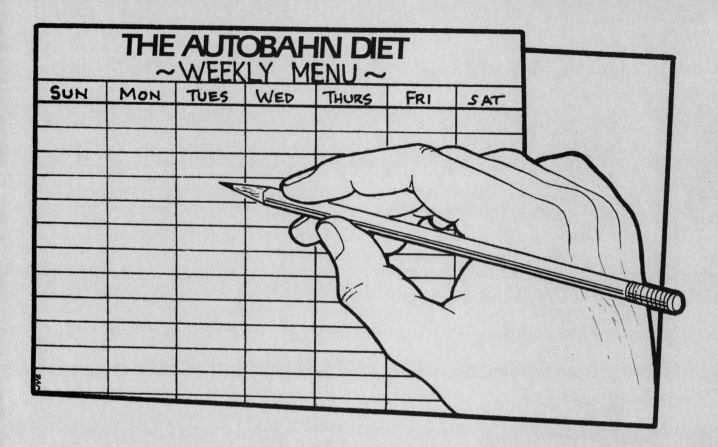

THE AUTOBAHN DIET
~ WEEKLY MENU ~

SUN	MON	TUES	WED	THURS	FRI	SAT

AUTOBAHN SHOPPING LIST

4 lbs. short grain brown rice
2 lbs. pearled barley
3 lbs. millet
2 lbs. oats
1 lbs. aduki beans
1 lbs. chickpeas
1 lbs. lentils
1 lbs. kidney beans
1 Pkg. wakame sea vegetable
1 Pkg. kombu sea vegetable
2 Pkgs. ramen whole wheat noodles
2 Pkgs. rice noodles
Mugi barley miso
Tofu
Sunflower and pumpkin seeds
SPICES: garlic, bay leaves, thyme,
   majoram, dill weed, oregano,
   cinnamon, dry mustard
FRESH VEGETABLES: Squash,
   onions, garlic, carrots, turnips,
   scallions, greens, green or red
   peppers, broccoli, cauliflower,
   celery, lettuce, parsley, daikon
   radish, cabbage, etc.

1 Pkg. Shiitake mushrooms
Rice cakes
4 ozs. bancha twig tea
Grain coffee
4 ozs. arrowroot or kuzu
2 pkgs. agar-agar
Barley malt syrup
Rice syrup
Brown rice vinegar
Tamari
Sea salt
Sesame oil
Corn oil
Raisins
Almonds and walnuts
Apple butter
SUPPLIES: Suribachi bowl and
   wood pestle; stainless steel pressure
   cooker, stainless steel or cast-iron
   soup pot, pans and skillet, trivet
   (Do not use aluminim cookware.)
FRESH SEAFOOD AND POULTRY
FRESH FRUIT: Apples, peaches, blue-
   berries, strawberries, pears, etc.

* All recipes can be found in the Journey For Health recipe section.

THE AUTOBAHN MENU

	BREAKFAST	LUNCH	SNACKS	DINNER
DAY 1	1 Bowl Autobahn Miso Soup Quick Start Breakfast Cereal 1 Cup Grain Coffee or/ Bancha Tea	1 Bowl Autobahn Miso Soup Ramen Noodles and Vegetables Tofu Eggsalad on Bed of Lettuce Pickle Beverage	Seeds and/ or Nuts	1 Bowl Autobahn Miso Soup Brown Rice and Millet Steamed Carrots, Cauliflower and Broccoli Salad with Autobahn Dressing 4 - 6 Ozs. Broiled White Meat Fish with Lemon Wedge Peach Cobbler Beverage
DAY 2	1 Bowl Autobahn Miso Soup Daytona 500 Start Up Cereal 1 Cup Grain Coffee or/ Bancha Tea	1 Bowl Autobahn Miso Soup Brown Rice and Barley Fruit Bean Casserole Sauteed Cabbage and Carrots Pickle Beverage	Rice Cake with Apple Butter	Unleaded Miso Soup Casserole Monte Carlo 2 Tbs. Fruit Bean Casserole Sweet and Sour Carrots Steamed Greens with Orange Slices Rice Pudding Beverage
DAY 3	1 Bowl Unleaded Miso Soup Cinnamon, Oatmeal and Fruit Cereal 1 Cup Grain Coffee or/ Bancha Tea	1 Bowl Unleaded Miso Soup Brown Rice and Corn Bugatti Bonanza Spread on a bed of lettuce Slice of Tomato and Sprouts Pickle Beverage	Brown Rice Crispies Snack	1 Bowl Unleaded Miso Soup Steamed Brown Rice and Corn Fish Kebabs Salad with Brown Rice Vinegar Dressing Steamed Broccoli Glazed Carrots Barley Apple Pudding Beverage
DAY 4	1 Bowl Unleaded Miso Soup Hot Cream of Wheat and Fruit Cereal 1 Cup Grain Coffee or/ Bancha Tea	1 Bowl Filter Miso Soup Brown Rice and Garbonzo Beans Vegetable and Nut Delight 1 Oz. Cheese Pickle Beverage	Rice Crackers	1 Bowl Filter Miso Soup Steamed Brown Rice and Garbonzo Beans BBQ Shiitake Mushrooms Vegetable and Nut Delight Glazed Onions Green Beans and Almonds Strawberry-Apple Custard Beverage

THE AUTOBAHN MENU CONTINUED

	BREAKFAST	LUNCH	SNACKS	DINNER
DAY 5	1 Bowl Turnpike Miso Soup ½ Grapefruit Watkin's Glen Special Cereal 1 Cup Grain Coffee or/ Bancha Tea	1 Bowl Turnpike Miso Soup Lentil Bulghur Burgers Salad/Choice of Dressing Sprouts Beverage	Apple	1 Bowl Turnpike Miso Soup Millet-Shrimp Creole Sauteed Mustard Greens and Radish Orange-Green-White Vegetables Peach Compote Beverage
DAY 6	1 Bowl Turnpike Miso Soup Sliced Orange Millet and Oats Cereal 1 Cup Grain Coffee or/ Bancha Tea	1 Bowl Five Liter Miso Soup Brown Rice and Barley Broccoli Parmesan Carrots and Green Beans with Tofu Beverage	Our Granola	1 Bowl Five Liter Miso Soup Brown Rice and Barley, Steamed Broiled Fillet of Sole Cabbage Salad Hot Turnips Steamed Turnip Greens and Carrots Apple Stuffed Acorn Squash Beverage
DAY 7	1 Bowl Five Liter Miso Soup Stewed Prunes Grand Prix Cereal 1 Cup Grain Coffee or/ Bancha Tea	1 Bowl 911 Miso Soup Stuffed Baked Chicken and Vegetables Steamed Greens with Sweet and Sour Pumpkin Seed Dressing Applesauce Strawberry Pudding	Popcorn	1 Bowl 911 Miso Soup Brown Rice Delight Sweet and Sour Vegies Steamed Broccoli, Cauliflower and Carrots Peach Crisp Beverage
DAY 8	1 Bowl Bridgestone Miso Soup Stewed Apples and Peaches Cream of Oats ½ Cup Grain Coffee or/ Bancha Tea	1 Bowl Bridgestone Miso Soup Noodles and Leeks 1 Oz. Camembert Cheese Pickle Beverage	Seeds and/ or Nuts	1 Bowl Bridgestone Miso Soup Brown Rice and Barley Fruit Bean Casserole Sauteed Mustard Greens and Radish Dynaflow Salad with Dressing Shrimp and Broccoli Delight Strawberry Pudding Freeze Beverage

THE AUTOBAHN MENU CONTINUED

DAY	BREAKFAST	LUNCH	SNACKS	DINNER
9	1 Bowl Bridgestone Miso Soup Three Gear Cereal 1 Cup Grain Coffee or/ Bancha Tea	1 Bowl Toll Booth Miso Soup Power Shift Burgers 2 Tbs. Fruit Bean Casserole 2 Slices Tomato and Lettuce Pickle Beverage	Rice Cake with Rice Syrup	1 Bowl Toll Booth Miso Soup Chinese Millet and Sauce 2 Tbs. Fruit Bean Casserole Fuel Injected Power Vegetables Power Glide Salad and Dressing Blueberry Pie Beverage
10	1 Bowl Toll Booth Miso Soup Cracked Wheat with Apples 1 Cup Grain Coffee or/ Bancha Tea	1 Bowl Toll Booth Miso Soup d'ELEGANCE Salad 1 Oz. Cheese 1 Apple Pickle	Toasted Pumpkin Seeds	1 Bowl Escort Miso Soup 2 Ears Fresh Corn on the Cob Fish Chowder Sauteed Mustard Greens and Radish Italian Salad with Dressing Peach Compote Beverage
11	1 Bowl Escort Miso Soup Barley Breakfast Cereal 1 Cup Grain Coffee or/ Bancha Tea	1 Bowl Escort Miso Soup Fried Rice Tofu Eggsalad on Bed of Lettuce Pickle Beverage	Sliced Apple	1 Bowl Escort Miso Soup Brown Rice and Kidney Beans Vegetable Stew Steamed Kale with Orange Slices 1 Oz. Cheese Squash Pie Beverage
12	1 Bowl Lamborghini Lentil Soup Cinnamon Oatmeal and Fruit Cereal 1 Cup Grain Coffee or/ Bancha Tea	1 Bowl Lamborghini Lentil Soup Rice Burgers Lettuce and 1 Slice of Tomato 1 Apple Pickle Beverage	Seeds and/ or Nuts	1 Bowl Lamborghini Lentil Soup Noodles and Mushrooms 4 - 6 Oz. Broiled Fish Cabbage Salad Steamed Carrots, Radishes and Turnip Greens Rice Pudding Beverage

THE AUTOBAHN MENU CONTINUED

	BREAKFAST	LUNCH	SNACKS	DINNER
DAY 13	1 Bowl Lamborghini Lentil Soup Grain Combo and Fruit 1 Cup Grain Coffee or/ Bancha Tea	1 Bowl Bronco Aduki Bean Soup Rice and Vegetable Casserole ½ Cup Fresh Strawberries Pickle Beverage	Our Granola	1 Bowl Bronco Aduki Bean Soup Barley Delight Chinese Chicken Sweet and Sour Carrots Oriental Vegetables Salad with Autobahn Dressing Steamed Sliced Apples Beverage
DAY 14	1 Bowl Bronco Aduki Bean Soup ½ Grapefruit Heavy Duty Porridge 1 Cup Grain Coffee or/ Bancha Tea	1 Bowl Bronco Aduki Bean Soup Corn Casserole Steamed Broccoli Pickle Beverage	Raisins	1 Bowl Autobahn Soup Millet Delight Steamed Kale, Carrots and Tofu Salad with Brown Rice Vinegar Dressing Oyster Stuffed Broiled Sole Applesauce Beverage

* The same soups can be used for two days. Just refrigerate when cooled. This will save you time. However, if you prefer you may make a fresh soup daily. Simply cut the recipes given in half. You may choose any of the soup recipes, listed in the book, that contain Miso, with the EXCEPTION of those containing grains and miso. You are not to use those recipes for 30 days.

**Save all leftover grain, they are excellent when preparing a breakfast cereal or the grain can be steamed for lunch or you may use them in casseroles.

WEIGHT LOSS TIPS

A. DRINK BEFORE OR AFTER MEALS, NOT DURING A MEAL.

B. CHEW EACH MOUTHFUL, 20 - 25 TIMES.

C. DO NOT DRINK COFFEE FOR 30 DAYS.

D. REMEMBER YOUR DAILY LIQUID CONSUMPTION.

E. AFTER A MEAL WAIT 15 MINUTES BEFORE HAVING A DESSERT.

Exit 10
MISO AND TAMARI

The Octane Boosters!

A Tale of Two Soy Sauces

Tamari, a by-product of miso, is the soy sauce which has formed as excess liquid and is drained off the miso after fermentation. "TAMARI" is used to specify **wheat free** soy sauce. "SHOYU" is the usual everyday soy sauce, made from soybean, wheat and salt. Chemical soy sauce in America is usually called "Soy Sauce" a la kikkoman and La Choy. **Shoyu** is the recommended soy sauce for everyday use by most people. It has a more adaptable flavor, a more diverse culture, and a better variety of amino acids. These qualities are due to a combination of bean and grain used in the making. Tamari is more of a specialty seasoning, especially appropriate for use with sushi or in seasoning crackers. These comprise most of its uses in Japan, however it is also used in certain other specialty dishes. Tamari may be used liberally for regular seasoning wherever the particular flavor seems right, (with certain vegetables, soups and beans, etc.). It is for wheat-sensitive people. Tamari is recommended for all seasonings. But beware, not all soy sauce labeled "Tamari" is wheat free. The label must be carefully inspected for ingredients. Most reputable natural food companies are beginning to comply with these accepted definitions. In the recipes on the following pages that call for "TAMARI", I am referring to the wheat-free tamari, or, you may use Shoyu.

MISO

In simple words, miso, as well as tamari, is produced by combining cooked soybeans, salt, various grains, and allowing fermentation to occur. After the initial cooking, one other step must be taken to complete the process. The grain-bean-salt mixture must be dusted with a type of mold which produces certain enzymes. These actually begin to digest the mixture and cause fermentation. With the correct application of salt, time, and pressure, the process is carefully controlled so that only the beneficial fungal and bacterial cultures survive. The result for **you** is more than just an aid to digestion, because miso supplies protein, calcium, iron and B-vitamins.

Miso also works in the same way as lactobacillus, found in yogurt, providing antibodies within and strengthening the human digestive system. If you do not form bacteria in your intestines, even the best quality food will not be digested or assimilated by your body. In fact, of the many micro-organisms present in miso, almost all are **antagonistic** to the bacteria which cause food poisoning. Veterans of the Second World War can attest to the fact that many survived the ravages of dysentary and nutritional edema only because of their captors frequent food use of fermented soybeans.

Miso looks like a dark paste, and has a salty and slightly spicy flavor. It makes a soup base look as though it were created from beef broth. We can avoid all the disadvantages of animal foods, yet we can still create the sensory pleasures of a rich, dark color and hearty, fragrant aroma.

There are many types of miso sold in natural food stores and some supermarkets today. The history of miso goes back for many centuries. Miso was eaten by Zen Buddhist monks and Samurai warriors alike, and many of them were strong and kept their vitality to a ripe old age. No matter which type is used, be sure it is processed from natural, organic ingredients with no chemicals or preservatives added. It is preferable that it not be pasteurized. The pasteurization will prevent mold formation, but it may also destroy some of the beneficial enzymes. Therefore, when using miso in soup recipes, always add the miso at the end of cooking and **NEVER BOIL** the miso. It is best to merely simmer for 3 - 5 minutes.

Unfortunately, the types of miso sold in most Oriental markets in this country have either been artificially fermented or have MSG or sugar added. This type of miso should be avoided.

The most common type of miso which can be used year around is MUGI miso. The grain used in its manufacturing is barley, and it is aged in wooden barrels for eighteen months. When brown rice is used as the grain, the miso is called GENMAI, if white rice is used it is called KOME, and if one sees the word HATCHO miso it contains no grain but is made from soybeans alone. The rice misos are lighter in taste and especially good in summer months or hotter weather. Hatcho is a more contracted miso, fermented over three years under heavy pressure, and is best eaten in colder climates. It is too strong for everyday use or for anyone living in southern United States. Another favorite miso of mine is Cold Mountain brand. They make several varieties called light yellow miso, red miso and mellow white miso. They are not pasteurized. They are excellent when used in salad dressing and seasoning vegetables.

There are other uses for miso, such as sauces, spreads and condiments. In these cases miso can be boiled, if desired, as long as some miso is eaten regularly in the form of soup, without being boiled. When refrigerating soups containing miso, it is best, after 24 hours, to add a little more miso to the soup to revitalize the enzymes.

Since soybeans are a principal ingredient of miso, and miso is the foundation for the soup course in a **BALANCED** everyday diet, it is worthwhile to look more closely at its composition. Soybeans contain 36% protein and have been called vegetable meat. Although the vegetable protein found in soybeans does lack certain amino acids, these are provided in miso soup by the addition of chopped, fresh scallions and bonita flakes. Soybeans are hard to digest in both raw or cooked form because of a digestion inhibiting enzyme called triptin. However, when they are fermented, such as in miso or tamari, the digestion inhibiting enzyme is destroyed. In addition, there are only 2 sources of vitamin B-12 in vegetable foods. These are sea vegetables and fermented soy products. Your daily miso soup will contain both. Now you will get the benefit of the protein without the adverse effect of indigestion. Soups loaded with animal fat almost surely contribute to indigestion.

In fact, animal protein also clogs and overworks the pores in the kidney. It leaves a residue in these tiny organs, whose size is no larger than the human ear, and whose thousands of tiny pores or nephrons must process all human waste. Miso soup helps remove the fermented meat residue in the kidney and intestines. Dr. Metchnicoff, a Russian physician, once said, "The most effective way to promote longevity is to prevent the poisoning of the intestines." He recommended lactic acid every day, an abundance of which is present in miso. Animal protein residue can produce toxins that damage the heart, arteries, and the nervous system. The benefits of learning to use miso regularly cannot be over-emphasized. **An Alkaline condition withstands infection and produces a strong constitution.** Also, miso soup is a good aid for anyone suffering from anemia or arthritic conditions. It helps in **BALANCING** the metabolism.

Soybeans also contain 18% vegetable fat. Since we have been told so often that excessive fat becomes poisonous to the system, it is important to become aware of the distinction between types of fat and the role they play in our body-mind relationship as a whole.

Your intake of fat should be primarily **unsaturated**, in the form of vegetable oils, along with the natural fats supplied by grains, seeds, nuts and fresh vegetables.

Fish and seafood are also desireable, because they are more **unsaturated** in quality than red meat. Saturated fats have been linked to cancer and heart disease, and are to be avoided. Saturated fats are found in meat, eggs, butter and cheese. They generally come from animal products. An exception to this is coconut oil, which is a saturated fat.

The consumption of both types of fats in this country has risen about 27% since the 1900's, when most people consumed about 31% of their caloric intake from fat. By the mid 1950's this had jumped to about 43%. Today it is estimated that the average American consumes about 160 grams of fat per person, per day.

While it is good news that of the total fat intake the percentage of unsaturated fat intake has risen, this is not an indication of real **BALANCE** in the American diet. Much of the current trend towards poly-unsaturated margarines is coupled with added intake of chemical preservatives and artificial ingredients. Also affecting the statistics, which show a 43% increase in total unsaturated fat intake in 1976, is the fact that meat consumption for that year also increased to 30% of the total daily fat intake. While we are happy to see increased use of vegetable or unsaturated type fats, it is just as important for a **BALANCED** view to see a decrease in animal fat consumption. Remember that your body uses proteins, carbohydrates and fats for its needs, but any excess in either form will be stored by your body only in the form of fat. **This storage of excess fats has a tendency to occur around more compacted organs such as the heart, liver and kidneys.**

Fat plays an important part in the production of bile and sex hormones. Small amounts of fat should be taken regularly and will be when the diet is in **BALANCE**. United States Senator George McGovern, chairman of the Senate Select Committee on Nutrition and Human Needs in 1977, made several very valuable recommendations, among them was to "eat less meat." Under pressure from the American National Cattlemen's Association and the American Meat Institute, he was persuaded to change the recommendation to "eat less animal fat." This is vague and misleading to our population since there is much evidence that there may be many adverse effects from consuming too much animal protein. Also, it would seem clear to a body-mind in focus, that the surest way to reduce consumption of animal fat is to EAT LESS MEAT.

Another contributor to high consumption of saturated fats in many diets is milk and milk products. It would be wise to consider why cow's milk contains far more saturated fat than a nursing mother's breast milk, even though they both contain approximately the same amount of total fat. The unsaturated fat which is more prevalent in breast milk (by two to four times the amount in cow's milk) is called linoleic acid, and it is important to our diets for several reasons. Scientists doing research with linoleic acid now believe it may play a significant role in preventing heart attacks. Dr. Ancel Keys has stated that, ". . . a little over two parts of linoleic acid may offset the harmful effects of one part saturated fat."

Linoleic acid is also a valuable contributor towards beautiful skin. Babies who are not adequately supplied with it develop scaly, itchy skin which also may have sores and break easily when scratched. Other research has been done regarding the role of linoleic acid in over-eating. These results indicate that when linoleic acid was given supplementally to babies, the total caloric intake was spontaneously decreased. When another type of fat was given in its place, the infants tested ate far more.

You will be pleased to know that linoleic acid is present in sources other than just breast milk. The best additional sources are found in oils pressed from grains, seeds and nuts. Corn oil, for example, contains 57% linoleic acid and the vegetables in **your daily miso soup** are lightly sauteed in this type of oil.

A **BALANCED** view of a modern diet leads us to the use of these foods assuring us of a well-functioning body-mind relationship.

SUMMARY

The value of using miso, from a nutritional point of view, is its beneficial character-istics. Miso is a fermented, aged soybean paste. It contains living enzymes which aid in digest-ion and provides a nutritious **BALANCE** of natural carbohydrates, essential oils, vitamins, enzymes, protein, as well as linoleic acid. Miso aids the blood in helping to promote cell and tissue building, which nourishes the skin and hair. Soybeans contain 34% protein, 31% carbohydrates and 18% fat. They have nearly twice as much protein as red meat and fish and ten times as much as milk. In addition, soybeans are rich in calcium, phosphorus, iron, lecithin and other minerals. They contain nearly maximum proportions of amino acids es-sential to man's diet.

Miso paste is added at the end of cooking. Place miso in a suribachi bowl, add ½ cup of hot broth and puree. Add the miso puree to the soup and continue to simmer for 3 - 5 min-utes. PLEASE DO NOT boil the miso, as boiling destroys the essential enzymes and minerals.

STOCKS FOR SOUP

To further enhance the nutritional value of your daily soup course, a little effort in setting aside the ingredients for a stock will pay big dividends. It is not only economical, since most of these products would otherwise be discarded, your soup will be tastier and the broth richer.

Several basic items, such as water retained from preparing beans, noodles and veg-etables, can be strained, saved, and stored in glass containers in the refrigerator. These provide the liquid called for in soup recipes, in place of water. Keep a container with a tight lid, saving all the cut ends of root vegetables; onions, carrots, turnips, squashes, scallions, celery, etc. A delicious stock can be made from these ends by simply boiling them in 7 - 8 cups of water for 20 to 30 minutes. Strain the broth, then either discard the cooked ends or throw them on a compost pile.

Be sure to use the broth immediately or allow to cool to room temperature then refrigerate for later use.

To make an instant stock when no scraps are available we suggest using two table-spoons of bonita flakes (dried fish flakes) in five cups of boiling water, simmer for three minutes and strain the flakes from the broth.

Another basic stock is to take a 3" x 7" piece of Kombu, sea vegetable, wiping off the white residue with a dry cloth, and boiling the kombu for 20 minutes in five cups of water. Simmer the stock for an additional five minutes, strain and use the liquid for stock. Save the kombu to use in a delicious sea vegetable dish.

Remember that any liquid which has been used in cooking is suitable for stock. The following recipes will be easily adapted to the use of your own creative stocks. Exercise your imagination further by choosing to thicken any of these recipes for a creamy soup with the following grains:

1. Barley flour, toasted
2. Buckwheat flour, toasted
3. Oat flakes, rolled or ground into flour
4. Semolina, toasted in oil
5. Cornmeal, toasted in oil
6. Rice flour

In using the following recipes, flexibility is advised. There are many things which may change the cooking times that are given, so do not adhere blindly to the suggested ones. Your heat will vary, your cooking utensils may be heavier or lighter, or your liquid quantity may change slightly. For example, a soup for fifteen people will take longer to cook than a soup for four people. As a creative art form, cooking should not be a carbon copy of any recipe.

Strive to keep vegetables crisp; when sauteing, do not overcook. Remember they will be simmered for an additional period of time. If certain vegetables are not available, allow your intuition to substitute others. Stay with the creation of the food itself. Watch, smell, observe, and be guided by the process that is happening. **Do not leave the kitchen** or try to do too much at one time. **LOVE** the art of cooking. Leave your problems at the door of your kitchen. Your attitude will surely reflect in your finished product. **You are creating the body and mind of tomorrow.**

Remember before adding miso to your soup that you dilute the miso with a little hot soup broth and mix it till it becomes a puree. This should be done in a suribachi bowl. Add miso at the **end of cooking, and allow to simmer for a few minutes. NEVER BOIL MISO. If your soup is stored in the refrigerator for 24 hours or longer, add a small amount of miso to rejuvenate the enzymes. You may choose to season your soups with sea salt or tamari; add them also at the end of cooking.

SOUP

Soup is an excellent way to begin a meal, as well as a wonderful way to start the day. Although Americans do not traditionally eat soup for breakfast, many other societies or groups within societies are fortunate enough to have overcome this cultural aversion. They benefit by receiving a better quality vegetable protein boost to help meet their stamina needs for the day.

Soup, taken at the beginning of a meal, helps prepare the digestive system for the foods which follow. This is the reason I prefer to consume miso-based soups daily. It is a very important food to take for good health.

SOUP RECIPES

TO GET YOU ON THE ROAD

**Wakame, a sea vegetable, can be cut into tiny pieces with scissors while it is in its dry form, then soaked for 5 minutes, drained, discarding the liquid, and added to the soup stock. Or you may soak the strips for 5 minutes, chop into tiny pieces and add to the soup.

***You may garnish soups with sliced scallions, or chopped parsley or small squares of tofu.

TURNPIKE MISO SOUP

6 Cups vegetable soup stock or water
1 Tsp. Bonita flakes (Optional)
1/3 Cup dried wakame, cut tiny (soak, discard water)
1 Tsp. corn oil
2 Onions, chopped
3 Carrots, finely chopped
¼ Small cabbage, chopped
2 TBS. Miso (Barley or mugi, diluted/pureed with broth from soup)
1 Sheet tofu, fried 1/8" thick, cut into 1" squares
1 Scallion, sliced thin, use for garnish

Saute vegetables separately in the corn oil for a few minutes over a low flame. (Start with the onions.) Bring water or stock to a boil and add the bonita flakes. Add the drained wakame and vegetables and lower the flame. Cover and cook on low heat for 25 minutes (or until the carrots are tender). Add miso at end of cooking, (be sure that it is in puree form), simmer for 5 minutes. Garnish with finely chopped scallions and a square of tofu on top.

UNLEADED MISO SOUP

6 Cups of vegetable soup stock or water
¼ Cup of wakame, cut in tiny pieces
    (soak, discard water)
1 Onion, diced
1 Carrot, diced
½ Butternut squash, cubed (or you may
    use any other hard winter squash)
1 Turnip, diced
2 TBS. of Mugi Miso, diluted and pureed

Bring stock to a boil, add the presoaked wakame and cook covered for 10 minutes. Then add vegetables, allow to cook for 5 - 10 minutes or until soft. (Do not over-cook.) Add the pureed miso at end of cooking, cover and allow to simmer for 5 minutes. Serve hot. Garnish with parsley or scallions.

FILTER MISO SOUP

4½ Cups vegetable soup stock or water
½ Cup wakame, cut in tiny pieces
1½ Cups of daikon radish, sliced in
    ½" pieces
1 TBS. of Mugi Miso

Bring water or stock to a boil, add daikon radish, lower flame and cover. Allow to cook for 5 minutes. Add the wakame and cook over low flame until soft, 10 - 15 minutes. Add miso at end of cooking, allow to simmer for 3 minutes. Garnish with sliced scallions.

AUTOBAHN MISO SPECIAL

6 Cups of vegetable soup stock or water
½ Cup fresh mushrooms, sliced thin
3 Scallions, sliced diagonally - ¼"
2 TBS. Mugi Miso, diluted and pureed

Bring the broth to a boil, add the mushrooms and scallions, lower the flame and simmer for 5 minutes. Dilute and puree the miso, add the miso puree to the soup and simmer for 3 - 5 minutes. Serve.

FIVE LITER MISO SOUP

7 Cups of vegetable soup stock or water
1 Clove of garlic, minced
1 Onion, diced
1 Turnip, diced
1 Carrot, diced
¼ Cup wakame, cut into tiny pieces. (soak,
    discard soaking water)
1 Shiitake mushroom, soaked, quartered
    and stem removed
2 TBS. Miso, diluted and pureed

Bring the vegetable soup stock to a boil, add the wakame, lower the flame and cook for 7 - 10 minutes. Lightly saute the vegetables in a little sesame oil. Add the sauteed vegetables to the soup and cook until tender. Puree the miso and add to the soup, continue to simmer for 3 - 5 minutes. Garnish the soup with chopped greens.

HEEL AND TOE MISO SOUP

6 Cups of vegetable soup stock or water
2 Cloves of garlic, minced
7 Scallions, sliced or/ 2 onions, diced
1 Shiitake mushroom, soaked, quartered
    and stem removed (You may soak
    it in the broth from the soup stock)
1 Cup of daikon radish, sliced (use regular
    radish if daikon is not available)
2 Tbs. Miso, diluted and pureed
Small amount of sesame oil

Lightly coat a soup pot with the sesame oil, saute the garlic and scallions first, then add the mushroom and daikon radish. Saute for 3 - 4 minutes. Add the soup stock and bring to a boil, lower the flame and simmer for 10 minutes. Puree the miso and add to the soup and continue to simmer for 3 minutes. Serve.

TARGA MISO SOUP

6 Cups vegetable Soup Stock or water
1 Clove garlic, minced
2 Onions, diced
1 Carrot, diced
¼ Cabbage, shredded
Sesame oil
2 TBS. Mugi Miso, diluted and pureed

Lightly coat a soup pot with oil. Saute garlic, onion and carrot over a medium flame, for 4 minutes. Add cabbage, saute for 2 minutes. Add soup stock. Bring to a boil, lower flame and simmer for 20 minutes. Dilute and puree the miso and add to the soup at end of cooking. Simmer for 2 minutes and Serve.

BRIDGESTONE MISO SOUP

6 Cups of water or vegetable soup stock
¼ Cup wakame, cut in tiny pieces (soak, discard water)
1 Large butternut squash or acorn squash, peeled and cubed
2 Onions, sliced
1 Carrot, cut in ¼" diagonals
2 TBS. Mugi Miso, diluted and pureed

Place wakame, onions, squash and carrots in a pot. Add water or stock, SLOWLY pouring the liquid down the sides of the pot. Bring to a boil. Lower flame and cook covered until the carrots are tender. Add miso at end of cooking, cover and allow to simmer for 5 minutes. Serve.

DELOREAN MISO SOUP

4 - 5 Cups of water or vegetable soup stock
½ Cup of wakame, cut in tiny pieces (soak, discard water)
2 Medium onions, cut into 1/16th pieces
1 Carrot, diced
1 Tsp. sesame oil
1 TBS. Miso-pureed, Cold Mountain Miso (Red)
1 Scallion, sliced

Saute onions and carrots separately in the sesame oil. Bring the soup stock to a boil, add the wakame and lower flame and cook for 10 minutes. Add vegetables and cook on med. flame for 20 minutes or until carrots are tender. Add miso at the end of cooking, cover and allow to simmer for 3 minutes. Remove from flame and allow to set for 2 minutes covered. Garnish with sliced scallions and serve.

TOLL BOOTH MISO SOUP

6 Cups of water or vegetable soup stock
½ Cup wakame, cut in tiny pieces (soak, discard water)
2 Onions, cut in 1/16th pieces
½ Butternut squash, cubed
5 Crescent pumpkin pieces, cubed
2 Carrots, ¼" diagonally cut
2 Turnips, ¼" sliced rounds
2 Stalks of celery, ½" diced
2 TBS. Mugi Miso, diluted and pureed

Place wakame in bottom of a soup pot. Layer all vegetables on top of the wakame, in the order given. Gently pour the soup stock slowly down the sides of the pot, to avoid disturbing the layers. Cover, and bring to a boil, lower flame and simmer for 20 minutes or until the vegetables are tender. Add miso at end of cooking and allow to simmer for 3 minutes.

NISSAN TAMARI SOUP

7 Cups of water or vegetable soup stock
3 Large onions, diced
2 Scallions, diced
2 Cloves of garlic, minced
1 Fertile egg, beaten
2 TBS. of tamari

Lightly saute, garlic, onions and scallions in a pot, add soup stock, bring to a boil, lower the flame and simmer 10 - 12 minutes. Add the beaten egg, slowly to the soup, add the tamari, stir. Turn off heat and allow to set for 2 minutes. Serve.

RALLY GREEN MISO SOUP

5 - 6 Cups vegetable soup stock or water
1 Clove of garlic, minced
2 Medium onions, diced
1 Zucchini squash, ¼" rounds
1/8 Tsp. oregano or Italian spice
1 TBS. Miso - diluted and pureed

Saute garlic, onions and zucchini in a pot, add soup stock and bring to a boil. Add seasoning and lower the flame, allow to cook until the vegetables are tender. Add miso at end of cooking, simmer for 3 minutes.

ESCORT MISO SOUP

6 Cups vegetable soup stock or water
1 Cup of celery, diced ½"
2 Medium onions, diced
2 TBS. Mugi Miso, diluted and pureed

Saute onions and celery in a pot with a little sesame oil. Add 2 cups of soup stock and bring to a boil. Add remainder of the stock and lower flame, cook until vegetables are tender. Add miso at the end of cooking. Allow to simmer for 5 min.

FRAZER MISO SOUP

7 Cups of water or soup stock
1 Clove of garlic, minced
2 Cups of yellow summer squash, ½ pieces
3 Onions, diced
1 Carrot, matchsticked (Option)
2 TBS. of Miso, diluted and pureed
Pinch of thyme

Lightly coat a soup pot with sesame oil, saute garlic, onions, squash and carrots. Add soup stock and bring to a boil, lower the flame, add thyme and simmer until vegetables are tender. Add miso at the end of cooking and simmer for 5 minutes.

MOSPORT MISO SOUP

7 Cups of water or vegetable soup stock
¼ - ½ Cabbage - sliced and chopped
2 Cups of green beans, cut ½" diagonal cuts
2 Medium onions, chopped
1 Carrot, sliced very thin, use as garnish
2 TBS. of Miso, diluted and pureed

Lightly coat a soup pot with sesame oil, saute onions, green beans and cabbage. Add soup stock and bring to a boil, lower flame and simmer till vegetables are tender. (10 - 15 minutes) Add miso at end of cooking, simmer 5 minutes. Serve with a garnish of carrots.

911 MISO SOUP

6 Cups of soup stock or water
Tofu, sliced 1/8" and cubed
4 - 5 Scallions, sliced
2 TBS. of Mugi Miso, diluted and pureed

Bring the soup stock to a boil, add tofu cubes, lower the flame and simmer for 5 minutes. Add the miso and continue to simmer for 3 - 5 minutes. Add the scallions, turn off the flame and allow to set for 1 minute. Serve hot.

WARM UP-QUICK MISO SOUP

6 Cups of water or vegetable soup stock
1 Clove garlic, minced
1 Onion, diced
1 Small carrot, diced
1 Handful fresh green beans, cut in halves
2 TBS. wakame, pre-soaked for 5 minutes (discard the soaking water)
2 TBS. Mugi Miso, diluted and pureed

Lightly saute all the vegetables together, add the soup stock and wakame. Bring the mixture to a boil, lower the flame and allow to simmer until the vegetables are tender. At the end of cooking add the seasonings.

WENDY'S PENICILLIN SOUP
(FOR COUGHS AND SPUTTERS)

A soup for all seasons, when you feel a cold coming on, or a sore throat aches and pains. The ingredients are for adult portions. Children's portions should be cut in half.

5 - 6 Cups of vegetable soup stock or water
5 - 6 Slices of daikon radish, diced
1/3 Cup wakame, cut into pieces, soaked (soaking water discarded)
4 - 6 Shiitake Mushrooms, soaked for 30 minutes, destemed (soaking water discarded)
3 TBS. of Miso (Mugi or hatcho) diluted with stock

Bring the soup to a boil, add the mushrooms, lower the flame to medium. Allow to cook for 10 minutes. Add the daikon radish, allow to cook for 5 minutes. Add the wakame, and allow to cook for another 10 - 12 minutes. At the end of cooking add the miso and allow to simmer 3 - 5 minutes. Serve.

BANDIT MISO SOUP

3 Cloves garlic, minced
5 - 6 Medium onions, cut into 1/16ths
2 Scallions, sliced
2 TBS. wakame, pre-soaked for 5 minutes (discard the soaking water)
2 TBS. cooking sherry
1 TBS. Miso, diluted and pureed
5 Cups of soup stock or water

Bring the soup stock to a boil, add the wakame and garlic, lower the flame and simmer uncovered for 5 minutes. Add the onions and bring back to a boil, lower the flame and cover. Simmer for 5 minutes. Add the sherry and dilute the miso. Add the miso at the end of cooking and allow to simmer for 2 minutes. Serve with croutons or a thin slice of camembert cheese or both. Top with sliced scallions.

SOUPS WITH BEANS

LAMBORGHINI LENTIL SOUP

7 Cups of vegetable soup stock or water
1½ Cups of lentils, rinsed and drained
3 Onions, diced
1 Carrot, diced
¼ Cup wakame, cut into tiny pieces (soaked, discard soaking water)
2 TBS. of Miso/ or 2 TBS. of tamari to taste

Bring soup stock to a boil, add lentils and boil on a low flame for 10 - 15 minutes, add wakame, cook for 10 minutes. Now add the onions and carrots and allow to cook for 10 minutes or until tender. Add miso/ or tamari at the end of cooking. Allow to simmer for 5 minutes. Garnish with sliced scallions and serve.

BRONCO ADUKI BEAN SOUP

6 - 8 Cups vegetable soup stock or water
1 Cup aduki beans, rinsed and drained
1/3 Cup wakame, cut into tiny pieces
    (soak, discard water)
1 3" Piece of kombu
2 Onions, cut into 1/8ths
1 Carrot, ¼" diagonals
2 Stalks of celery, ¼" diagonals
½ Butternut squash (or any hard winter
    squash), cubed
1 Turnip, cut in half moons
½ Tsp. sesame oil
3 TBS. tamari/ or 2 TBS. Mugi Miso,
    diluted and pureed

Put 4 cups of water in a pressure cooker and add aduki beans and a 3" piece of kombu. Bring to pressure and cook for 30 minutes. Remove from heat and bring pressure down quickly by running the cooker under cold water. While beans are cooking, saute all vegetables in a cast-iron skillet, beginning with onions. Place beans, vegetables and liquid in a soup pot, add 2 - 3 more cups of soup stock and the wakame. Bring to a boil, lower flame and simmer for 10 - 15 minutes. Add miso/ or tamari at end of cooking, allow to simmer for 5 minutes. Garnish and serve.

PERSONAL NOTES:

COL. BELANGER'S FAST BACK SOUP

4 Cups of vegetable soup stock or water
1 Cup black beans, rinsed and drained
2 Medium onions, diced
2 Carrots, diced
1 Bay leaf
1 Stalk of celery, chopped
½ Tsp. sea salt
1 Tsp. of tamari (optional)

Saute onions with the bay leaf, add water or stock and beans. Bring to a boil. Simmer for 2 hours. Add carrots, salt, celery and simmer for 15 minutes. If vegetables are added too soon, the bean juice will turn vegetables black. Add tamari to taste. Garnish with chopped parsley or scallions. Serve.

CONTINENTAL BARLEY SOUP

7 Cups of water or soup stock
½ Cup barley, rinsed and drained
¼ Cup aduki beans, cooked (Added to
    the soup at the end)
1 Onion, diced
1 Carrot, diced
¼ Butternut squash, diced
2 Stalks of celery, diced
3 Shiitake mushroom, (Soak for 30 min-
    utes, destem and slice)
½ Tsp. sea salt
Pinch of thyme
1 Tsp. sesame oil
1 TBS. tamari

Lightly saute all vegetables and set aside. Bring soup stock and barley to a boil. Add salt and cover, lower flame and simmer for 20 minutes. Add vegetables, beans, thyme, cover and simmer for 10 minutes. Add tamari at end of cooking, stir and allow to set for 2 minutes. Garnish and serve.

MILAN MINESTRONE SOUP

7 Cups of water or soup stock
1/3 Cup wakame, cut into tiny pieces
    (soak, discard water)
½ Cup garbonzo beans (80% cooked)
2 Onions, cut into 1/16th
1 Carrot, diced
2 Scallions, sliced
¼ Green pepper, diced
1 Turnip, cut into matchsticks
1 Stalk of celery, sliced
1 Zucchini, cut 1" thick slices
1 Clove garlic, minced
¼ Tsp. oregano
½ Tsp. Sea salt
½ Cup fresh Romano cheese, grated
¼ - ½ Cup red Chianti wine
1 Bay leaf
1 TBS. parsley, chopped
2 TBS. tamari
1 Cup whole wheat elbow macaroni

Lightly saute all vegetables in 2 Tsp. of sesame or corn oil. Saute garlic and onions separately and place sauteed vegetables in a bowl. Bring soup stock to a boil. Add partially cooked beans and all vegetables to the stock. Lower flame, add bay leaf, oregano and cover. Simmer for 25 minutes. Add elbow macaroni and salt, bring to a rapid boil stirring constantly, lower flame, cover and simmer for 15 minutes. Stir occasionally. Add wine, simmer for 5 minutes, add tamari. Serve with grated cheese.

G.M. NAVY BEAN SOUP

5 Cups of water or soup stock
1 Cup Navy beans, rinse and soak 4 hours
2 Onions, diced
3 Fresh ears of corn, remove kernels
    from the cob
2 Stalks of celery, diced
½ Tsp. Sea salt

Bring soup stock and beans to a boil. Cover, lower flame and simmer for 45 minutes to an hour. Add vegetables and salt, cover and simmer 15 minutes or until beans are tender. Season to taste with miso (pureed) or tamari. Serve.

LANCIA LIMA BEAN SOUP

4 Cups of water or vegetable soup stock
1 Cup lima beans
1 Onion, diced
1 Carrot, diced
1 Stalk celery, diced
¼ Tsp. Sea salt
1 Small bay leaf
1 TBS. Miso/ or 1 TBS. tamari

Place the lima beans and soup stock in a soup pot, add the bay leaf. Cover and bring to a boil. Lower the flame and simmer for 35 minutes or until the lima beans are tender. Add the vegetables and sea salt, bring back to a boil, lower the flame and cook until the vegetables are tender. Add the miso or tamari and serve.

DAYTONA SPLIT PEA SOUP

6 Cups of water or soup stock
1 Cup split peas, rinsed
½ Cup rolled oats
2 Onions, diced
2 Carrots, diced
1 Stalk of celery, diced
1 Sweet potato, diced
¼ Cup wakame, cut into tiny pieces
     (soak, discard water)
2 Cloves garlic, minced
½ Tsp. Sea salt
1 TBS. of tamari
½ Butternut squash, diced
¼ Cup sesame seeds, toasted and crushed
2 Tsp. sesame oil
1 Bay leaf
1/8 Tsp. thyme
Pinch of rosemary
Croutons

Bring peas and stock to a boil. Lightly saute onions, carrots, celery, squash and garlic. Add sauteed vegetables with raw potato to peas and soup stock. Add ½ cup rolled oats. Lower flame and simmer for 15 minutes. Remove from flame, allow to cool. Place mixture in a blender and blend until smooth. Pour mixture back into soup pot and bring to a boil. Lower flame and add sesame seeds, all spices and seasonings and wakame, stir occasionally. Cover and simmer for 40 minutes, stir occasionally. Garnish with croutons and serve.

KONI-KIDNEY BEAN SOUP

7 Cups of water or soup stock
1½ Cups of kidney beans, rinsed and
     drained
2 Onions, diced
2 Stalks of celery, diced
4 Shiitake mushroom, (Soak for 30 minutes, destem and slice)
2 TBS. of Miso-pureed

Bring soup stock and beans to a boil, cover and lower flame. Simmer until kidney beans are 80% cooked. Add onions, celery, mushrooms and simmer for 15 minutes. Add pureed miso at end of cooking, simmer for 5 minutes. Serve.

*PERSONAL NOTES:

SOUPS WITH GRAIN

*When cooking a soup that contains grain, it is suggested that you add only enough water to cover your grain. As your grain cooks and the water is absorbed, you may add just enough liquid to cover until the grain is cooked. You may add as much or little, as you prefer, depending on how thick or thin you wish your soup to be.

A WHOLE GRAIN SOUP MIX

1 Cup brown rice
1 Cup barley
½ Cup lentils
½ Cup split peas

Place all the ingredients in a sealed glass jar and use in the following soup:

COUPE SOUP

1 Cup of soup mix
7 Cups of water or vegetable soup stock
¼ Tsp. Sea salt
1/8 Tsp. rosemary
1/8 Tsp. thyme
1/8 Tsp. oregano

Place the mix in a saucepan or soup pot with the water and add the seasonings and sea salt, bring to a boil, lower the flame, cover and simmer for 30 - 40 minutes. Now add the following:

2 Cloves of garlic, minced
3 Small onions diced
1 Carrot, diced
2 Stalks of celery, diced
1 Turnip, diced

Add all the vegetables to the soup mixture and bring back to a boil, lower and simmer until the vegetables are tender. Serve.

STRAIGHT 8 VEGETABLE SOUP

8 Cups of water or vegetable soup stock
2 Onions, diced
2 Carrots, diced
2 Stalks of celery, diced
2 Yellow summer squash, diced
½ Buttercup squash, diced
¾ Cup brown rice, barley or millet
1 Tsp. Sea salt
Corn oil
1 Clove garlic, minced
¼ Tsp. dill weed
1/8 Tsp. marjoram
½ Tsp. savory
2 TBS. tamari

Saute the garlic and all the vegetables in a large cast-iron skillet, add all the spices and grain. Mix together well. Saute for 3 - 4 minutes. Add the water in a saucepan and add all the sauted ingredients, bring to a boil, add the sea salt and lower the flame. Cover and allow to cook until the grain is tender. For additional seasoning add sea salt or 2 TBS. of tamari at the end of cooking. Serve.

HIGH CAM MILLET SOUP

7 Cups of water or soup stock
1 Cup tempeh, diced (Cook tempeh first
    in water seasoned with tamari,
    3 - 5 minutes)
½ Cup millet, rinsed and drained
2 Onions, diced
1 Carrot, diced
½ Cup green beans, ½" pieces (add
    10 minutes before end of cooking)
¼ Tsp. Sea salt
1 Bay leaf/ or pinch of thyme
Tamari to taste

Layer all ingredients in the following order, onions, carrot, tempeh, millet and a pinch of sea salt. Gently and slowly pour enough liquid down the sides of the pot to cover ingredients. Cover and bring to a boil, lower flame and simmer. When the millet expands, add enough water to cover. This is repeated until the millet is done. Now add 3 cups of cold liquid, salt and bay leaf, allow to simmer for 10 minutes. Add green beans, bring to a boil, lower and simmer for 10 minutes more. Add tamari to taste. Serve.

ROCKET RICE SOUP

1 Onion, diced
1 Carrot, diced
1 Turnip, diced
1 Stalk of celery, diced in ½" pieces
½ Cup brown rice, rinsed and drained
6 Cups water or soup stock
Pinch of Sea salt
1 TBS. tamari

Layer all vegetables in the order given, along with the brown rice. Gently and slowly pour liquid down the sides of the pot. Add sea salt, bring to a boil and cover. Lower flame and cook for 25 minutes or until the rice is tender. Add tamari and stir. Serve.

MUSTANG MILLET SOUP

8 Cups of water or soup stock
1 Cup of millet, rinsed and drained
2 Onions, chopped
1 Carrot, diced
1 Cup green beans, thin diagonal cuts
¼ Tsp. Sea salt
1 Tsp. corn oil
1 Bay leaf
Tamari to taste

In a heavy cast-iron skillet, saute onions, carrots. Saute green beans and set aside. Bring soup stock to a boil, add millet and sea salt. Lower flame, add sauteed vegetables and bay leaf. Stir well and cover. Simmer for 30 minutes. Add green beans and simmer for 10 minutes more. Add tamari or miso if additional flavor is desired. Serve.

CARRERA MISO SOUP

2 Stalks of celery, diced
2 Onions, diced
½ Butternut squash, cubed
½ Cup brown rice, rinsed and toasted
6 Cups water or soup stock
2 TBS. Miso, pureed

Rinse the brown rice and toast in a skillet. Lightly coat the bottom of a soup pot with sesame or/ corn oil. Layer all vegetables in the order given, and spread the toasted brown rice evenly over the vegetables. Gently pour the liquid down the sides of the pot. Cover and cook on a medium flame until the rice is tender. Add the pureed miso at the end of cooking, simmer for 2 minutes. Serve with sliced scallions as garnish.

YOKOHAMA BARLEY SOUP

6 Cups of water or soup stock
½ Cup barley, rinsed and drained
2 Onions, diced
2 Carrots, diced
2 Parsnips, diced
2 Stalks of celery, diced
4 Shiitake mushrooms, sliced (Soak for
    30 minutes, destem)
1½ Tsp. sesame or corn oil
½ Tsp. Sea salt
Pinch of thyme
Freshly chopped parsley for garnish

Place barley and mushrooms in a heavy soup pot with soup stock, and bring to a boil. Add sea salt, cover, lower flame and simmer for 25 minutes. Saute vegetables in a skillet. When the barley is tender, add the sauteed vegetables to the stock. Add a little more sea salt, thyme and simmer for 15 - 20 minutes. Serve with parsley as garnish.

SUPRA VEGETABLE SOUP

2 Onions, diced
2 Stalks of celery, diced ½" pieces
½ Butternut squash, cubed
½ Acorn squash, cubed
3 - 4 Pieces of crescent pumpkin, cubed
7 Cups of water or soup stock
½ Cup brown rice or/millet, rinsed and
    drained
2 TBS. of Miso-pureed

Layer all vegetables, in a heavy soup pot, in the order given, EXCEPT celery (which will be added 10 minutes before end of cooking time). Gently pour the liquid down the sides of the pot to avoid disturbing vegetables. Place grain on top. Cover and bring to a boil, reduce flame and simmer for 25 minutes or until grain is tender. Add celery, miso puree and allow to simmer for 5 minutes. Serve.

G.T. MUSHROOM BARLEY SOUP

7 Cups of water or soup stock
2 Cloves of garlic, minced
2 Onions, diced
1 Carrot, diced
½ Lb. of fresh mushrooms, sliced
½ Tsp. Sea salt
½ Cup barley, rinsed and drained
Sesame oil
3 TBS. tamari
Freshly chopped parsley for garnish

Bring barley to boil in 2 cups of liquid add a pinch of sea salt. Cover and lower flame, cook for 30 minutes. In a cast-iron skillet, add sliced mushrooms to the DRY skillet, sprinkle on sea salt, cover and cook dry over a medium flame. Pour off excess liquid and set aside. Now lightly coat the skillet with sesame oil, saute vegetables, beginning with garlic, onions, etc. including mushrooms. Add all sauteed vegetables to the barley, plus the additional liquid. Cook for 10 - 15 minutes. Season with tamari at end of cooking. Serve with parsley as a garnish.

LE BARONE MISO SOUP

7 Cups of water or soup stock
½ Cup wakame, cut into tiny pieces
    (Soaked, discard soaking water)
3 potatoes, peeled and quartered
2 Pumpkin or butternut squash, diced
1 Carrot, diced
½ Cup brown rice or/millet, rinsed and
    drained
2 Scallions, sliced fine for garnish
1 TBS. Miso, pureed

Layer all vegetables in the following order, wakame, potatoes, squash, carrot and grain. Gently and slowly pour liquid down the side of the pot enough to cover the ingredients. Bring to a boil, lower flame and cover. Simmer for 30 minutes or until tender. Add pureed miso at end of cooking, simmer for 3 minutes. Garnish with scallions and serve.

BERLINETTA MISO SOUP

7 Cups of water or soup stock
1 Cup of barley, rinsed and drained
2 Onions, diced
¼ Head of cabbage, sliced
1 Carrot, pencil cut
1 Turnip, matchstick cut
½ Butternut squash, cubed
3 - 4" Strips of wakame, cut in tiny pieces
    (soak, discard soaking water)
1 Tsp. sesame oil
1 TBS. Miso - pureed

Bring soup stock to a boil, add barley and a pinch of sea salt. Cover and lower flame. Simmer for 20 minutes. Saute all vegetables separately in sesame oil and set aside. Add wakame, along with all the vegetables, EXCEPT cabbage. Bring back to a boil, lower flame and simmer for 15 minutes. Add cabbage and simmer for 10 minutes more. Add miso at the end of cooking, allow to simmer 2 - 3 minutes. Serve.

ELECTRA 225 SOUP

2 Onions, diced
3 Stalks of celery, diced
1 Cup of oats
1/3 Cup lentils, rinsed and drained
¼ Tsp. Sea salt
6 Cups of water or soup stock

Layer all ingredients in a soup pot in the order given. Gently pour the liquid down the sides of the pot. Cover, and bring to a boil, lower flame and cook for 25 - 30 minutes. Add sea salt and simmer for 10 minutes more. Serve garnished with scallions.

TALADEGA VEGETABLE SOUP

6 Cups of water or soup stock
1 Cup garbonzo beans, soaked overnight
½ Cup brown rice, rinsed and drained
2 Onions, diced
1 Carrot, diced
1 Butternut squash, cubed (or any other
    hard winter squash)
½ Tsp. Sea salt
Tamari or pureed Miso to taste

Place grain and beans, in a soup pot with soup stock. Bring to a boil, cover and lower flame. Simmer until beans are 60% - 70% done. Add vegetables and salt, bring to a boil, lower flame, simmer until tender. Add tamari or miso at end of cooking. Serve.

RICE RUNNER SOUP

1 Onion, diced
1 Carrot, diced
1 Turnip, diced
1 Cup lentils, rinsed and drained
½ Cup brown rice, rinsed and drained
7 Cups of water or soup stock
¼ Tsp. Sea salt
2 TBS. tamari (Optional)

Layer all vegetables in the order given, placing the lentils then rice on top. Gently pour the liquid down the sides of the pot. Cover, bring to a boil, then lower flame. Cook for 25 minutes, add sea salt, allow to simmer for 10 minutes more or until the rice is tender. Add sea salt or tamari to taste. Serve.

FERRARI AND FRIENDS

1 Onion, diced
2 Stalks of celery, diced
1 Carrot, diced
1 Cup whole wheat macaroni
¼ Tsp. Sea salt
7 Cups of water or soup stock
2 TBS. of tamari

Layer vegetables and macaroni in the order given. Gently pour the liquid down the sides of the pot. Add sea salt, cover, and bring to a boil. Lower flame and simmer until vegetables and macaroni are tender. Add tamari at the end of cooking and simmer for 2 minutes. Serve.

VELOCE LIMA BEAN SOUP

7 Cups of water or soup stock
1 Cup of lima beans, rinsed and drained
1 Cup whole wheat elbow macaroni
2 Onions, diced
1 Carrot, diced
½ Tsp. Sea salt
1 Bay leaf
2 TBS. of tamari (Optional)

Place lima beans and water in a soup pot, add bay leaf. Cover and bring to a boil. Lower flame and simmer for 35 minutes or until the lima beans are tender. Add macaroni and vegetables, along with sea salt, bring back to a boil, lower flame and cook for 10 minutes or until the vegetables are tender. Add tamari at the end of cooking and simmer for 3 minutes. Serve, add parsley as a garnish.

BLUEFLAME 6 SOUP

4 - 5 Ears of fresh corn, remove kernels
    from the cob
2 Stalks of celery, diced·
2 Onions, diced
1/3 Cup lentils or navy beans, rinsed and
    drained (If using navy beans,
    precook)
¼ Tsp. Sea salt
6 Cups of water or soup stock
Tamari to taste

Place onions, celery, corn and beans in a soup pot. Add water or soup stock, cover and bring to a boil. Lower the flame and simmer until the beans are tender. Add salt and tamari at the end of cooking. Allow to simmer for a few minutes more. Garnish with chopped scallions and serve.

*PERSONAL NOTES:

CREAMED SOUPS

RECARO MUSHROOM SOUP

7 Cups of cold water or soup stock
1/3 Cup wakame, cut into tiny pieces
    (soaked, discard soaking water)
1 LB. fresh mushrooms, rinsed and sliced
4 Onions, diced
1 Potato or rutabago, diced
1 Cup celery, diced
2 Scallions, sliced
2 Cloves garlic, minced
2/3 Cup oat flour (Rolled oats may be
    put through the blender)
½ Tsp. Sea salt
3/4 Tsp. sesame oil
1 TBS. of Miso-pureed (or tamari to taste)
3 TBS. of fresh parsley, for garnish

Saute all vegetables separately in sesame oil beginning with garlic, then onions and so on. Then set the vegetables aside. Dissolve the oat flour in a little cold liquid to prevent lumping. Add the remaining liquid slowly until dissolved, then bring to a boil, stirring constantly. Cook about 3 minutes or until the mixture thickens. Add the wakame and sauteed vegetables and the sea salt. Reduce the flame, cover and simmer for 20 minutes. Add the miso or tamari at the end of cooking and simmer for 3 minutes more. Garnish with chopped parsley and serve.

* It is best to dry roast the mushroom first before sauteing. Place sliced mushrooms in a dry skillet, sprinkle lightly with sea salt, cover and cook over medium flame. Pour off excess liquid and set mushrooms aside.

VOYAGER RICE SOUP

7 Cups of cold water or soup stock
5 TBS. of roasted rice flour
1½ Tsp. sesame or corn oil
2 Onions, chopped
2 Scallions, sliced
1 Turnip, diced
1 Carrot, diced
1 Stalk of celery, diced
½ Butternut squash, peeled and cubed
¼ Tsp. Sea salt
1 TBS. Cold Mountain red miso, pureed
½ Cup croutons, for garnish

Gradually stir rice flour into the six cups of cold liquid, until dissolved. Slowly bring the mixture to a boil. Cover, lower flame and cook for 15 minutes. Saute vegetables separately in a little sesame oil. Then add all vegetables to the rice cream, along with one (1) more cup of water and the sea salt. Cook over a low flame for 10 minutes. Cool slightly and pour ingredients into a blender and blend until creamy. Return to the soup pot and cook over a low flame for an additional 15 minutes. Add the pureed miso at the end of cooking and simmer for 3 minutes. Serve hot with croutons for a garnish.

*PERSONAL NOTES:

CELERY 928 SOUP

7 Cups of water or soup stock
1/3 Cup oat flour
1 Clove garlic, minced
2½ Cup celery, diced
1½ Cups onions, diced
¼ Tsp. Sea salt
Tamari to taste

Place garlic, celery, onions and 6 cups of water or soup stock into a pot. Bring to a boil, add a pinch of sea salt. Reduce the flame to low, cover and simmer for 15 minutes. Mix the oat flour in the remaining cup of cold water and mix until dissolved. Slowly add the mixture to the soup, stirring constantly to prevent lumping. Bring to a boil, add salt, lower flame and simmer for 20 minutes. Add tamari at end of cooking. Serve.

MAZDA CARROT SOUP

5 Carrots, cubed
3 Onions, diced
4 TBS. roasted barley flour or/
    rice flour
2 TBS. freshly chopped parsley
    (for garnish)
1 Clove garlic, minced
Pinch of thyme
1 TBS. sesame oil
¼ Tsp. Sea salt
7 Cups water or soup stock
Tamari or Miso to taste

Saute the onions, carrots and garlic in sesame oil over a high flame for 3 minutes, then over a medium flame for an additional 3 minutes. Add 2 cups of soup stock and simmer for 5 minutes. Cool slightly and place in a blender and blend until creamy. Bring 5 cups of soup stock to a boil, add ingredients from the blender and stir. Lower the flame, add barley flour, mixing thoroughly. Bring to a rapid boil, lower flame add sea salt and thyme, cover and simmer for 30 minutes. Add miso or tamari at end of cooking, allow to simmer for 3 minutes. Serve and garnish with parsley.

OYSTER BUGATTI

6 Cups of water
1 Dozen fresh oysters
2 Onions, diced
1 Carrot, diced
4 Scallions, sliced ¼"
8 - 10 Red or white radishes, sliced
1 TBS. Miso - pureed
Freshly chopped parsley for garnish

Scrub and wash oysters well. Place oysters in a pot with water and boil until the shells open. Remove the oysters from the pot and remove the meat from the shell. Set oysters aside. Drain the cooking water through a fine strainer, except for the last inch which contains sand. Place the oyster broth in a pot and bring to a boil. Add vegetables and simmer until tender. Add scallions, and oysters and pureed miso, allow to simmer for 2 minutes more. Serve garnished with chopped parsley.

B.M.W. SOUP

1 Lb. of fresh Alaskan crab legs
2 Cloves garlic, minced
1 Onions, diced
5 Scallions, diced
1 Cake tofu, cut into 1" pieces
¼ Tsp. Sea salt
1 TBS. tamari
5 Cups of water

Bring water to a boil, add sea salt and crabs. Lower flame and simmer until crab is tender. DO NOT OVERCOOK. Remove crab from the pot and cool. Add tofu squares and tamari to the crab broth and bring to a boil. Add vegetables, lower the flame and simmer for 5 - 7 minutes. Remove crab meat from shell, place in a soup bowl and pour the soup over the meat. Serve.

MARQUIS CLAM CHOWDER

1 Dozen fresh clams
2 Quarts of water (8 cups)
1 Cluster broccoli stems, sliced
2 Onions, diced
½ Butternut squash, peeled and cubed
2 Potatoes, unpeeled and diced
2 Stalks of celery, diced
¼ Cup wakame, cut into tiny pieces
     (soak, discard soaking water)
Pinch of thyme
Pinch of oregano
1 Bay leaf

Clean and scrub clams thoroughly. Bring water to a boil, cook clams until the shells open. Pour liquid through a fine strainer, except for the last inch, which will contain sand. Save the liquid for soup stock. Add onion, broccoli, carrots, squash and wakame to the clam broth. Bring to a boil and cook for 4 minutes. Remove the clams from their shells and mince very fine. Add potatoes, celery, minced clams, bay leaf and oregano to the soup. Simmer over a low flame for 35 minutes. Remove the bay leaf before serving. Add miso or tamari to taste at the end of cooking.

DUNLOP CHEESE SOUP

2 Cups vegetable soup stock or water
3 Cups oat milk, rice milk, or almond milk
½ Pound cubed cheese, Gruyere or cheddar
1 TBS, corn oil
2 Cloves garlic, minced
2 Onions, diced
½ Green pepper, diced
3 Stalks celery, chopped
2 Potatoes, cubed
2 Carrots, chopped
½ Cup whole wheat flour
3 TBS. tamari
¾ Tsp. Sea salt
½ Tsp. chile powder
¼ Tsp. thyme

Lightly coat a large saucepan with corn oil and saute the vegetables in the order given. Saute for 3 - 4 minutes. Add the sea salt, thyme and chile powder, mix together with the vegetables. Add the soup stock, raise the flame and cook until the mixture thickens and the vegetables are tender, (Approximately 20 minutes). In a separate bowl mix the whole wheat flour and almond milk until smooth, then add to the soup along with the cheese cubes. Lower the flame and simmer until the cheese begins to melt. Add the tamari and simmer for 3 - 4 minutes. Serve garnished with chopped parsley and fresh fruit. This is a delicious sauce for over grains.

*PERSONAL NOTES:

CORVETTE CHICKEN AND RICE SOUP

2 Cloves garlic, minced
2 Onions, diced
2 Stalks of celery, diced
2 Small potatoes, diced
1 Carrot, diced
¼ Butternut squash, diced
¼ Tsp. sea salt
¼ Tsp. sage
2/3 Cup brown rice
6 Cups chicken soup stock

Place 3 TBS. of chicken soup stock in a soup pot. Saute the garlic, onions then add the remaining vegetables and rice. Mix together well. Add the sage and sea salt, along with the remainder of the chicken stock. Bring to a boil, lower the flame and simmer for 25 - 30 minutes or until the rice is tender. If you desire further seasoning, add 1 TBS. of tamari at the end of cooking.

*PERSONAL NOTES:

Exit 11
THE GRAIN GROUP

Stars Of The Show

OUR CLOUDED WINDSHIELD

Our country is the youngest major nation in the world, yet the first one to almost completely abandon the use of whole cereal grains to feed her people. It is interesting to note the majority of the world's agriculture is centered on the production of grain and we are the largest producer. Yet, we have only been able to see the monetary benefits in grain. Recently however, we have begun to understand the relationship between degenerative diseases and the absence of whole cereal grain in our diets.

I believe the time has come to return to eating that which has been, for centuries, the most important food for humanity -- WHOLE CEREAL GRAINS.

Our taste buds have, through improper eating, become so jaded that the body they serve can no longer trust them. It is unfortunate, but true, that when a diet high in spices and artificial, chemicalized foods has been eaten for a period of time, the tongue and palate are no longer sensitive to the subtleties and natural sweetness of the most important and basic items. A **BALANCED** diet will include whole cereal grains. When you take the first step towards **BALANCED** eating and begin to prepare 30% - 40% of your meals around grains, you will also be **re-educating** your physical being to an appreciation of the taste long forgotten, but ready to guide you once again.

Most grains may be pressure-cooked, simmered, or boiled, and if they are prepared with a peaceful attitude, they will always turn out deliciously. Your individuality in cooking will soon reflect new ideas, such as selecting the right grains to fit the weather and season.

117

The health of the persons for whom you will be cooking is another factor to which you will increasingly be attuned, since their changing condition can be accomodated by making foods more contractive or expansive. As your self-awareness deepens you will find that your cooking becomes the most satisfying expression of inner spirituality possible. You will have taken a giant step toward freedom by abolishing the slavery to prepared foods.

Grains (or cereals) then, are the most suitable food for man. The unrefined, whole grains, (ones that would grow if planted) are the most nutritive and afford complete nourishment. Refined, separated, processed grains, (Notably ones which have had additives or "enriched" labels) are the least complete. An example of this is white flour, we will discuss flours in more detail later. All flours to some degree have lost their original value, however, freshly ground grains are the most acceptable. Whole grains are very high in vitamin B and have six of the needed ten amino acids. **The other amino acids will be supplied by eating beans, vegetables, seeds and nuts, along with the grain dish.**

It is often thought that grain is acid forming in the system, but this is misleading. Whole grains, chewed well, become alkaline in the human body. Todays modern man is notorious for being in a hurry. His meals are fast food and he forgets to chew, preferring to drink his food.

There are eight grains generally classified as cereals. They are: buckwheat, brown rice, wheat, millet, barley, rye, oats and corn. Buckwheat and millet are usually considered the most **contracted** and the best season for their use is winter. Oats and corn are the most **expanded** of the grains, and summer is the time to enjoy them. Corn is harvested in late summer or early fall. Rice, millet and rye are harvested in the fall. Wheat and barley are harvested in both May and October. Therefore, the wheat and barley that ripen in May are more expansive than the wheat and barley that ripen in October. Barley and wheat are considered more expansive than rice and millet, and are more suitable for summer enjoyment. Rice and millet give more warmth. Oats are the richest grain in fat content. Corn is the second richest. Oats are richest in mineral salt, barley is next. Oats, buckwheat, and whole wheat are the richest grains in protein. Buckwheat is the richest in magnesium, calcium and amino acids. Its protein more than equals the best animal protein.

The cook who knows how to prepare grains in a variety of delectable ways enjoys more than a culinary talent. As Michel Abehsera put it in *Cooking for Life*, "Don't call a doctor, I need a cook."

BROWN RICE

The Best of the Grain Group

Whole grain brown rice is the most **BALANCED** food for our daily consumption. Approximately one-half of the people in the world still regard it as their chief food, some of them eating as much as a pound a day. It contains most of the essential amino acids, is high in protein, calcium, iron, the B-vitamins and minerals. Brown rice is beneficial for the nervous system and the brain and contains the germ phytic acid, which aids in expelling toxins from the body.

Brown rice has **seven** skins called bran coats. The outer, or hull, is not edible, but because most of the minerals and vitamins in the grain are just underneath in the brownish colored bran coats, it should be husked very carefully. The white rice you usually find in the market is not satisfactory for your nutritional needs. Commercial rice mills use machines which rub off most of the bran coats, thus destroying much of the nutrition in the process of making the grain appear white and uniform in appearance. Processors, then polish the grains, sometimes even stain them, and may finish by covering them with talc and glucose. The natural oil is removed by these processors, and only the starchy kernel is preserved.

While some care must be given to brown rice to prevent the oil from becoming rancid during storage, the benefit is to retain its original food value.

Rice, always remember, is the best and most **BALANCED** whole cereal grain. This is why it is the principal food, (not the only food) in our diet. When I speak of rice hereafter, I will always mean **organic brown rice.**

Always buy well-stored, good quality rice. The way to shop for rice is at a natural food store or the natural foods section of a super-market. Choose a rice that is appropriate for the climate. In a cold climate, short grain is preferred. In moderate seasons of the year, medium grain is best. In hot climates, use long grain in your daily meals. Make certain the rice is not too old, greenish in color or badly broken.

Learn to use a pressure cooker in preparing your rice. It is fast and conserves cooking fuel. It also allows you to control the consistency of the finished product. It takes less water than simmering, and you are less likely to make mistakes. A stainless steel pressure-cooker is recommended, since this metal is less porous than aluminim. It will clean easier, and most important of all, cooking under pressure brings out the full, delicious flavor of the grain. Rice can be pressure cooked at different temperatures which will produce different tastes.

For example; one method in pressure cooking is to use high heat and to bring the pressure up rapidly. Most pressure cookers are fitted with a regulator which jiggles when full pressure has been reached. If yours has different weight selections, the 15 pound weight will probably be correct. Allow your regulator to reach maximum pressure, then reduce your heat to low. From this point you time your rice for 45 minutes, then remove it from the heat and allow it to lose pressure gradually, about 5 - 7 minutes. **Make sure all the pressure** is gone, then remove the lid. Using a moistened rice paddle or wooden spoon, loosen the rice around the edges. To remove the rice, gently mix the top and bottom layers so that they are blended together. DO NOT attempt to scrape the bottom until all the grains are placed in one dish. Then you may scrape the bottom and set this aside in another dish. The kernels that cook close to the heat are **more contracted** than those that cook further away.

Another method is to begin pressure cooking with a very low heat, allowing the pressure to come up gradually. This method is more expanded and produces a very peaceful and calming feeling, as well as a sweeter flavor. You are allowing the grains to adapt slowly to a high temperature.

Another method is to begin cooking with a low heat and gradually increase the temperature to high over a span of 30 minutes.

Still another method is to rinse and drain your rice, place it in the pressure cooker, add the required amount of water and sea salt, place the lid on and allow to soak for several hours before cooking. This is an excellent way to prepare rice if you have an upset stomach or are experiencing digestive problems.

Climate is a factor that influences the way a pressure cooker is used. In moist climates the grain requires less water in preparation. In dry climates the general amounts of water may have to be increased. The more water you add per cup of rice (or any other grain) **the softer** the grain will be. The less water you add, the harder and chewier it will be. I have found that a proportion of 1¼ to 1½ parts of water for each part of rice, serves as a useful standard.

Other cooking methods require slightly different amounts. Freshly harvested rice will always contain more moisture than rice that has been stored for a time, and for that reason requires less water in its preparation.

When cooking small quantities, it is wise to use a little more water.

When the rice you are cooking fills your pot more than halfway, the greater quantity of water you add will come to a boil slowly and the rice kernels may absorb more than you had intended and the rice may turn out too soft. A good rule of thumb is, when cooking large quantities, lessen the amount of water used per cup until a minimum of equal parts of rice and water is reached. One or two attempts should yield perfect results.

We add a **small** amount of **sea salt** to **all** our grains when cooking to bring out their full flavor. We will discuss a condiment called sesame salt later (which can be sprinkled on the rice when served for a more salty taste), however, making rice less salty is impossible after cooking, so use a light hand.

Children and elderly adults are usually happier with a soft, moist, lightly salted rice. Young and middle aged adults generally prefer a chewier, saltier variety.

Always **wash** rice (and other grain, as well as seeds and beans) before using. Place the rice directly into the pot and cover it with water. Swirl lightly with your hand, removing hulls or other particles that may rise to the surface and then drain through a strainer. Repeat this process until the water is clear. When cooking grain in combination with another grain or with seeds or beans, always wash each ingredient separately before combining them in a pot. Certain grains are heavier than others and will stick to the bottom of the pot, so be sure you know which grain to place nearest to the bottom of the pot.

The more contracted grains are generally the ones to put at the bottom, and certain combinations should not be mixed together. For example, rice and corn make an excellent combination. The rice is cleaned separately, placed on the bottom of the pot, add the water and place the corn gently on the top.

Some recipes will call for dry - roasting or sauteing a grain or flour to make it sweeter or more contracted. When dry-roasting, you may start with a cold skillet or saucepan. When you saute, preheat your pot or pan until a drop of water sprinkled upon it's surface will dance before evaporating. Then coat the pot evenly with oil. If the oil smokes, both the oil and your pan are too hot.

After cooking rice, the bottom of your pressure cooker may be slightly scorched. The yellowish rice that forms a layer above it is the richest in minerals. This is called bottom rice. This may be used as a crunchy, chewy snack. Dry completely, then fry in a little oil. The scorching will wash out easily if you pour cold water into the pot or pressure cooker after removing the grain and allow it to sit for some time before washing.

I recommend you do not fill your pressure cooker more than 70% capacity, allowing the pressure to come down naturally. Always remove the pressure cooker from the burner when done. Again, wet a wooden rice paddle or spoon and remove the rice from the pressure cooker or pot as soon as the pressure has reached normal. If the rice is allowed to set in the pot, the moisture that it contains will have an expanded effect on the grains. The rice will be tasteless, soft and wet. Place the grain in a wooden bowl and cover with a bambo mat. It will cool slowly and permit moisture to escape. Use either a heat dispersing pad or metal trivet underneath the pressure cooker, depending on the type of stove you have.

BROWN RICE RECIPES

* All grains may be garnished with sliced scallions, sesame salt, or finely chopped parsley. There are also many sauces you may choose from to use with your grain. Rice used is organic brown rice. When cooking grains, be sure to add a small amount of sea salt to bring out the flavor.

BROWN RICE (Pressurized)
(Serves two)

1 Cup brown rice, rinsed and drained
1 1/3 Cups of water
Pinch of Sea salt

Combine the ingredients in a pressure cooker, cover, place a trivet under the pot and bring to full pressure over high heat. Reduce heat to low and simmer for 45 minutes. Remove from heat and allow pressure to return to normal. Uncover and mix gently with a moistened wooden rice paddle or spatula. Place in a wooden bowl, cover with a wooden mat for a few minutes, and serve.

BROWN RICE (Simmered)
(Serves four)

2 Cups brown rice, rinsed and drained
5 Cups of water
Pinch of Sea salt

For a lighter, fluffier dish, simmer the rice in a heavy cast iron pot. Combine the ingredients, place a trivet under the pot and bring to a boil rapidly over high heat. Reduce heat to low and cover with a tight fitting lid. Cook for 45 - 60 minutes, or until most of the water has evaporated. Depending on the humidity, this could take as long as 1½ hours. Toss lightly with a wooden rice paddle or spatula and let stand in a wooden bowl for a few minutes before serving.

CABRIOLET RICE

1 Cup brown rice, rinsed and drained
5 Cups of water
¼ Tsp. Sea salt

Place rice and water in a pressure cooker. Cover , place trivet under pot and bring to full pressure. Reduce heat to low and cook for 1 hour. Remove from heat and allow pressure to return to normal. Once uncovered, it will reveal a layer of rice milk on the surface of the grain. With a wooden spoon, gently stir the grain back into the rice milk and serve hot. This is an excellent breakfast for infants or elderly people who are unable to chew their food properly. It is also an ideal food to take during an illness of any kind and aids in the problem of constipation.

BROWN RICE AND BARLEY
(Serves 4)

1½ Cups brown rice, rinsed and drained
½ Cup barley, rinsed and drained
2 2/3 Cups water
Pinch of Sea salt

Place rice and water in a pressure cooker, then gently sprinkle barley and salt on top. Cover, place trivet under the pot and bring to full pressure. Reduce heat to low and cook for 45 minutes. Remove from heat and allow pressure to return to normal. Uncover and gently mix with a wooden spatula. Place in a wooden bowl, cover with a wooden mat for a few minutes, then serve.

BROWN RICE AND YELLOW CORN
(Serves 4)

1½ Cup brown rice, rinsed and drained
½ Cup fresh corn, removed from the cob
2 1/3 Cups water
Pinch of Sea salt

Place rice and water in a pressure cooker. Gently place corn kernels and salt on top. Cover, place a trivet under the pot and bring to full pressure. Reduce heat to low and cook for 40 minutes. Remove from heat and allow pressure to return to normal. Uncover and mix gently with a moistened wooden spatula. Place in a wooden bowl, cover with a wooden mat for a few minutes, then serve.

BROWN RICE AND MILLET
(Serves 4)

1½ Cups brown rice, rinsed and drained
½ Cup millet, rinsed and drained
2 ¾ Cups of water
Pinch of Sea salt

Place rice and millet in a pressure cooker, add the water and sea salt. Cover, place trivet under the pot and bring to full pressure. Reduce heat to low and cook for 50 minutes. Remove from heat and allow pressure to return to normal. Uncover and mix gently with a moistened spatula. Place in a wooden bowl and cover with a wooden mat for a few minutes. Serve.

BROWN RICE, TAMARI AND BANCHA TEA
(Serves 2)

1 Cup brown rice, rinsed and drained
1½ Cups of bancha tea
Pinch of Sea salt
¼ Tsp. tamari

Place rice in a pressure cooker, add bancha tea, sea salt and tamari. Cover, and place on a trivet. Cook as per regular brown rice instructions. Serve.

BROWN RICE WITH WHEATBERRIES
(Serves 4)

1½ Cups of brown rice, rinsed and drained
½ Cup whole wheatberries, rinsed and
        soaked overnight
2 2/3 Cups of water
Pinch of Sea salt

Place rice and water in pressure cooker, then gently sprinkle wheatberries and salt on top. Cover, place trivet under the pot and bring to full pressure. Reduce heat to low and cook for 1 hour. Remove from heat and allow pressure to return to normal. Uncover and gently mix with a moistened spatula. Place in a wooden bowl and cover with a wooden mat for a few minutes. Serve.

BROWN RICE AND GARBONZO BEANS
(Serves 4)

1½ Cups brown rice, rinsed and drained
½ Cup garbonzo beans, rinsed and soaked
        overnight
2 2/3 Cups of water
¼ Tsp. Sea salt

Place rice and water in a pressure cooker. Add pre-soaked garbonzo beans (gently) on top and sea salt. Cover, place on trivet and bring to full pressure. Reduce heat to low and cook for 45 minutes. Remove from heat and allow pressure to return to normal. Uncover and gently mix with a moistened spatula. Place in a wooden bowl and cover with a wooden mat for a few minutes. Serve.

**Be sure that when using recipes that contain wheatberries and garbonzo beans that you soak them in water overnight.

BROWN RICE, BARLEY AND COMPANIONS
(Serves 4)

1½ Cups brown rice, rinsed and drained
½ Cup barley, rinsed and drained
1 Onion, diced
1 Carrot, diced
1 Cup butternut squash, cubed
2½ Cups of water
1 TBS. tamari

Place rice and water in a pressure cooker. Add barley, onions, butternut squash and carrot on top in that order. Add a pinch of sea salt, cover, place pot on a trivet and bring to full pressure over high heat. Lower the flame and cook for 45 minutes. Remove from heat and allow pressure to return to normal. Serve.

BROWN RICE AND PINTO BEANS

1½ Cup brown rice, rinsed
½ Cup pinto beans, rinsed
2 ¾ Cup Water
¼ Tsp. Sea salt

Place the rice and water in a pressure cooker. Add the pinto beans on top. Add the sea salt. Cover, place on a trivet and bring to full pressure. Reduce heat to low and cook for 45 minutes. Remove from heat and allow pressure to return to normal. Uncover and gently mix with a moistened spatula. Place in a wooden bowl and cover with a wooden mat for a few minutes. Serve.

*PERSONAL NOTES:

BROWN RICE AND KIDNEY BEANS
(Serves 2)

1 Cup brown rice, rinsed and drained
½ Cup kidney beans, rinsed
1¼ - 1½ Cups of water
¼ Tsp. Sea salt

Place beans in a pot and cover with water, bring to a boil, lower flame to medium heat and cook for 30 minutes. Place rice and water in a pressure cooker, gently add the beans and sea salt. (You may use the water from the beans or save it for soup stock). Cover, place on trivet and bring to full pressure on high heat. Reduce heat to low and cook for 45 minutes. Remove from heat and allow pressure to return to normal. Uncover and mix gently with a moistened wooden spatula. Place in a wooden bowl, cover with a wooden mat for a few minutes. Serve.

SWEET BROWN RICE WITH ADUKI BEANS
(Serves 2)

1 Cup sweet rice, rinsed and drained
¼ Cup aduki beans, rinsed
1 TBS. unhulled sesame seeds
1½ Cups of water
¼ Tsp. Sea salt

Place rice and water in a pressure cooker, then gently place aduki beans on top. Sprinkle roasted, unhulled sesame seeds next then add sea salt. Cover and place on trivet, bring to full pressure on high heat. Reduce heat to low and cook for 45 minutes. Remove from heat and allow pressure to return to normal. Mix gently with a moistened spatula and place in a wooden bowl. Cover with a wooden mat for a few minutes then serve.

BROWN RICE WITH SESAME SEEDS
(Serves 2)

1¼ Cups brown rice, rinsed and drained
¼ Cup unhulled sesame seeds, rinsed
1½ Cups of water
Pinch of Sea salt

Wash sesame seeds in a strainer, drain off all water and place seeds in a dry cast-iron skillet. Dry roast over a medium flame stirring constantly. When seeds turn light brown they will release a nutty fragrance. Remove from heat and let cool. Place rice and water in a pressure cooker, sprinkle sesame seeds and sea salt on top. Cover and cook according to regular brown rice recipes.

FRIED RICE
(Serves 2)

1½ Cups of cooked rice
1 Onion, diced
1 Carrot, diced
1 Stalk of celery, diced
2 TBS. Tamari
1 TBS. Sesame Oil
1 Fertilized egg (optional)

In a cast iron skillet saute diced vegetables in sesame oil. Add the cooked rice to the sauteed vegetables, cook on a medium flame, stir occasionally (The rice has a tendency to stick). When rice and vegetable have browned, add tamari and a little water and stir into the mixture. Simmer for 3 - 5 minutes. Beat the egg and drizzle over mixture. Cook for 5 minutes. Serve.

*PERSONAL NOTES:

CURRIED EGGS WITH BROWN RICE
(An occasional treat)

1 Cup brown rice, rinsed
1/8 Tsp. thyme
2½ Cups water or vegetable soup stock
¼ Tsp. Sea salt
1 Tsp. corn oil

Bring the brown rice and stock to a boil, add the thyme and sea salt. Cover and lower the flame. Simmer until the rice is done. 20 - 30 minutes. When the rice is done add 1 Tsp. corn oil and mix in well.

In a separate pan, boil 3 - 4 fertile eggs until hardboiled. Cool and cut into halves.

2 Tsp. arrowroot, dissolve in ¼ cup cool
    water
1 Clove garlic, minced
2 Onions, diced
¾ Tsp. curry powder
3 TBS. unbleached white flour
1½ Cups oat or rice milk (or use bancha
    tea)
1 Fresh lemon
¼ Tsp. Sea salt

Heat a skillet with a little corn oil, saute the garlic, onions and add the curry powder, stir until the curry is completely dissolved. It will give off its own distinctive odor. Add the flour, stirring in evenly, add the milk or bancha tea, and the arrowroot mixture. Bring to a boil, stirring constantly. Lower the flame and allow to cook until smooth and creamy. Add ¼ Tsp. Sea salt, stirring, add the egg halves, close the flame, cover and allow to set for 2 - 3 minutes.

Place the cooked rice on a platter in a mound. Squeeze the juice of a fresh lemon over the rice. Pour the eggs and sauce over the rice and top with freshly chopped parsley.

BROWN RICE DELIGHT
(Serves 4)

1 Cup brown rice, rinsed
2 Ears of fresh corn, sheared off the cob
1 Large sweet onion or 2 regular onions, diced
1 Carrot, diced
Handful of fresh mushrooms, sliced thin
¼ Tsp. dill weed
1 Tsp. corn oil
¼ Tsp. Sea salt
1¾ Cups of water

Lightly coat a heavy sauce pan with the corn oil and saute the onions, carrot, corn, and mushrooms, then add the brown rice, salt, all the spices. Saute all the ingredients for 3 minutes. Add the water, bring to a boil, lower the flame, cover and allow to cook for 25 - 30 minutes. Stir occasionally. At the end of cooking you may add for additional flavor: a little sea salt or tamari or 1 Tsp. butter (Butter used should be raw butter). Allow to set covered for 1 minute. Serve.

BROWN RICE WITH SQUASH OR PUMPKIN
(Serves 4)

2 Cups brown rice, rinsed and drained
1 Small acorn squash or 1 Cup of pumpkin (peeled and cubed)
2½ Cups of water
¼ Tsp. Sea salt

Place rice, water and sea salt in a pressure cooker, then gently place the squash on top. Cover, place on trivet and bring to full pressure on high heat. Reduce heat to low and cook for 40 minutes. Remove from heat and run under cold water, bringing pressure down rapidly. Uncover and mix gently, place in a wooden bowl and cover with a wooden mat for a few minutes. Serve.

RICE 356
(Serves 4)

2 Cups of brown rice, rinsed
2½ Cups of water
¼ Tsp. Sea salt
1 Tsp. sesame oil
2 Cloves garlic, minced
2 Small carrots, diced
1 Medium onion, diced
½ Green pepper, diced
1 LB. Shrimp, peeled and deveined
2 TBS. Tamari

Combine rice and water in a pressure cooker, add salt and cover. Place on a trivet and bring to full pressure over high heat. Reduce heat to low and cook for 40 minutes. Remove from heat and allow pressure to return to normal. While rice is cooking, heat a cast-iron skillet lightly coated with sesame oil. Saute garlic and onions over medium flame gently stirring for 2 - 3 minutes. Then saute carrots, stirring constantly so they are coated evenly with oil, 3 - 4 minutes. Saute green pepper and add shrimp for 1 minute. Combine all ingredients in skillet, cover and simmer for 10 - 12 minutes on low heat. Add tamari and mix together. Turn off heat.

When the rice is cooked, uncover and mix lightly. Gently stir in shrimp and vegetables. Recover the pressure cooker with the lid and regulator and allow to set for 5 minutes undisturbed. *You may place it back on the stove but DO NOT put the burner back on. The flavor of the vegetables and shrimp will spread evenly throughout the dish. Serve.

BROWN RICE AND ALMONDS

1 Cup brown rice, rinsed
1/3 Cup almonds, ground into meal
1½ Cups of water
¼ Tsp. Sea salt

Place the brown rice and almond meal in a pressure cooker. Add the water and sea salt. Cover and bring to pressure, lower the flame and simmer for 45 minutes. Allow the pressure to return to normal and serve.

BROWN RICE, FRUIT AND NUT

1½ Cups brown rice, rinsed
¼ Cups almonds, chopped in half
¼ Cups raisins
2 Cups of water
Pinch of Sea salt

Place the brown rice in a pressure cooker, add the raisins and almonds on top. Gently pour the water down the sides of the pressure cooker. Bring to full pressure, reduce the flame and simmer for 45 minutes. Allow pressure to return to normal. Serve.

BROWN RICE AND SHIITAKE MUSHROOMS
(Serves 2)

1 Cup brown rice, rinsed and drained
3 - 4 Shiitake mushrooms, sliced thin, stems removed (*soak for 30 minutes in 1 1/3 cups of water)
1 1/3 Cups of water (Use soaking water)
Pinch of Sea salt
1/8 Tsp. tamari

Cook as per instructions for pressure cooked rice. Serve.

FIESTA RICE
(Serves 4)

2 Cups brown rice, rinsed and drained
¼ Cup wild rice, rinsed
1/8 Tsp. tumeric
1/8 Tsp. curry
1/8 Tsp. ginger
1/8 Tsp. sage
Pinch of cinnamon
Pinch of nutmeg
1 Cup of apple juice/or fresh squeezed lemon or orange juice may be used
1¼ Cups of water
¼ Tsp. Sea salt

Place the brown rice in a pressure cooker, add the liquid, then sprinkle the wild rice on top, then add all the spices. Cover, place on a trivet, and bring to full pressure, lower the flame. Simmer for 50 minutes. While rice mixture is cooking saute the following vegetables in a cast iron skillet:

2 Onions, diced
1 Clove garlic, minced
2 Stalks celery, diced
1 Carrot, matched sticked
¼ Green or red pepper, diced

Lightly coat the skillet with sesame oil, saute vegetables starting with garlic, onions, then add peppers, celery and carrots. Saute for 5 - 7 minutes. Set aside and allow to cool. When rice is cooked, gently stir in the sauteed vegetables and mix together. Serve.

*PERSONAL NOTES:

GRAIN AND SUNFLOWER BAKE
(Serves 4)

1½ - 2 Cups of cooked whole grain (brown
    rice, millet, barley or combination
    of any of the grains)
1 Cup of sunflower seeds
¼ Tsp. Sea salt
1 TBS. corn oil
3 Cloves garlic, minced
2 Onions, diced
2 Stalks of celery, chopped
½ Green pepper, chopped
3 TBS. tamari, diluted in 1 - 2 cups of
    water
1 Tsp. cumin
3 TBS. freshly chopped parsley

Saute the garlic, onions, celery, pepper and sunflower seeds. Add the sauted ingredients to the cooked grain, along with the cumin, tamari and water. Mix well. Place in a lightly oiled casserole dish and bake for 30 minutes at 350°. Serve.

RICE AND VEGETABLE CASSEROLE
(Serves 2)

1 Cup cooked rice or leftover grain
2 Onions, diced
1 Clove garlic, minced
1 Cup mushrooms, sliced
1 Cup broccoli, flowerettes
    (You may also use cauliflower)
¼ Cup tamari mixed with ¾ cup water
1 Pkg. tofu

Saute the garlic, onions and mushrooms, set aside. Saute broccoli floweretts, set aside. Place rice in the bottom of a glass baking dish, place onions, garlic and mushrooms on top. Pour the tamari/water mixture evenly over the casserole. Layer broccoli evenly over the top. Bake at 350° for 15 minutes. Squeeze out tofu and crumble over casserole, bake 5 - 10 minutes, until brown. (*You may want to add additional flavor to the tofu by sprinkling a small amount of tamari over the top.) Serve.

CASSEROLE MONTE CARLO

1 Cup cooked brown rice/ or leftover grain
2 Onions, diced
¼ Green pepper, diced
1 Tomato, sliced thin then quartered
Mix ¼ cup tamari with ¾ Cup of water
Thin slices of cheddar cheese, camembert
    brie or tofu

Place grain in the bottom of a glass baking dish. Spread evenly, then top evenly first with onions, pepper and tomatoes. Pour the tamari/water mixture evenly over the casserole. Bake at 350° for 20 minutes. Then add the tofu or slices of cheese on top of the casserole. Bake for an additional 10 minutes or until cheese has melted. Serve.

RICE TOFU CASSEROLE
(Serves 3)

1½ Cups cooked brown rice - set aside
1 Pkg. tofu, cut into ¼ cubes, steamed
    for 5 minutes
2 Onions, diced
1 Clove garlic, minced
½ Green pepper, diced
2 Stalks of celery, diced
1 Tsp. corn oil
½ Tsp. Sea salt
¼ Tsp. oregano
1 TBS. barley malt syrup
2 Cups of mock tomato sauce (See Sauces)

Saute the onions, garlic, green pepper and celery in corn oil until tender. Add the tofu, barley malt syrup and sea salt, stir well, and add the mock tomato sauce. Cover all the ingredients and simmer for 10 minutes on a low heat. Stirring occasionally. Spoon the mixture over the cooked brown rice that has been placed in a casserole dish. Heat in the oven at 325° for 15 - 20 minutes. Serve.

LAYERED BROWN RICE AND CHEESE CASSEROLE
(Serves 4)

2 Cups of cooked brown rice
8 ozs. of sharp raw chedder cheese, grated
2 Cups onions, sliced
2 Cloves garlic, minced
3 Stalks of celery, chopped
1 Pound of fresh mushrooms, sliced
1 Cup of watercress, chopped
1 Tsp. paprika
1 Tsp. Sea salt
½ Tsp. freshly grated ginger juice
1 TBS. sesame oil
1 TBS. tamari diluted in ¼ cup of water

Coat a cast iron skillet with sesame oil and saute the onions, garlic, celery, mushrooms and watercress. Add the seasonings of sea salt, paprika and ginger juice. Lightly coat a casserole dish and begin layering with the brown rice, then sauteed vegetables, grated cheese, repeat the layers. Add the diluted tamari and water over the top of the casserole. Place in the oven and bake at 350° for 25 - 30 minutes. Serve hot with a garnish of freshly chopped parsley. Serve.

BAKED BROWN RICE

1 Cup brown rice, rinsed
½ Cup raisins or dried fruit of your choice
2 Cups soya milk
¼ Tsp. Sea salt

Place the rice, raisins, soya milk and sea salt in a saucepan. Bring to a boil. Then gently pour all the ingredients into a baking dish, cover and bake at 300° for 2-3 hours. If the milk boils over, your oven is too hot. This is a great dish for the winter months.

GRAIN, FRUIT AND NUT CASSEROLE
(Serves 4)

2 Cups of cooked brown rice (or any grain combination)
½ Cup raisins
½ Cup dried apples
¼ Cup sunflower seeds, toasted
½ Cup sesame seeds, toasted
¼ Cup almonds, chopped
¼ Cup walnuts, chopped
2 Stalks celery, chopped
1½ Cups scallions, chopped
1 Cup grated raw chedder or gruyere cheese

Coat a cast-iron skillet with a little sesame oil and saute the scallions, celery, seeds and nuts. Add the cooked grain and fruit, heat thoroughly. Place the mixture in a lightly oiled casserole dish, top with the grated cheese. Place in the oven and bake at 300 degrees or until the cheese melts. Serve.

RICE BURGERS
(Yields 5 - 7 patties)

1 Cup brown rice, cooked
¼ Cup rolled oats
¼ Cup corn meal
¼ Cup wheat germ
1 Small onion, diced
1 Stalk celery, diced
1 TBS. tamari
2 TBS. corn oil
1 Fertile egg, beaten well

Combine in a separate dish:

2 TBS. rice flour
2 TBS. wheat germ

Combine the brown rice, oats, cornmeal and wheat germ with the vegetables, add the egg and tamari. Form into patties, then dust with the rice flour and wheat germ mixture. Place the oil in a skillet, when the oil is hot, brown the patties on both sides. Serve.

GRAIN OMELETTE
(Serves 3)

1 Cup of leftover brown rice (or any grain
    combination)
¼ Green pepper, diced
1 Small onion, diced
1 Small clove garlic, minced
1 Scallion, diced
½ Cup cooked mushrooms
1 TBS. tamari
Pinch of Sea salt
1 Fertile egg, whipped with ¼ cup of
    bancha tea
Grated parmesan or mozzerelli cheese

In a cast-iron skillet coated with a little
sesame oil, saute the vegetables first, add
the leftover grain and heat. Spread evenly
in the skillet. Pour the whipped egg over
the grain and allow to cook over a low
to medium heat. When the egg begins
to set, turn the forming omelette over in
the skillet to cook on the other side. (You
might have to cut the omelette in half
or quarters to turn.) When you have
turned the omelette, sprinkle the grated
cheese over the top and allow to melt.
Serve with sliced tomatoes, a small portion
of steamed broccoli and a piece of fresh
fruit. Garnish with parsley. A good dish
for a cold winter day.

PUNGENT HEARTY RICE

1 Cup brown rice, rinsed
2 Onions, diced
1/8 Tsp. curry
¼ Tsp. thyme
¼ Tsp. basil
½ Tsp. marjoram
¼ Tsp. Sea salt
3 Cups soup stock or water

Coat a medium size saucepan with oil.
Saute the onions for 2 minutes, then add
the rice. Saute together for 3 minutes.
Add the remaining ingredients and mix
well. Add the soup stock, bring to a boil,
lower the flame and simmer for 25 - 30
minutes or until the rice is tender. Serve.

RICE STUFFING

1½ Cup of leftover rice and corn
3 Onions, diced
2 Stalks celery, diced
2 Small clove of garlic, minced
¼ Cup raisins
2 Apples, peeled and diced
¼ Cups toasted almonds, chopped
¼ Tsp. Sea salt
1/3 Cup apple juice
1/3 Cup water

Combine all the ingredients in a pot,
EXCEPT the grain, bring to a boil, lower
flame, add salt and allow to simmer for
10 minutes. Mix in leftover grain, stir
and allow to cook for another 10 minutes.
If using stuffing for an organic chicken,
be sure to clean and salt the cavity of the
chicken first, stuff the chicken and cook
for 1 hour at 350°. Put any remaining
stuffing in a side dish and bake. Serve.

*PERSONAL NOTES:

MOCHI

2 Cups sweet brown rice, rinsed
   and drained
2 - 2½ Cups of water
Pinch of Sea salt per cup of rice

Pressure cook sweet brown rice as per instructions for regular rice. Allow pressure to come down normally. Place rice in a large heavy wooden bowl.

With a large wooden pestle, pound the rice vigorously, until all the grains are broken. The rice becomes very sticky. This may take 40 - 50 minutes. Occasionally wet your pestle with cool water and sprinkle a few drops of water on the rice to prevent it from sticking. After your mochi has been sufficiently pounded, wet your hands and form the mochi dough into small cakes, place them on a cookie sheet that has been dusted with rice flour. You may also form the dough into oblong shapes about 10" long and 4" wide, and ½" thick. Sprinkle the mochi with rice flour, bake it at 350° till it puffs up and then eat it. You may store mochi in the refrigerator to prevent mold formation, and if mold does form, merely cut it off and eat the remaining part. You can also pan fry mochi over a low flame in a dry skillet. When pan frying cover the skillet, and occasionally turn the mochi to prevent burning. Cook until each piece expands and puffs up. You may eat as is or season mochi with a mixture of tamari and fresh grated ginger juice (just a few drops). You may also add mochi to your miso soup at the very end of cooking. Mochi is very good for pregnant or nursing mothers. *For the sweet tooth, spread a little barley malt or rice syrup on the mochi.

BROWN RICE STUFFED PEPPERS

2 Cups brown rice, cooked
6 Green peppers, pre-salted
¼ Cup peas
1 Stalk celery, chopped
1 Carrot, shredded
½ Cup caulifloweretts, chopped
3 Scallions, chopped
2 Hardboiled eggs (fertile), chopped

DRESSING:

2 TBS. rice vinegar
2 TBS. corn oil
1 TBS. lemon juice
1 Clove garlic, minced
½ Tsp. dry mustard

In a small bowl, combine all the dressing ingredients and set aside. Cut off the tops of the green peppers and remove the seeds. In a large bowl combine the rice and vegetables. Mix together well, then add the eggs and mix again. Add the dressing to the rice and vegetable mixture. Allow this mixture to set for 3 hours. You may refrigerate. Salt the interiors of the peppers and stuff with the rice mixture. Place the peppers in a casserole dish and add a little water to the bottom. Bake at 325° for 20 minutes or until done. Serve.

*PERSONAL NOTES:

MILLET

Millet is an **underrated** grain. It is grown to feed cattle in the United States, but in parts of Europe and Asia, especially Africa, India and Japan, it is still valued as a staple food. Its light bitterness, small size and alkalinity, give it the classification of being very contracted. It blends well with other grains. When cooked with onions and other vegetables it is a **BALANCED** and delicious dish. Millet is an excellent grain for body builders and weight lifters.

Although the growing plant is sensitive to cold, it is very hardy and insect and plant diseases do not usually attack it. Some varieties of millet mature in as little as two to three months, so it can be planted as early as May and as late as August depending on the location of the crop.

In the United States, a strain called foxtail millet is grown primarily in Kansas, Missouri, and Texas. In Wyoming, Montana and the Dakotas, a variety called broomcorn millet is grown.

The recipes given here are basic ones, which we hope will encourage you to further experiment. Millet is high in protein, iron and vitamin B-1. It also contains all but one of the essential amino acids. Its alkalinity makes it an excellent food for illnesses affecting the stomach, spleen or pancreas. It is very effective for treating bad breath.

Millet is a versatile grain, it can be used in soups, along with vegetables, stuffings, breads or muffins. It also may be eaten as a cereal.

MILLET RECIPES

MILLET (Pressure cooked)

1 Cup millet, rinsed
1¾ Cups of water
Pinch of Sea salt
1 Tsp. Sesame oil

You may toast millet as follows for either cooking method used. Use a cast-iron skillet or pressure cooker. Coat with sesame oil, saute millet over a medium flame, stirring constantly until lightly browned. Remove from stove and allow to cool. You may also dry roast.

For pressure cooked millet, add water and sea salt. Cover, place cooker on a trivet and bring to full pressure over high heat. Lower heat and simmer 45 minutes. Remove from heat and allow pressure to return to normal.

(Simmered)

When cooking millet in a pot, add 3 cups of water. Bring to a boil, add salt and cover. Reduce the heat to medium for 3 minutes. Then lower the heat and simmer for 30 minutes. If a softer consistency is desired, add additional water. If a dryer consistency is desired, use less water and extend the cooking time to 5 - 15 minutes.

MILLET DELIGHT

¾ Cup millet, rinsed
2 Cloves garlic, minced
2 Onions, diced
1 Carrot, diced
¼ Red pepper, diced
2½ Cups water
Corn oil
¼ Tsp. Sea salt
¼ Tsp. thyme
¼ Tsp. marjoram

Lightly coat a heavy sauce pan with the corn oil and saute the garlic, onion, pepper and carrot, then add the millet along with the spices. Saute all the ingredients for 2 minutes. Add the water and bring to a boil, add the sea salt, lower the flame, cover and cook for 25 - 30 minutes. Stir occasionally. At the end of cooking you may add for additional flavor: a little sea salt, tamari or 1 Tsp. of butter. After you add the additional seasonings, turn off stove, stir and allow to set covered for 1 minute. Serve. (When using butter be sure to use raw butter) Excellent dish when accompanied with steamed broccoli and sweet potatoes.

CHINESE MILLET

1¼ Cup millet, rinsed
½ Cup cashews, ground
3½ Cups of water
¼ Tsp. Sea salt

SAUCE:

2 Small onions, diced
1 Clove garlic, minced
2 Cups fresh mushrooms, sliced
2 TBS. tamari
2 TBS. arrowroot
1 Cup cold water
Corn oil

In a deep sauce pan bring the millet and water to a boil, add sea salt. Lower the flame and simmer for 15 minutes. Add the cashews and cook for an additional 20 minutes or until tender. Gently mix and remove from the stove. In a separate skillet, saute the onions, mushrooms and garlic. Dilute the arrowroot in 1 cup of water. Pour into the mushroom mixture and stir until the sauce thickens. Use the sauce over the Chinese millet. Serve.

MILLET STEW

1 Cup millet, rinsed
3 Cups water
1 Tsp. Sea salt
2 Cloves garlic, minced
3 Onions, quartered
1 Carrot, cubed
3 Potatoes, diced
1 TBS. tamari
Sesame oil

Lightly coat a saucepan with sesame oil and toast the millet until golden brown. Add all the ingredients, except tamari and saute for 3 minutes. Add the water and bring to a boil. Lower the flame and simmer until vegetables are tender and millet is cooked. Season with tamari and serve.

MILLET MASERATI
(Serves 4 - 5)

1½ Cups millet, rinsed
½ Cup lentils, rinsed
2 Carrots, ½" diagonal slices
2 Onions, cut into 1/8ths
½ Green pepper, stripped lengthwise
½ Butternut squash, cubed
1 Stalk of celery, chopped
1 TBS. corn oil
4 Cups of water
2 TBS. tamari
10 Drops of freshly grated ginger juice

Lightly oil the pressure cooker, add the millet and lightly toast. Remove from cooker and allow to cool. Then in your pressure cooker saute the vegetables beginning with onions. Add lentils, then millet. Gently pour water down the sides of the cooker. Cover, place cooker on a trivet and bring to full pressure over a high heat. Reduce heat to low and simmer for 25 minutes. Remove from heat and allow to return to normal pressure. Meanwhile, add ginger juice to the tamari and dilute with 1/3 cup of water. Uncover the millet and pour over the grain-vegetable mixture. Stir gently and serve.

MILLET AND CAULIFLOWERETTS

1 Cup millet, rinsed
2 Cups caulifloweretts
1 Onion, diced
3½ Cups boiling water
1 Tsp. sesame oil
¼ Tsp. Sea salt

Lightly brush the sesame oil in the bottom of a cast-iron skillet. Saute the onions, then add the caulifloweretts and saute for 4 - 5 minutes. Add the millet and saute for another 3 - 4 minutes, stir constantly to avoid sticking. Add boiling water and sea salt. Bring the mixture to a boil, cover, reduce flame to low and simmer for 30 - 35 minutes. Serve.

MILLET-SHRIMP CREOLE
(Serves 2)

3 Cups water
1 Cup millet, toasted
¼ Cup aduki beans, presoaked for 4 hours
1 Large onion, cut in eighths
1 Carrot, chopped
½ Cup pumpkin or squash, cubed
1 Tsp. sesame oil
2 TBS. tamari, diluted in 1/3 cup of water
½ Green pepper
1 lbs. Shrimp, peeled and deveined

Lightly coat a skillet with oil and saute all of the vegetables. Saute shrimp and set them aside. Place millet and water in a pressure cooker. Add soaked aduki beans and gently put in all sauteed vegetables. Cover, place trivet under pot, bring to full pressure over high heat. Lower flame and simmer for 30 minutes. Remove from stove and allow pressure to return to normal. Uncover, add the shrimp and the diluted tamari mixture, stir gently. Recover and let flavor develop for 3 - 5 minutes. Uncover and serve.

MILLET BURGERS

3 Cups millet, cooked
1/3 Cup lentils, cooked
2/3 Cup sunflower seeds
1 Onion, minced
½ Small carrot, minced or grated
¼ Tsp. Sea salt
2/3 Cup whole wheat flour
¼ Tsp. oregano

Combine millet, lentils, sunflower seeds, onion and carrot in a bowl. Mix thoroughly, then add sea salt, oregano and enough flour to hold the mixture together. If the mixture is too dry sprinkle with a little liquid. Form mixture into burgers or patties, or any shape you like.

Put 1/3" of sesame oil or corn oil into a cast-iron skillet. Pan fry over a medium heat. Serve plain or with a sauce.

MILLET HUSHPUPPIES

1¼ Cups cooked millet
½ Cup corn meal, water ground
1 Small onion, diced very fine
2 TBS. grated carrots, fine
1 Sprig parsley, chopped fine
2 Cloves garlic, minced
½ Tsp. Sea salt
2 TBS. sesame oil
1 TBS. barley malt syrup
½ Cup of water (approximately)
Ginger-tamari sauce (See Sauces)

Combine all dry ingredients. Add finely chopped vegetables, syrup and oil, mix thoroughly together well with your hands. Add enough water to form a thick batter. Heat 1" sesame oil in a cast-iron skillet to 325%. Drop spoonfuls of batter into the oil and fry until golden brown. Place on a paper towel to drain off excess oil. Serve with the ginger/tamari sauce.

MILLET ON THE GREEN

1 Cup millet, toasted dry
1 Clove garlic, minced
2 Onions, diced
5 Scallions, diced
2 Cups, broccoli floweretts
1 Small lemon, juiced
1/3 Cup tamari
1 TBS. parsley, chopped
¼ Tsp. Sea salt
3 Cups of water

Bring water to a boil, add the millet and salt. Allow to boil again. Cover, lower the flame and simmer for 25 minutes. Then lightly saute vegetables 4 - 5 minutes. Add the vegetables to the millet. Mix the tamari and lemon juice with ¼ cup of water. Add the liquid to the millet, allow to simmer for 5 minutes. Garnish with parsely and serve.

MILLET V-12

½ Cup of millet, cooked
1 Cup lentils, cooked
1 Clove garlic, minced
2 Scallions, diced
2 Cups of spinach, chopped
2 Apples, grated
1 Fertile egg, beaten
1 TBS. lemon juice
1 Tsp. coriander
2 TBS. corn oil

In a lightly oiled medium size skillet, saute garlic and scallions, add the spinach and mix well, sauteing for 2 minutes. Add cooked millet and lentils to the sauteed vegetables then add all the remaining ingredients to the mixture. Preheat oven to 350° . Place the mixture into a lightly oiled casserole dish and bake for 30 - 40 minutes or until golden brown. Serve.

MILLET-ALMOND CASSEROLE

1 Cup millet, cooked
1 Cup almonds, ground
½ Cup almond milk
¼ Cup wheat germ
¼ Cup chopped parsley
1/8 Tsp. sage
1/8 Tsp. marjoram
1 Fertile egg, beaten
1 Tsp. corn oil
½ Cup of water

Lightly coat a cast-iron skillet with corn oil and saute the onions. Combine the millet and almonds in a mixing bowl, add the wheat germ, sauteed onions, parsley, almond milk, egg and water. Blend together. Add the seasonings. Place ingredients into a lightly oiled casserole dish. Bake at 325° for 25 minutes or until lightly browned. Serve.

MILLET, VEGETABLE CASSEROLE
(Serves 3)

2 Cloves of garlic, minced
2 Onions, diced
½ Green pepper, diced
10 - 15 Fresh mushrooms, sliced
1 Carrot, diced
1 Cup toasted millet
3 Cups of water
3 - 5 Whole tomatoes, chopped
½ Cup Freshly grated parmesan cheese
2 TBS. Tamari, diluted in ½ cup of water

Layer the first six ingredients in a saucepan, in the order given. Slowly and gently pour the water down the sides so as not to disturb the order of the vegetables. Add a pinch of sea salt and bring to a rapid boil. Lower the flame and cook for 30 minutes or until the millet is soft. Mix well and place the mixture into a lightly oiled casserole dish. Pour the diluted tamari over the mixture, top with the chopped tomatoes and cheese. Place in the oven and bake at 350 degrees for 15 minutes. Serve hot.

HI-BOOST MILLET
(Serves 4)

1½ Cups millet, rinsed
½ Cup brown rice, rinsed
3 Cups of water
¼ Tsp. Sea salt

Place rice, millet, salt and water in a pressure cooker. Cover, place on a trivet and bring to full pressure over high heat. Reduce heat to low and cook for 50 minutes. Remove from heat and allow pressure to return to normal. Remove cover and place in a serving bowl.

HI TURBO MILLET

1 Cup cooked millet
1 Cup rice vinegar
¾ Cup barley malt syrup
2 Cups pitted prunes
1 Cup toasted slivered almonds
3 - 4 Apples, peeled, cored and cubed
1 Tsp. sage
1 Tsp. Sea salt

In a small stainless steel sauce pan bring the vinegar and barley malt syrup to a boil over a medium heat. Remove from the flame and add the prunes, set aside and allow to cool. Stir occasionally.

Pre-heat the oven to 350 degrees. In a large bowl combine the cooked grain, almonds, prunes, sage, sea salt and apples. Strain off the vinegar liquid from the prunes, add to the millet, mix together. Add just enough of the vinegar liquid for flavor to taste. Will make 6 - 8 cups of stuffing. Place in an organic chicken or turkey or bake in a side dish.

*PERSONAL NOTES:

BUCKWHEAT

For Heavy Duty Hauling

Buckwheat, although technically not a cereal, is usually grouped with them. It is a seed grass and is more contracted than any of the other cereals. It is grown only in colder climates. It grows very quickly, maturing in only two months and can be harvested in spring, summer, and fall. Buckwheat is quite different from wheat, which has a long growing time, even longer than rice.

In appearance, buckwheat is a three-sided seed, it is such a hardy grain that few pests or diseases affect it. It can thrive on very poor soil and is even grown on land which is too wet to produce other grains. It grows so densely that it even smothers weeds.

When eaten regularly as a staple food, it produces a very strong constitution. Russian athletes at an Olympic game in Germany were unable to eat their favorite dish, buckwheat. They left the Olympics and returned home greatly annoyed. They felt that without the source of their great strength it would be senseless to participate.

Buckwheat can be eaten in the form of noodles, as a cereal, or as a stuffing for cabbage, green pepper, or squash in place of meat. It is excellent for cold weather since it produces heat quickly. If eaten in warm weather, it should be consumed in the evening.

Called "kasha" by the American Jewish population, buckwheat is high in vitamin E, and is a good blood-building food and beneficial for the kidneys. It is also high in protein, calcium, iron, and vitamin B-1 (Niacin). Besides generating body heat and strength, it is good for the lungs and helps eliminate fluid retention. It is not, however, recommended for small children, nor for adults as a daily food IF they are living in a **hot** climate.

In the recipes that follow, you will notice that we **never** use a pressure cooker to prepare buckwheat. It grows faster than other grains, and will cook faster. It is very useful to be able to lift the lid and check to see if the water has all evaporated or if it is about to burn.

When buckwheat is used as flour it makes an excellent addition to other flours, to create a dark bread. It is too strong of a grain to be used alone, so try it with whole wheat flour.

It can be used in soups, as a cereal, as a casserole, vegetable grain pies and pancakes. You can make delicious noodles or buy them already made.

BUCKWHEAT RECIPES

KASHA CASSEROLE

1 Cup cooked buckwheat groats
1 Cup whole wheat macaroni shells, cooked
½ Cup garbonzo or aduki beans, cooked
1 Onion, chopped
2 Scallions, chopped
1 Small butternut squash, peeled and diced
2 Tsp. sesame oil
¼ Tsp. Sea salt

Saute vegetables, place in a bowl, add all other ingredients and mix ingredients together thoroughly. Place in a lightly oiled casserole dish and bake at 350° for 20 - 30 minutes. Serve.

BUCKWHEAT-KASHA-GROATS

1 Cup buckwheat groats
2¼ Cups of water
¼ Tsp. Sea salt

Bring water to a boil, add groats. When water comes to a boil again, add salt, lower the flame, cover and simmer for 20 minutes. Check occasionally and stir to be sure grain does not burn on the bottom. If water is not evaporated when grain is soft, leave uncovered for a few minutes. Serve. Garnish with parsley.

136

BENZ PATTIES

2 Cups buckwheat groats, cooked
¾ Cup unbleached white flour/or whole
    wheat flour
1 Medium onion, diced
1 Carrot, diced
7 - 10 Fresh mushrooms, sliced thin
1 Ear corn, kernels removed from cob
½ Green pepper, chopped
1 Tsp. sesame oil
1 TBS. tamari, diluted in ¼ cup of water
1 Cup bread crumbs or corn meal
Pinch of sea salt

Saute all vegetables and set aside to cool. Combine vegetables with groats, add tamari and a few drops of water. Mix thoroughly. Add enough flour to hold mixture together. Form patties and set aside. Combine the remaining flour, add salt with the water to form a thin batter.

In a cast-iron skillet, pour ½" oil and heat to 360° F. Dip patties into the batter, roll in the bread crumbs until completely covered. Place in the hot oil and fry 3 - 4 minutes or until golden brown. Place the patties on a paper towel to remove excess oil. Serve.

CABBAGE 6.9

Use the buckwheat/vegetable recipe for
    stuffing
1 Chinese cabbage

Steam or parboil a medium Chinese cabbage (this has curly leaves). Separate the leaves carefully and set them aside to cool. Place the groat mixture carefully on top of a cabbage leaf. Place another leaf on top and fold in the leaf side to form a cabbage roll. Place cabbage rolls in a lightly oiled casserole dish and bake at 350° for 20 minutes. Serve with Bechamel sauce topping. DELICIOUS!

BUCKWHEAT WITH VEGETABLES

1 Cup buckwheat groats
2¾ Cups of water
1 Tsp. Sea salt
3 TBS. tamari, diluted in ½ cup of water
1 Onion, minced
2 Scallions, chopped
1 Carrot, diced
7 - 10 fresh mushrooms, sliced thin
1 Ear of corn, kernels removed from the
    cob
1 Handful parsley, chopped
1½ Tsp. sesame oil

In a deep saucepan, bring water to a boil, add groats. When the water comes to a boil again, add ¼ Tsp. sea salt, lower flame, cover and simmer for 18 - 20 minutes. Check occasionally to prevent evaporation and burning. Saute vegetables separately in a cast-iron skillet. Allow vegetables to cool and then add to the cooked groats. Mix thoroughly. Add tamari/water mixture for flavor. Serve topped with chopped parsley.

*Use this recipe to stuff peppers. Salt inside the green peppers, fill and bake in a glass dish at 350° for 30 minutes. Since peppers are a very expanded vegetable, the **BALANCE** between them and the very contracted grain is a desirable one.

*PERSONAL NOTES:

BARLEY

This easy to digest grain may have been the first cereal cultivated by man. Grains found in Egypt are believed to be 5,000 years old. Scientists feel it may have orginated in Ethiopia or central Asia. They do know colonists from England brought barley to America in the 1600's. The Dutch people brought varieties of the grain from Europe and the Spanish colonists contributed a variety from North Africa.

Nearly five billion bushels of barley are produced annually; the largest production comes from Russia, France and Great Britain. In the United States, North Dakota, Montana and California produce the most barley, averaging yields of about 40 bushels per acre. Sadly, about 65% of our barley in this country is used for animal feed. In contrast, other countries consider barley a staple. In Tibet, for example, it is still regarded as their most important food.

There are some varieties which are free of the chaff which normally covers the threshed grain, but others must have the hull removed. In a process which results in "pearled" barley, the grain is ground in a revolving drum until both hull and germ are removed. This leaves only a starchy ball. It takes 100 pounds of barley to produce 35 pounds of barley "pearls". It may be wise when shopping to try to locate "pot barley," which has only been processed long enough to remove the husk.

Although some plant diseases such as smut, stem rust, and mildew, do affect barley yields, it will grow nearly anywhere in the temperate zone and there are both spring and winter varieties.

A popular use of barley, is the sprouting of the grain, drying it and making it into a malt. Malting barley is much more expansive and this product can then be used for making beer and other alcoholic beverages, malt flavorings, my favorite sweetner is barley malt syrup. However, barley can also be roasted, unhulled, and boiled in water to make a delicious tea. If ground after roasting and mixed with other grains, it makes a delicious coffee-substitute which can be purchased commercially, or prepare your own grain coffee. (See Beverage Section)

It is a wonderful grain for use in stuffings, thickening soups or served with vegetables. Barley flour makes an interesting variation to any bread recipe as well as making an excellent baby cereal. Fermented, barley is a major ingredient in making miso.

BARLEY RECIPES

BARLEY SIMMERED
(Serves 2)

1 Cup barley, rinsed and drained
3 Cups of water
¼ Tsp. Sea salt

You may prefer to dry roast barley in a skillet over a medium flame, stirring constantly until brown, before cooking.

Combine ingredients in a cast-iron saucepan. Bring to a boil, add sea salt, lower the flame, cover and simmer for 25 - 35 minutes. Remove from the stove and stir lightly. Recover and let set for a few minutes before serving.

PRESSURIZED BARLEY

1 Cup of barley, rinsed
1½ Cups of water
¼ Tsp. Sea salt

Place the barley in the pressure cooker. Add the water and sea salt. Cover and place on a trivet. Bring to pressure, lower the flame and cook for 45 minutes. Remove from heat and allow pressure to come down. Serve hot. Garnish with sesame salt, parsley or your favorite sauce.

BARLEY DELIGHT

½ Cup barley, rinsed
1 Clove garlic, minced
2 Onions, diced
1 Carrot, diced
1 Stalk celery, diced
¼ Green pepper, diced
1½ Cups of water
½ Tsp. Sea salt
Sesame oil
1/8 Tsp. rosemary
1/8 Tsp. marjoram
Pinch coriander

Lightly coat a heavy sauce pan with the sesame oil and saute the garlic, onions, celery, carrot and green pepper, then add the barley along with sea salt and spices. Saute all the ingredients for 2 minutes. Add the water and bring to a boil, add the sea salt, lower the flame, cover and allow to cook for 25-30 minutes, or until tender. Stir occasionally. At the end of cooking you may add for an additional flavor: a little sea salt., tamari or 1 Tsp. butter. (Butter used should be raw butter.) Allow to set covered for 1 minute after additional flavoring is added. Serve.

BARLEY NUT CASSEROLE

2 Cups barley, rinsed
5 Cups water
1 Tsp. Sea salt
½ Cup bread crumbs
2 Carrots, diced
2 Onions, diced
2 Leeks, sliced/ or use 4 scallions, sliced
¾ Cup pumpkin or squash, peeled
    and cubed
½ Cup chopped almonds

Place the water, barley and sea salt in a saucepan. Bring to a boil, lower heat, cover and simmer for 30 minutes. Lightly coat a cast-iron skillet with a little sesame or corn oil and saute the onions and leeks, set aside. Then saute the pumpkin and carrots. Add the onions to the pumpkin and carrots, lower the heat and cook together for 10 minutes. After the barley has been cooked and is tender, mix together in a large bowl with all of the ingredients and cooked vegetables. Place the mixture in a lightly oiled casserole dish, top with the almonds. Bake at 350° for 30 minutes. Serve.

POWER SHIFT BURGERS

2 Cups barley, cooked
2 Small onions, minced
2 Scallions, sliced thin
1½ TBS. Miso, diluted in ½ cup hot water
1 TBS. sesame butter
Sesame oil for frying
Flour, as needed

Combine all the ingredients in a large bowl and mix together well. Add flour as needed to thicken the mixture. Form into patties. Heat the sesame oil in a skillet and fry the patties on both sides. Serve on whole wheat rolls, along with lettuce, pickle, relish, etc.

BARLEY WITH VEGETABLES
(Serves 2)

1 Cup barley, rinsed
1 Onion, diced
1 Carrot, diced
1 Cup broccoli, floweretts (buds or heads)
3 Cups of water
Pinch of Sea salt
½ Tsp. sesame oil

In a cast-iron skillet, lightly coated with oil, saute vegetables. Place barley in a pot, add water and sea salt, bring to a boil, lower the heat and sauteed vegetables. Cover and simmer 25 minutes. Serve.

BARLEY-EGGPLANT BAKE

2 Cups cooked barley
2 Cloves garlic, minced
3 Cups eggplant, diced ½", peeled
1 Cup onions, diced
½ Cup green pepper, diced
2 Cups tomatoes, chopped
¼ Cup grated parmesan cheese
Sea salt
Corn oil

Lightly coat a cast-iron skillet with oil and saute garlic, onions, and peppers until slightly browned. Add the eggplant and allow to cook for 5 minutes. Add the tomatoes, mix well and cook for 2 minutes. Then add the cooked barley, mix together and cook for an additional 2 minutes. Place ingredients into a lightly oiled casserole dish and bake at 325° for 30 minutes. Season with sea salt and top with freshly grated parmesan cheese and serve.

BAKED BARLEY PARMESAN
(Serves 5 - 6)

2 Cups cooked barley
1 Clove garlic, minced
1 Onion, minced
1 Carrot, diced
1 Small zucchini squash, 1/3" rounds
1 Turnip, diced
1 Tsp. corn oil
1 Tsp. tamari, diluted with 1/3 cup water
½ Cup bread crumbs
¼ Cup freshly grated parmesan cheese

Saute vegetables separately, beginning with garlic and onion for 2 minutes. Then saute carrots, squash and turnip. Combine all vegetables in a cast-iron skillet, add tamari diluted with water. Cover and simmer for 10 minutes, stirring occasionally.

Place cooked barley in a lightly oiled casserole dish and cover the grain with the cooked vegetables. Top with bread crumbs and parmesan cheese. Bake at 325° for 15 - 20 minutes. Serve hot.

*PERSONAL NOTES:

WHEAT, BULGHUR, AND CRACKED WHEAT

Wheat fields cover more of the world's surface than any other food crop. Conversely, in our relative scale of values, and from a **BALANCED** point of view, it is the least important grain for our daily consumption.

Although ten billion bushels are grown in the world each year, very little of this is consumed as a whole grain; instead, three-fourths of the 26 billion pounds of flour ground yearly in the U.S. alone finds its way into commercial preparation of bread, rolls, cookies, cakes, pies and other bakery items.

There are some valid reasons for our national acceptance of the processing that is given the whole wheatberry. One reason is whole wheat is difficult to digest and must be cooked very well, and subsequently chewed well.

Most Americans do not seem to realize that the "enrichment" performed upon wheat once it has already been broken down into flour does not restore it to full nutritional value. Most of the vitamins are in the bran layers and the germ of the wheat, both of which are removed in the milling of WHITE flour. Whole wheat flour, on the other hand, retains these parts and there is only the loss of the integrity of the grain.

Wheat is believed to have been cultivated first in Asia 6,000 years ago, in what was then called Mesopotamia, now known as Iraq. Wheat is referred to in biblical writings, thus we know it was considered an important food in Palestine and Egypt. Columbus brought wheat to the West Indies in 1493, and Cortez introduced it in Mexicao in 1519. From Mexico, missionaries took it to Arizona and California. The pilgrams are known to have planted it as early as 1618, but it did not grow as well as the corn the Indians had planted.

Since wheat is still subject to a variety of diseases today, scientists are continually cross-breading different strains to try to improve resistance. In fact, seven different kinds of the fourteen species are grown in the U.S. today. Of these fourteen species there are as many as 30,000 **varieties** grown in various parts of the world. The U.S. Dept. of Agriculture has collected 15,000 varieties for experiments in combining the better qualities of each strain. It would seem that of all the grains this one has been tampered with by man to the greatest degree and is furthest from nature's own hardier, more adaptable creations. Is this possibly the reason why more people experience food allergies to wheat products than any other grain? Could it be that the glutamic acid, which is a by-product of wheat and is used in making monosodium glutamate, (MSG - used as a flavor enhancer) is frequently associated with headaches? It is much used in modern Chinese restaurants and some persons experience immediate effects from its consumption.

The leading producer of wheat in the world today is Russia, however, her food needs are **even greater** than her production. She imports much of her wheat from the U.S. when trade restrictions permit. On the contrary, the U.S. (second in wheat production) has usually been able to store **more than** one year's supply of wheat to meet her domestic and export needs.

There are two general groups of wheat; winter wheat and spring wheat. Each major group has varieties of hard wheat and soft wheat. For example, hard, red, winter wheat is high in gluten and protein and more suitable for bread making. Soft, pastry wheat is lower in both protein and gluten and used mostly for sauces or pastry products. Durhum wheats are lower still in protein, have almost no gluten, however, their coarse particles are excellent for noodles, macaroni, and spaghetti products.

Bulghur is a par-boiled grain which has been dried. It is unlike cracked wheat, which is not pre-cooked but merely partially milled. Couscous is another word sometimes encountered in wheat products. It is not a whole grain but made from unbleached, cracked, refined whole wheat. These can all be cooked, if desired, by steaming. Their use is not recommended on a daily basis because of the loss of nutritional value.

WHOLE WHEAT BERRIES

1 Cup wheat berries (soak overnight)
3½ Cups of water
¼ Tsp. Sea salt
½ Tsp. corn oil
1 Medium onion, sliced in 1/8
2 Small carrots, diced

Soak wheat berries overnight. Place in a pressure cooker, add water and salt. Place trivet under pot, bring to full pressure over high heat, reduce heat and simmer for 2 hours. Saute onion, carrots in a skillet. When wheat berries are cooked, allow pressure to return to normal, uncover and add the onions and carrots, mix together. Cover and let set for a few minutes before serving.

d'ELEGANCE SALAD

1 Cup of bulghur, soaked in 4 cups of
    water for approximately 2 hours
    or until the bulghur is soft
1 Onion, diced
2 Stalks of celery, diced
1 Carrot, diced
½ Cucumber, peeled and sliced
¼ Green pepper, diced
4 - 5 Red radishes or daikon radish, sliced
Handful of freshly chopped parsley
¼ Tsp. Sea salt

Drain off the liquid from the bulghur. Mix the bulghur and vegetables together in a large wooden salad bowl. Prepare the following dressing and blend well with the bulghur and vegetables, chill and serve.
Dressing:

¼ Cup corn oil
1 TBS. Rice vinegar

COUSCOUS

1 Cup of couscous, rinsed
Equal amounts of water
A pinch of Sea salt

In a pressure cooker, add all ingredients. Place trivet under pot and bring to full pressure over high heat. Lower the heat and simmer for 4 minutes. Remove from the stove and allow to stand covered for ten minutes. Serve with your choice of vegetables.

COUSCOUS

Rinse couscous in a strainer. Place in a steamer and steam for five minutes, in a small amount of water. Remove from steamer, stir and place in a serving dish.

BULGHUR AND VEGETABLES

2 Cups of bulghur, rinsed
4 Cups of water
½ Tsp. Corn oil
1 Medium onion, cut in 1/8 or half moons
1 Small carrot, diced
½ Butternut squash, peeled and cubed
Handful of freshly chopped parsley
1 Tsp. Sea salt
Pinch of thyme

Dry roast bulghur over a medium heat, 3 - 5 minutes, stirring constantly. Allow to cool. Add water, thyme, and salt. Bring to a boil. Cover and lower the heat, simmer for 20 minutes, heat a cast-iron skillet and coat with oil. Saute onions, carrots, squash separately. Then combine all vegetables together and add a pinch of sea salt. In just enough water to cover the vegetables. Bring to a rapid boil. Cover and lower heat, simmer until vegetables are tender. When the bulghur is ready, add vegetables together and mix thoroughly. Sprinkle with chopped toasted almonds and serve.

COUSCOUS AND COUSINS

1 Cup couscous, rinsed
½ Cup garbonzo beans, cooked
2 Onions, diced
1 Carrot, matchsticked
Pinch of Sea salt
¼ Cup of raisins

Steam the couscous and raisins for 5 minutes. Set aside in a separate bowl. Lightly saute onions and carrots, add a little water to cover and allow to simmer for 5 minutes. Add the vegetables to the couscous along with beans and sea salt, toss and serve.

WHEATBERRIES AND BEANS

1 Cup wheatberries, soak overnight (discard water)
½ Cup adulki beans
1 - 6" Strip of kombu
2 2/3 Cups of water

Place the kombu on the bottom of the pressure cooker. Add the pre-soaked wheatberries, then the beans. Gently pour the water down the side of the pressure cooker. Bring to full pressure, lower the flame and simmer for 1 hour. Allow pressure to return to normal. Add a pinch of sea salt and let set for a few minutes. Serve.

BULGHUR SIMMERED

1 Cup bulghur, rinsed
2 Cups of water
Pinch of Sea salt
1 Small bay leaf
Dash curry powder

Coat a sauce pan with oil and saute bulghur over a medium flame. Stir constantly for five minutes. Add water and bring to a boil. Add salt, and bay leaf, lower flame and simmer for 20 minutes. Remove from heat, take out the bay leaf, add a dash of curry powder and mix thoroughly. Cover and let set for a few minutes. Serve plain or with bechamel sauce.

*PERSONAL NOTES:

RYE

A cereal grain similar in appearance to wheat and barley, rye has been cultivated since the days of ancient Rome. Its origin from wilder species has been less affected by human intervention because rye pollinates in the open; wheat, oats and barley do not. This makes it difficult to keep varieties pure. Man has thus been unable to experiment with cross-breeding and hybridization. Hooray for Mother Nature!

Russia is the leading producer of rye, with Poland second, and since it grows better than any other small grains in cold weather, it is easy to understand why it is a popular crop in those countries. It also grows well in poor or sandy soil.

The rye bread made in Europe is a darker, heavier loaf, as compared to our American made rye bread. In this country it is usually mixed with whole wheat flour since the rye grain itself contains less gluten than whole wheat. Due to the lack of gluten, yeast does not raise rye flour as easily as whole wheat. We prefer to create our rye bread **without** the use of yeast and are very happy with the solid, heavier loaf it yields.

Distillers use malt made from rye in whiskey and gin production. Rye whiskey has rye grain as its chief mash ingredient.

The food value of rye is nearly as good as wheat and both give energy and endurance. In the U.S. most rye is grown in North Dakota, South Dakota and Nebraska. Rye yields about 20 bushels to the acre in this country, which is a very low yield, therefore, farmers generally prefer to grow wheat. Rye is sometimes grown alternately with other crops to protect the soil and called a "cover crop." Frequently it is also used in feeding livestock.

It might be wise for nursing mothers to avoid over-consumption of rye during lactation since cows which graze on rye sometimes produce an unusually strong tasting milk. Also, a popular misconception is that rye tastes like caraway seeds, since bakers generally add these to commercial rye bread for flavor. Actually the rye flour tastes quite differently, as I discovered once when I used whole rye seeds in my bread, thinking I was duplicating the bakery product. The result was a lovely bread with unchewable seeds which did not have the taste I had long associated with rye.

There is one poisonous enemy of rye grain. It is a fungus called "ergot" which, while it also can attack wheat and barley, it most commonly affects rye. It replaces the grain with a blackish body several times larger than the normal grain. In certain instances whole villages have been affected by consuming this affected grain or its by-products. Symptoms of poisoining are like an epidemic of LSD usage since convulsions and hallucinations are common and cases of persons jumping from windows have been traced to this disease called "ergotism." This same fungus in controlled amounts, however, has been used in the production of a number of medications. Doctors can use them to produce contractions of involuntary muscles which, for example, can cause abortion or aid in childbirth. They can also use these drugs to control bleeding. Isn't it amazing that nature contains all the extremes and man is free to select the **BALANCE**. The same agent can be employed for man's benefit or his destruction.

RYE

1 Cup rye, rinsed
3 Cups of water
1 Tsp. corn oil
Pinch of Sea salt

Bring water to a boil and add all ingredients. Cover and allow to come to a boil again, lower the heat and simmer for 35 - 40 minutes. Serve with chopped parsley or sliced scallions.

DUNLOP RYE

1 Cup brown rice, rinsed
½ Cup rye, rinsed
1¾ - 2 Cups of water
Pinch of Sea salt

Place ingredients in a pressure cooker. Bring to full pressure over high flame, reduce the heat and cook for 40 minutes. Remove from heat and allow pressure to return to normal. Serve.

RYE CASSEROLE

1 Cup cooked rye
½ Cup cooked brown rice
¼ Cup cooked pinto or kidney beans
1 Onion, diced
1 Stalk of celery, chopped
2 Tomatoes, chopped
1/8 Tsp. sage
¼ Tsp. dill weed
¼ Tsp. Sea salt
2 TBS. tamari
¼ Cup grated cheese, set aside

Place all the ingredients in a bowl, EXCEPT the cheese, and mix together thoroughly. Moisten with a little water if necessary. Place the mixture in a lightly oiled casserole dish and bake at 350° for 30 minutes. Sprinkle with the grated cheese and bake an additional 10 minutes. Serve.

RYE AND LENTIL DELIGHT
(Serves 4)

½ Cup rye, cooked
½ Cup green lentils, cooked
1 Clove garlic, minced
1 Onion, diced
1 Carrot, diced
2 Stalks celery, diced
¼ Tsp. sage
A pinch of Sea salt
1 TBS. corn oil
1 TBS. tamari
1 Cup vegetable soup stock

Coat a medium size sauce pan with oil and saute all the vegetables, beginning with onions and garlic. Add the cooked rye and lentil, herbs, tamari and sea salt. Mix all the ingredients together thoroughly. Add the vegetable soup stock, cover and simmer over a medium heat for 10 - 15 minutes. Serve.

* For rye bread recipe, see the bread chapter.

*PERSONAL NOTES:

OATS

Belonging to the same family of plants as wheat, rye, barley, corn, and rice, oats have the distinction of being the grain highest in protein and fat. It is believed they developed from wild grasses and were first grown in Asia. Although they may not have been widely used in earlier times, by the 1200's oats were grown in England and known there as "pilcorn." They are best suited to a cooler, more moist climate but some varieties have been grown as far north as the Artic circle. They are sown mostly in the spring except in the southern regions where they may be sown in the autumn.

The United States is the leading country in oat production with Russia second and Canada third. Our highest producing states are Minnesota, South Dakota and Wisconsin.

Rich in iron and calcium, oats are most commonly used as a breakfast cereal or in muffins and cookies. They can be purchased in three ways; whole, rolled or steel cut.

The whole grain looks much like a rye or wheat grain although thinner, longer and more pointed on the end.

Whole, **rolled** oats are flat, whitish and most familar. The "quick-cooking" variety can be distinguished from whole rolled oats by the appearance of smaller, broken pieces.

Steel cut oats are whole grains which have been cut into smaller pieces. They make an excellent cereal, but with a more firm consistency than the rolled oats, which are creamier when cooked. Both are delicious.

A few raisins may be added near the end of cooking time for variety. Oat milk is very useful in creating custards, puddings and other desserts. Oats may be added to make dishes fluffy or crisp depending on their preparation.

* OAT MILK . . . see beverage section!

OAT RECIPES

TUNED OATMEAL

1 Cup rolled oats
½ Cup millet, rinsed
3¼ Cups of water
¼ Tsp. Sea salt
2 Scallions, sliced very thin

Bring 3 cups of water to a boil. Add oats, millet and sea salt. Mixture will begin to rise in the pan so add the additional ¼ cup of cold water. Lower the heat and cover, simmer for 25 minutes, stirring occasionally. Uncover and simmer for 3 minutes. Serve with sliced scallions, parsley, and/or sesame salt.

FLAKES OF VEGETABLE

1 Cup of oat flakes
3 Cups of water
¼ Tsp. Sea salt
1 Onion, minced
1 Carrot, diced
2 Tsp. corn oil

Dry roast flakes in a saucepan over a medium heat, stirring constantly, to prevent burning, approximately 5 minutes. Set aside and allow to cool. Coat a cast-iron skillet with the corn oil. Saute onions and carrots for 5 - 6 minutes. Add the vegetables to the flakes. Add 3 cups of boiling water and salt. Lower the heat and cover, simmer for 25 minutes, stirring constantly. Serve with sesame salt.

STEEL CUT OATS

1 Cup Steel cut oats
2 Cups of water
Pinch of Sea salt

In a saucepan add the steel cut oats, water and sea salt. Bring the mixture to a boil, stirring constantly to avoid sticking. Lower the flame, cover and allow to cook for 25 - 30 minutes. Stir occasionally to avoid sticking. Serve with chopped parsley or chopped toasted almonds and cinnamon.

See the breakfast section for recipes using oatmeal . . .

* PERSONAL NOTES:

CORN

Botanists believe corn first grew somewhere in North America. Fossilized pollen grains from corn plants have been found in Mexico which date back around 60,000 years, and tiny ears of corn as old as 3,000 years were found. Early explorers found the American Indians growing all the main kinds of corn used today in areas as far North as Canada and south to the tip of South America.

Before the discovery of the new world by Christopher Columbus, the word "corn" was used in the British Isles to refer to other grains, such as wheat, oats, barley, and rye. Europeans had no knowledge of corn as we know it today. When Columbus landed in Cuba in 1492, his crew, on exploring the island, returned to tell him about "a sort of grain called maize." Today corn is the most valuable crop grown in the United States. In fact, this country produces one-half of the world's total corn.

The corn crop covers about 71 million acres of land in the U.S. alone. Although much of it is fed to livestock, it is also used in the manufacturing of other products such as; adhesives, antifreeze, antiseptics, dyes, felt, fertilizer, fuel, paint, paper, pastes, photographic film, plastics, safety glass, soaps, solvents, varnishes and whiskey.

The "Corn Belt" is an area stretching across the U.S., this area provides the rain during the growing season, the climate, and the warm weather needed after pollination. It includes the top producing states of Illinois, Iowa, and Indiana. The next highest ranking states in production are Minnesota and Nebraska, however, today corn grows in almost every state.

Man eats corn in many forms, in addition to the "corn on the cob" kernels. These foods include; popcorn, hominy grits, corn meal products such as corn bread, pancakes, tamales, cereals and fritters. Products refined from corn that find their way to our tables are starches, syrups, sugars and oil. There are many items, such as margarines, baking powders, catsup, vinegar, yeast, and even chewing gum, which use some form of a corn base, and almost any sweet processed food contains at least one additive from corn.

Industrial uses range from cleaning compounds to the use of corn starch in cosmetics, explosives, electric batteries, and drugs.

There are six main kinds of corn; dent corn, flint corn, sweet corn, popcorn, flour corn, and pod corn.

The kind the Indians taught the settlers to grow was flint corn. Although flint and dent corn are also fed to animals, sweet corn is mainly grown for human consumption. It is most tasty when freshly picked and a milky fluid still fills the kernels, and is less delicious when harvested after the kernels have begun to harden.

Popcorn has a tough outer coat covering each kernel. When heated quickly, moisture rapidly builds up inside the kernel causing the outer shell to crack and the entire inside blows or puffs up. Other kinds of corn crack when heated but do not pop. As a snack its nutritional value is comparable to other kinds of corn and it is fun to eat.

Flour corn is a soft corn grown by the Indians. It can be ground into flour by hand because of its softer kernels and it is one of the oldest types of corn.

Pod corn alone has a separate covering around each kernel and is believed to be the ancestor of all other types. It has never been grown commercially because these coverings make it hard to use.

Corn cannot reproduce for more than a few seasons without man's intervention. Seeds from wild corn fall too close to the parent plant for proper growth. Today, most breeders control corn pollination by hand breeding methods which allow them to cross-fertilize one plant with another and obtain selected qualities of each. More than 9/10ths of the corn grown is thus "hybridized."

Corn is subject to a host of insects and diseases. Many farmers use insecticides and other poisons to help prevent damage. If one is fortunate enough to be able to purchase "organically grown" corn, it would be the most desireable. If not, we suggest buying corn in season and leaving it in the husk until used.

The corn flour and meal products are also subject to differing methods of processing. If the grain is soaked and treated chemically before grinding, the method used is called, "wet milling." "Dry Milling," is a process of grinding the grain into its separate parts; hull, endosperm, and germ. Repeated grinding reduces them to particles of any desired size, the most common ones being coarse hominy, grits, corn meal, and corn flour.

Sometimes you can find a better corn meal product ground by a process known as the "old process" or "water-ground" process. There are only a few water mills still using this method, however, one that we know of is located in a small town in the State of Virginia. Its name is Mabry Mills and information on buying water-ground meal can be obtained by writing to: Mabry Mills, Meadow of Dan, Virginia 24120. The benefit to this method, which grinds whole corn between water driven, rotating stones, is that in water-ground meal the germ is left in the meal, improving the flavor and nutritional value.

The slight disadvantage is that the corn meal must then be refrigerated, therefore most stores which place corn meal products on the shelves would not be inclined to stock it. For the cooks who truly desire **BALANCE** in the foods they prepare, this minor effort is well worthwhile. All our flours which are not ground just before using are refrigerated for maximum freshness, and the final food creations reflect the differences in flavor.

When eaten in hot weather, fresh corn-on-the-cob produces a cooling effect in the body. The natural sugar found in corn is a polysaccharide which is released slowly into the bloodstream. This gives high energy and is good for the heart. Corn, like wheat, must be chewed thoroughly for proper digestion or assimilation of these benefits will not occur.

There are simple instructions for removing corn from the cob. Simply remove husks and silk and rinse ears in cold water. Holding the ear upright (either in a deep bowl or on a cutting board), use a sharp knife, cut downward, removing the kernels from the cob. One ear of corn makes about ½ cup cut kernels.

Corn should be kept cool, so when selecting corn hold it in your hand, if it is warm put it back on the shelf. Also look for dark green husks and make sure the kernels are fully developed.

Fresh corn can be enjoyed on a picnic or camping. To roast, turn back the husks and remove the silk. Sprinkle with cold water and pull the husk back over the corn. Twist the top to secure and place at the outer edge of the hot coals. Turn occasionally, cook about 20 minutes.

CORN RECIPES

CORN MEAL CEREAL

1 Cup corn meal
4 Cups of water
¼ Tsp. Sea salt
¼ Tsp. Corn oil

Coat a saucepan with oil. Saute the corn meal over a medium flame, stirring constantly until golden, about 5 minutes. Add water and bring to a boil, add sea salt. Cover and lower the flame, simmer for 30 minutes. Stir gently and allow to set a few minutes before serving.

BAKED CORN-ON-THE-COB

To bake corn, remove silks from the ears of corn, pull husks back over the corn, or wrap the corn in foil. Preheat the oven to 450° and bake for 12 - 15 minutes.

CORNMEAL (POLENTA)

2 Cups corn meal
8 Cups water
1 Tsp. Sea salt
1 TBS. corn oil
½ Cup raisins and/or chopped almonds

Coat a saucepan with oil. Saute the corn meal over a medium flame, stirring constantly, until fragrant, about 10 minutes. Remove from heat and allow to cool. Return pot to the stove and gradually add water, stirring until smooth. Bring to a boil over high flame, add sea salt, cover and lower the flame. Simmer one hour, occasionally stirring. If it thickens before cooking time is over, add a little water. This may then be served hot accompanied by a vegetable or pour it into a loaf pan or decorative mold which has been rinsed in cold water. Allow to cool and harden. When it is firm, cut into pieces and serve with apple butter or nut butter. Add raisins and/or almonds before simmering for one hour.

R.P.M. CORN

2 Cups cooked corn kernels
1 Onion, diced
¼ Green pepper, diced
½ Tsp. Sea salt
1 TBS. corn oil
2 Squares of tofu
1 Tsp. Freshly grated ginger juice
2 TBS. tamari
1/3 Cup water

Lightly coat a cast-iron skillet with corn oil, saute onions, pepper for 5 minutes. Add corn and salt and saute for 1 minute. Squeeze the liquid from the tofu and crumble tofu into small pieces. Add to the skillet, along with grated ginger juice, tamari, and water. Cook over a medium flame, stirring constantly for 5 - 7 minutes or until tofu is done. Serve hot along with a leafy green vegetable.

CORN CHOWDER

2 Cups of fresh corn, kernels removed from cob
2 Medium onions, diced
2 Stalks of celery, diced
1 Potato, peeled and diced
2 - 3 Cups of oat milk (See beverage section)
1 Clove garlic, minced
1½ Cups of water
½ Tsp. Sea salt
1/8 Tsp. thyme
1 TBS. tamari
½ - ¾ Tsp. corn oil

Saute onions, celery, and garlic, then add potato, corn, salt, thyme and water. Bring mixture to a boil, lower the flame and simmer for 15 minutes. Add tamari and simmer 3 more minutes. Add the oat milk, mix thoroughly, simmer a few more minutes and serve.

CORN CASSEROLE

5 - 6 Ears of fresh corn - remove the kernels from the cob
¾ Cup corn meal
1 Fertile egg
¼ Green pepper, diced
½ Onion, diced
1 Clove of garlic, minced
1/3 Cup freshly grated romano cheese
¼ Cup of water
Pinch of Sea salt

Mix all the ingredients together and place in a lightly oiled casserole dish. Add the salt and the ¼ cup of water, top with the grated cheese and bake at 350 degrees for 30 minutes. Serve.

TABOULY-BO
A cold summer meal

4 Ears of corn, uncooked, kernels removed
    from cob
1 Carrot, medium, diced
2 Onions, chopped fine
1 Turnip, diced
1 Cup broccoli, floweretts
1 Scallion, sliced
1 TBS. corn
2 TBS. tamari diluted in ¼ cup of water

1 Package Tofu
Juice of 1 orange
Pinch of Sea salt
Handful of freshly chopped parsley

Saute lightly in a cast-iron skillet in this
order; Onion, carrot, turnip, broccoli,
corn. As each vegetable is done, set aside
and when all are sauteed combine again
in the skillet. Add tamari and water, mixing
with vegetables for 1 minute. Turn into a
casserole dish and add scallion, mixing
gently. Allow to cool and refrigerate.
Cream the tofu with a little broth or
water in a suribachi bowl with a wooden
pestle. Add juice of one orange and sea
salt to taste. When mixture is smooth
spread on top of vegetables as you would
if icing a cake. Refrigerate again and serve
cold. Garnish with chopped parsley. Serve.

CORN-ON-THE-COB

4 Ears of corn, silks and husks removed
Water
Pinch of Sea salt

Put 3 inches of water in a pot and bring to
a boil. Add corn and salt. Cover and lower
flame, simmer for 15 minutes. Serve.

PRESSURIZED CORN

Use one inch of water. Add corn, a pinch
of sea salt, and place trivet under the pressure cooker. Bring to full pressure over
high flame. Lower flame and simmer for
3 - 4 minutes. Allow pressure to return to
normal. Uncover and serve.

CORN AND BROWN RICE

2 or 3 Ears of corn kernels removed
    from cob
1 Cup of brown rice, rinsed
¼ Tsp. Sea salt
1¼ - 1¾ Cups of water

Place brown rice and water in a pressure
cooker. Sprinkle kernels of corn gently
on top of rice, add sea salt. Bring to full
pressure over high flame. Lower flame
and simmer for 40 minutes. Remove
from stove and allow pressure to return
to normal. Mix and serve.

*PERSONAL NOTES:

Exit 12
BREAKFAST

The High Power Starter

"Whole grain cereals, the breakfast for good health and true champions."

The delicious way to start any day, winter or summer, is with a hot bowl of whole cereal grains. This will give you all the protein and energy needed to start your engine. Replace the processed, refined, sugar frosted cereals that give you a fast but false start. They are high in empty calories. There are many different ways to prepare a wholesome breakfast. You may use whole cereal grains (toasted and untoasted), cracked wheat, bulghur, oats, flakes, home-made cereals and granolas, pancakes, waffles or freshly baked grain muffins. Cereals and pancakes can be topped with fresh or dried fruits and natural sweeteners such as barley malt syrup, rice syrup, honey and maple syrup. You may also use toasted or raw nuts and seeds, sprinkled on your choice of cereals.

Since I do not advocate the daily use of cow's milk, many people ask me what can be used on cereals. Most whole cereal grains, when cooked properly, make their own creams. However, for a palate pleasing treat I use milks made from almonds, cashews, oats, rice and soya milk. I occasionally use bancha tea or apple juice. (See Beverage Section for easy to prepare recipes.)

CEREALS:

Brown rice	Whole wheat, creamed	Cream of oats	Cream of Barley
Brown rice cream	Cracked wheat	Steel cut oats	Buckwheat groats
Brown rice crispies	Bulghur wheat	Rolled oats	Buckwheat cream
Brown rice puffed	Shredded wheat	Flaked oats	Buckwheat pancakes
Brown rice waffles	Wheateena	Oatmeal	Puffed corn
Brown rice (leftover)	Whole wheat puffed	Muffins	Grits
Millet	Whole wheat pancakes	Waffles	Granola

FRUITS:

Blueberries	Apricots	Prunes	Honeydew
Strawberries	Cherries	Pears	Grapes
Raspberries	Raisins	Plums	Almonds
Peaches	Apples	Figs	Sesame Seeds
Grapefruit	Oranges	Canteloupe	Sunflower seeds
		Watermelon	Cranberries

153

WATKINS GLEN SPECIAL

½ Cup rolled oats
½ Cup buckwheat groats
½ Cup rice or oat milk
¼ Cup raisins
3 Cups of water
Pinch of Sea salt

Bring the water to a boil, add the sea salt, buckwheat groats, oats and raisins. Lower the flame, and simmer for 10 minutes. Stir in the oat milk, simmer 3 minutes. Serve.

QUICK START BREAKFAST CEREAL

3 TBS. millet, rinsed
1 Cup of water
1 Peach, peeled and diced
2 TBS. raisins
2 TBS. rolled oats¡
½ - 2/3 Cups of water
Pinch of Sea salt

Place the millet, 1 cup of water and sea salt in a sauce pan, bring to a boil. Lower the flame, cover and cook for 15 minutes. Add the remaining ingredients and bring to boil, lower the flame and cook an additional 10 minutes. Stir occasionally. Allow to cook uncovered for 2 minutes. Serve topped with cinnamon and/or chopped nuts.

CINNAMON, OATMEAL AND FRUIT

1 Cup rolled oats
½ Cup of raisins
1 Tsp. cinnamon
½ Tsp. vanilla
2 Cups of water
Pinch of Sea salt

In a medium sauce pan, bring water and raisins to a boil, add the oats, salt, cinnamon and vanilla. Cover and cook for 10 - 15 minutes. Serve as is or with almond milk.

CREAM OF OATS

1 Cup rolled oats
3 Cups of water
¼ Tsp. Sea salt
¼ Cup of dried peaches

Bring water to a boil. Add oats, peaches, sea salt and lower flame, cover and simmer for 15 minutes, stirring occasionally. Serve hot sprinkled with cinnamon or toasted almonds.

DAYTONA 500 START UP

1 Cup cooked brown rice or leftover grain
1 Cup rolled oats
2½ Cups water
Pinch of Sea salt
¼ Cup raisins, and 1 apple peeled and diced
(You may also add dried apricot)

Place all ingredients into a pot, bring to a boil, stirring, lower flame and cover. Allow to simmer for 25 minutes. This cereal is a very hearty and creamy dish. Serve with toasted, chopped almonds, or lightly sprinkle with cinnamon.

RICE CREAM CEREAL
(Breakfast for 4)

½ Cup of rice flour (prepare as below)
3½ Cups of water
Pinch of Sea salt

To make rice flour, place 1 cup of rice (rinsed and drained), in a cast-iron skillet and toast over a medium flame. Stir constantly to prevent burning for 8 - 12 minutes. Allow to cool. Place in a mill or grind in a blender until it becomes a fine flour. Place rice flour in a saucepan and add cold water. Bring to a boil, stirring constantly. Add salt, cover, place a trivet under the pan, lower the heat and simmer for 30 minutes, stirring occasionally to prevent burning. Serve with toasted or chopped almonds as a topping.

THREE GEAR CEREAL

1 Cup sweet brown rice, rinsed and drained
½ Cup brown rice, rinsed and drained
¼ Cup millet, rinsed and drained
2 Cups of water
Pinch of Sea salt
¼ Cup raisins

Place sweet brown rice and water in a pressure cooker. Add brown rice gently on the top and then millet over the regular rice. Add raisins and salt, cover, place on a trivet and bring to full pressure over a high heat. Lower flame and cook for 45 minutes. Remove from heat and allow pressure to return to normal before serving.

GRAND PRIX

1 Cup rolled oats, uncooked
½ Cup rice, cooked or leftover
3 Cups of water
1 Apple, peeled and diced
Pinch of Sea salt
Handful chopped toasted almonds

Place the rice, oatmeal, and water in a deep pot. Bring to a boil, add salt and raisins. Lower the heat, cover, and simmer for 25 minutes, or until creamy. Stir occasionally. Garnish with almonds and serve.

MILLET AND OATS

½ Cup millet, cooked
1 Cup oats
1 Cup apple juice
½ Cup raisin or apricots
¼ Tsp. Sea salt
1½ Cups of water

Place all ingredients into a saucepan, bring to a boil, lower the flame and simmer for 30 minutes. Top with chopped toasted almonds or cinnamon.

CREAM OF WHOLE WHEAT

½ Cup whole wheat flour
2 Cups of water
¼ Tsp. Sea salt
2 Tsp. corn oil

Coat a saucepan with oil. Saute flour over a medium heat, stirring constantly until fragrant. Remove from heat and allow to cool. Place trivet under pot. Add salt and gradually add water, bring to a boil, lower flame and cover. Simmer for 30 minutes, stirring occasionally.

Cooking with a pressure cooker, dry roast the flour in the pressure cooker, allow to cool then add water and salt. Place trivet under the cooker, bring to full pressure over high heat, reduce heat to low and simmer for 15 minutes. Remove from stove and allow pressure to return to normal.

RICE CREAM

1 Cup brown rice, rinsed and drained
4½ Cups of water
¼ Tsp. Sea salt

Place rice and water in a pressure cooker. Cover, place trivet under pot and bring to full pressure. Reduce heat to low and cook for two (2) hours. Remove from heat and allow pressure to return to normal. Uncover, allow to cool, ladle mixture into a piece of cheesecloth in a bowl. Wrap the cheesecloth tightly around the soft grains. Squeeze all the rice liquid through the cloth until only the rice grains remain and no more liquid can be extracted. Put the pulp aside for later use in bread or soup making. Use the rice cream for babies. It may be refrigerated and diluted with a little water to obtain the right consistency for bottle feeding.

WINTER PORRIDGE (A hearty breakfast for the coldest of days)

1 Cup brown rice, rinsed and drained
4 Cups of water
1 Tsp. sesame oil
1 Medium onion, cut into 1/8ths
1 Medium carrot, diced
1 Cup butternut squash, diced
2 TBS. Cold Mountain miso - diluted and
    pureed in ½ cup water

Combine rice and water in pressure cooker. Cover, place trivet under pot and bring to full pressure over a high heat. Reduce heat to low and simmer for 35 minutes. Remove from heat and allow pressure to return to normal. After removing rice from heat, begin to prepare your vegetables.

Heat a cast-iron skillet lightly coated with sesame oil. Saute onions over a medium flame until all the aroma from the onions is released. Place in a dish, then saute the diced carrots and squash together for 3 - 4 minutes over a medium flame. Add onions to carrots and squash and mix together. Reduce heat to low and continue to saute for 10 minutes, stirring lightly. Add pureed miso, bring to a boil, and turn off heat. Uncover the porridge and mix in the vegetables. Return the pot to the stove and simmer for 2 - 3 minutes. Serve with a sprinkle of sesame salt on top. Try serving this dish with a leafy green vegetable. It adds color and **BALANCE** and helps you shed some old ideas about breakfast.

BARLEY BREAKFAST CEREAL

1 Cup barley, rinsed
4½ Cups of water
¼ Cup of raisins
Pinch of Sea salt

Place barley and raisins in a heavy pot, add water and sea salt, bring to a boil. Cover, lower the flame and simmer for 1¼ - 1½ hours. Serve hot, garnished with parsley and sesame salt, or with toasted chopped almonds.

HOT CREAM OF WHEAT AND FRUIT

½ Cup whole wheat flour
2 Cups of water
2 Apples, peeled and diced
1/3 Cup of raisins
2 TBS. of barley malt syrup
Pinch of Sea salt
Almond milk to taste

In a medium sauce pan, bring the water to a boil, stir in the whole wheat flour and sea salt. Cover and lower the flame and simmer for 22 minutes, stirring occasionally. Add the apples, raisins, barley malt and cover. Simmer an additional 5 - 7 minutes. Serve with or without almond milk.

CRACKED WHEAT WITH APPLES

1 Cup cracked wheat or bulghur
1 Tsp. corn oil
Pinch of Sea salt
3 Cups of water
1 Apple, peeled and diced
Cinnamon or toasted sesame seeds

Coat a cast-iron skillet with corn oil and heat. Saute the grain until it releases a nutty fragrance, 3 - 5 minutes. Add the sea salt, water and apples. Bring to a boil, lower the flame, cover and simmer for 20 - 25 minutes, stirring occasionally. Top with cinnamon or sesame seeds.

HOT CRACKED WHEAT

¼ Cup cracked wheat
½ Cup raw almond meal
¼ Tsp. Sea salt
2¼ Cups of water
1/3 Cup raisins
3 TBS. barley malt syrup
½ Cup almond milk

In a saucepan place the water, cracked wheat, almond meal, raisins, and sea salt. Bring to a slow boil, stirring with a wire whisk. Add the barley malt syrup. When the cereal comes to a boil, lower the flame, cover and simmer for 15 minutes, stirring occasionally. Serve with almond milk.

WHOLE GRAIN COMBINATIONS

Dry roast each one of the following ingredients, separately, until they release a nutty fragrance. Mix them together and store in a glass sealed container or jar. (Be sure that the lid is air tight.) These grains may be used whole or you may grind them in a blender just before using (Not too fine).

2 Cups of brown rice
2 Cups of buckwheat groats
2 Cups of steel cut oats
2 Cups of triticale
½ Cup pearled barley

Cook the mixture as per cooking instructions for grains, adding fruit and nuts or:

1 Cup of grain combination
Pinch of Sea salt
3 Cups of water

Bring the water to a boil, add the grain and sea salt. Allow to come back to a boil, cover and lower the flame and cook on a medium flame for 10 minutes. Shut off the flame and allow to set overnight. Serve cold or re-heat, adding syrup, fruit, nuts or sesame salt.

MULTI-GRAIN AND FRUIT

1 Cup of grain combination
   (See Whole Grain Combination)
½ Cup raisins or apricots
3 Cups of water
Toasted almonds
Pinch of Sea salt

Bring water to a boil, add grain combination, sea salt and fruit, lower flame, cover, simmer until soft. Top with toasted almonds and barley malt syrup or top with fresh ripe strawberries.

BUCKWHEAT CREAM (A winter breakfast cereal) Serves 4)

½ Cup buckwheat flour
4 Cups of cold water
½ Tsp. Sea salt/ or 2 Tsp. tamari
2 TBS. sesame oil

To make buckwheat flour, place 1 cup of groats, rinsed, in a cast-iron skillet. Toast over a medium flame. Stir constantly to prevent burning and then allow to cool. Place the cooled groats in mill or grind in a blender until they become a fine flour. Heat a skillet and coat with oil. Saute buckwheat flour over medium flame 1 - 3 minutes, stirring constantly. Remove from the stove allowing it to cool. Return to stove and gradually stir in the cold water. Bring to a boil, lower heat, simmer for 10 minutes, stirring constantly. Season with sea salt or tamari, when the mixture becomes thick and creamy. Garnish with scallions and parsley. For a sweeter taste add ½ cup pureed butternut squash into the cream while it is simmering.

HEAVY DUTY PORRIDGE

½ Cup buckwheat groats
1/3 Cup raisins
2 TBS. barley malt syrup
2½ Cups of water

In a sauce pan, bring the water to a boil. Stir in the groats, cover and lower the flame. Simmer for 15 minutes. Add the raisins and barley malt syrup. Stir and cook for an additonal 5 - 10 minutes. Serve.

OATMEAL PANCAKES
(Yields 5 - 6 medium pancakes)

1 Cup rolled oats, blend fine in a blender
½ Cup whole wheat flour
¼ Tsp. Sea salt
1½ Tsp. baking powder (Rumford)
1 Fertile egg
1½ Tsp. corn oil
2 TBS. barley malt syrup
1 Cup almond or soya milk
½ Cup bancha tea or water

Mix all the dry ingredients. In a separate bowl, beat the egg and add to the corn oil, barley malt syrup, almond milk and water. Mix the liquid ingredients with the dry ingredients, blend together well. Lightly coat a skillet or griddle with oil, heat over a medium flame, when hot pour pancake batter into the skillet. When bubbles appear turn over. Serve with barley malt syrup or maple syrup.

APPLE NUT PANCAKES

1 Apple, peeled and grated fine
1 Cup apple juice
1 Fertile egg, beat well
½ - ¾ Cup of warm bancha tea
1 Tsp. dry yeast
1 Cup whole wheat pastry flour
¼ Tsp. Sea salt
¼ Cup toasted almonds, chopped fine
½ Cup wheat germ
½ - 1 TBS. corn oil

Mix the sea salt, wheat germ and flour together. Add the corn oil and mix again. Add the yeast to the warm bancha tea and when dissolved add to the flour mixture and mix well, using a wire whip. Beat the egg, apple juice and add to this the grated apple. Combine all the ingredients and mix together. Allow the batter to set in a warm place for 20 minutes. Lightly oil a cast iron skillet and cook the pancakes on a medium heat. Top with barley malt syrup or maple syrup.

WHOLE WHEAT PANCAKES

1 Cup whole wheat flour
½ Cup unbleached white flour
¼ Tsp. Sea salt
1½ Tsp. baking powder (Rumford)
1 TBS. grated apple
2/3 Cups apple juice
1 Fertile egg, beaten
2/3 Cups soya milk or bancha tea
1 TBS. corn oil

Mix all the dry ingredients together then add the egg and remaining ingredients. Mix together well. Lightly coat a skillet with corn oil, heat over a medium flame, when hot pour the batter into the skillet. When bubbles appear on top, turn over. Serve topped with apple compote or syrup.

SQUASH PANCAKES

2 Cups squash, shredded (use butternut
    or buttercup)
1 Large onion, chopped
¼ Cup sesame oil
¼ Tsp. thyme
1 Tsp. Sea salt
1 Cup flour (Use ½ whole wheat pastry
    flour and ½ unbleached white flour)
3 TBS. barley malt syrup
1 Tsp. baking powder (Rumford)
2 Fertile eggs, beaten
1 Cup of oat milk or bancha tea

In a cast-iron skillet, saute the squash and onions in a little sesame oil. Add the sea salt and thyme, mix thoroughly. Remove from the skillet, place in a separate bowl and allow to cool. In another bowl combine the rest of the dry ingredients, the barley malt syrup and the sesame oil. Stir the beaten eggs into the squash mixture and mix thoroughly. Add the mixture to the dry ingredients, mix well. Allow to cool in the refrigerator for 20 - 25 minutes before using. This mixture can also be prepared 24 hours ahead of time. Lightly coat a cast-iron skillet with sesame oil and heat until the oil dances. Drop in ¼ cup of the mixture and cook until done. Serve with a squash sauce. (See sauces)

BUCKWHEAT PANCAKES
Makes 6 skillet size cakes

1½ Cups buckwheat flour
½ Cup whole wheat pastry flour
½ Tsp. Sea salt
1 TBS. barley malt syrup
1 TBS. corn/or sesame oil
2 Cups of warm water
2 Tbs. Sourdough starter (see bread section)

Combine dry ingredients. Blend starter into the flour mixture. Add the oil and syrup to warm water and beat until liquid is whitish in color and the oil is not standing on top. A hand egg beater works best for this. Then turn the liquid immediately into the flour mixture, and beat with a whisk. Cover the dish with a paper towel to absorb excess moisture and then place a plate on top of that to keep it warm. Let the mixture set for 2 hours or overnight if possible.

Next morning, pre-heat a well oiled skillet or griddle, when a drop of water dances and disappears on its surface the skillet is ready. Pour skillet sized pancakes into the skillet. Turn the pancakes when air-bubbles have appeared in the center. Serve with barley malt or rice syrup.
* You may also add chopped nuts, raisins and/or fresh blueberries to pancake mixture after it has set all night.

PANCAKE OR WAFFLE TOPPING

2 Cups of strawberries, cleaned and stemmed
1/3 Cup barley malt sryup
2 TBS. freshly squeezed orange juice

In a saucepan, combine all the ingredients and heat. Pour over pancakes or waffles while hot.

RICE FLOUR WAFFLES

1 Cup of rice flour
1 Cup of bancha tea
2 Fertile eggs, separate the yolks and whites (Beat the egg whites until stiff)
½ Cup almond granola
1/8 Tsp. Sea salt

In a bowl, mix together, egg yolks, bancha tea, sea salt and rice flour. Add the granola, mix well. Now fold in the well beaten egg whites. Place in a hot waffle iron and cook until golden brown. Top with maple syrup or fresh fruit.

*For pancake topping you may wish to try the peach or apple compote. (See Desserts)

GRAIN OMELETTE
(Serves 3)

1 Cup of leftover brown rice (or any grain combination)
¼ Green pepper, diced
1 Small onion, diced
1 Small clove garlic, minced
1 Scallion, diced
½ Cup cooked mushrooms
1 TBS. tamari
Pinch of Sea salt
1 Fertile egg, whipped with ¼ cup of bancha tea
Grated parmesan or mozzarella cheese

In a cast-iron skillet coated with a little sesame oil, saute the vegetables first, add the leftover grain and heat. Spread evenly in the skillet. Pour the whipped eggs over the grain and allow to cook over a low to medium heat. When the eggs begin to set, turn the forming omelette over in the skillet to cook on the other side. (You might have to cut the omelette in half or quarters to turn. When you have turned the omelette, sprinkle the grated cheese over the top and allow to melt. Serve with sliced tomatoes, a small portion of steamed broccoli and a piece of fresh fruit. Garnish with parsley. A good dish for a cold winter day.

RAISIN NUT MUFFINS

2 Cups whole wheat pastry flour
1 Cup rice flour
1 Cup whole rolled oats
2 Cups apple juice
1 Cup water
1 Tsp. cinnamon
2 Tsp. corn oil
¼ Tsp. Sea salt
1 Cup raisins
½ Cup almonds, chopped
2 Tsp. baking powder (Rumford)

Mix all the dry ingredients together, thoroughly. Add the remaining ingredients to the dry mixture and stir until completely blended. Pour the mixture into individually oiled muffin tins and bake at 350° for 40 minutes or until done.

BLUEBERRY MUFFINS

1 Pint fresh blueberries
1½ Cups whole wheat pastry flour
1½ Cups unbleached white flour
2 TBS. corn oil
¼ Tsp. Sea salt
1 Tsp. cinnamon
1 Tsp. vanilla
1 Cup apple juice
½ Cup almonds, chopped
¾ Cup warm water
2 Tsp. dry yeast

In a separate bowl combine all the ingredients EXCEPT the yeast and blueberries. Dissolve the yeast in warm water then blend into mixture. Gently stir the blueberries into the batter. Allow to stand in a warm place for 10 minutes. Pour into lightly oiled muffin tins and bake at 350° for 40 minutes or until done.

ALMOND FLAVORED GRANOLA

1 Cup of almonds, chopped
1 Cup of rolled oats
1 Cup of triticale
½ Cup barley malt syrup
¼ Cup corn oil
½ Tsp. vanilla
¼ Tsp. cinnamon
¼ Tsp. Sea salt

Mix all the ingredients, then spread evenly on a cookie sheet and bake at 325 degrees for 20 - 25 minutes or until golden brown. Serve.

COLD CEREAL

2 Cups oats, dry roasted
½ Cup sunflower seeds, dry roasted
½ Cup walnuts, chopped
1/3 Cup cashews, chopped
1 Cup dried peaches, chopped

Mix all the ingredients together and store in an air-tight glass container. Serve with soya milk and top with barley malt syrup or rice syrup.

*PERSONAL NOTES:

THE EGG

The incredible, edible egg. A few questions which I have been asked many times, "Are eggs good for you? How many eggs should I eat? Do they contain high amounts of cholesterol?" I shall not attempt to advise the reader on the egg or its consumption. I will merely present you with some "food for thought" and "yolks" for the day.

Easter is not the only time for egg coloring. Hens, such as the Rhode Island Red, color their eggs while still in the uterus. These are known as brown eggs. Back in the 1850's, the average barnyard hen, laid 15 eggs per year. Today, with selective breeding, and of course modern scientific intervention, one (1) hen lays, on the average 300 eggs per year. In an article published by the Farmers Almanac, it is stated, "Genetics researchers at the University of Missouri College of Agriculture managed to coax hen number 2988 to lay 371 eggs between August 30, 1979, and August 29, 1980, - a world's record of 1.02 eggs a day for the entire year."

Whether eggs are brown or white, small or large, the average American consumes 280 eggs per year. To maintain that consumption level, it takes approximately 285 million hens working day and night.

Although I do not know which came first, the chicken or the egg, it is clear to me that if nature intended her hens to produce 300 eggs per year, she would have done so in the 1800's. **BALANCE** is the key to GOOD HEALTH.

1800's - 1 hen = 15 eggs
1983 - 1 hen = 300 eggs

You will have to decide how many eggs you are going to eat and whether eating eggs once or twice a week is healthier than eating eggs daily.

To check the egg for freshness, simply pick it up and shake it. If it rattles it is not fresh. If the egg is fresh, when broken and placed in a frying pan the yolk will appear firm and upright, and the white will not spread out too far.

AA means that the egg is less than 10 days old from packing, and Grade A, 30 days old. My grandmother tested the freshness of an egg simply by placing a few tablespoons of salt in several cups of water; if the egg bobbed up to the surface the egg was too old. If the egg is fresh, it will sink to the bottom and turn over on its side. Of course, I am speaking of an uncooked egg in the shell.

Our preference is always given to quality. Unwashed eggs, which are available at most health food stores, or purchased fresh from a local farm, will last five times longer than those commercially processed. Packers often coat their eggs with oil, as well as pack them in an oil based carton. The best egg for your consumption would be a fertile egg. Fertile eggs come from hens which are allowed to run outdoors and roam with the rooster and are free to eat worms, insects, grass and seeds. Their yolks are darker and full, and they are usually packed in an unoiled cardboard box.

Exit 13
LUNCH

Do you take lunch seriously? We Americans generally do not. Lunch has become a quick snack, something to hold you over for the real meal, dinner.

On our journey for health, we have traveled to many countries which have different cultural habits representing yet a different extreme. While visiting South America, Chile in particular, all the shops and factories would close at noon during the week and re-open at four P.M. Practically the entire afternoon is a glorious luncheon interlude, with ample time to prepare slow cooking delicacies, savor the local wine and frequent the local beach. It was a cultural difference to which we adapted easily. Across the ocean, some European countries still take several hours at noon to prepare their main meals, rest and enjoy their families. Since our American lifestyle does not afford us such luxury, somewhere between these polar opposite lifestyles lies a harmonious **BALANCE**.

We offer you a few dozen satisfying recipes in this section which will turn yesterday's cooked grain into today's sparkling Casserole Monte Carlo. Simple beans and fruits shall be transformed into a Bugatti Bonanza Spread, Salad Granada and Fruit Ferrari. Soups can be enjoyed all year long with your favorite sandwich mix, salads and casseroles. One of my favorites is Milan Minestroni soup and leftover millet delight, stuffed into whole wheat pita bread, topped with sprouts and freshly chopped tomatoes. All will make you famous as a creator of luncheon specialties which are healthy, **BALANCED** and pleasant to eat.

Ideally, the mid-day meal can be an opportunity to enjoy the company of your family, your friends and co-workers; the time for spirited interchange of ideas, suggestions and even positive, gentle criticism. The small effort and abundant love with which you, the cook and creator, invest in presenting an attractive lunch table will bring ample reward and satisfaction.

SESAME ALMOND SANDWICH MIX

½ Cup cooked pinto beans
½ Cup toasted almond butter
2 Cups toasted sesame seeds, ground
    into meal
1 Clove garlic, minced
2 Onions, diced
¼ Tsp. Sea salt
2 TBS. tamari
½ Tsp. dill weed

Place the garlic, dill, onions and tamari in a blender and blend together. In a separate bowl blend together the pinto beans, almond butter and sesame meal. Add the liquid mixture and blend together into a creamy mixture. Add the sea salt. Allow to set in the refrigerator for several hours before using. Serve on toast or rice cakes with tomato and lettuce.

CHICK-A-FU SANDWICH MIX

¾ Cup cooked chickpeas
4 Oz. tofu, steamed for 5 minutes
2 TBS. onions, diced
1 Clove garlic, minced
1 Tsp. dill weed
3 TBS. Miso nut butter (See Spread Section)
¼ Cup water
1 Scallion, sliced for garnish
Juice of 1 fresh orange

Place all the ingredients into a blender. Blend until it reaches a smooth consistancy. Place in a bowl and garnish with sliced scallion. Refrigerate 1 hour. Use in sandwiches or as a dip.

HOT OPEN FACE SANDWICH

2 Slices whole wheat bread (Autobahn
    Bread)
Cheese, Brie, Camembert, Gruyere or
    Raw Cheddar
1 Small onion, chopped fine
4 Slices of tomato
Lettuce
Stone ground mustard
Dill pickle

Spread mustard on the bread, then add the lettuce, tomato, cheese and top with chopped onion. Broil until cheese is melted. Serve with dill pickle.

BUGATTI BONANZA SPREAD

1 Cup garbonzo beans, cooked
2 Onions, diced
1 Clove garlic, minced
1/3 Cup toasted sesame seeds
½ Tsp. Sea salt
½ Tsp. coriander
2 TBS. freshly chopped parsley

Puree the garbonzo beans in a blender, add all the ingredients and mix well. Use as a filling for pita bread. Top with fresh sprouts or cheese and heat in the oven.

HUMMUS

1 Cup cooked garbonzo beans
2 Cloves garlic, minced
1 TBS. onion, minced
3 TBS. lemon juice
½ Cup tahini
Sea salt to taste

Place the lemon juice, garlic and onions in a blender, mix together. Add the tahini and beans and blend together until it becomes a puree. Spread this on pita bread, chapati or homemade whole wheat bread. Use stone ground mustard for a condiment and top with sprouts to make a delicious sandwich.

MILLET DELIGHT

¾ Cup millet, rinsed
2 Cloves garlic, minced
2 Onions, diced
1 Carrot, diced
¼ Red or green pepper, diced
2½ Cups water
¼ Tsp. Sea salt
¼ Tsp. thyme
¼ Tsp. marjoram
Corn oil

Lightly coat a heavy pot with corn oil and saute the garlic, onions, carrot and pepper. Then add the millet along with all the spices and saute for 2 minutes. Add the water and sea salt and bring to a boil. Lower the flame, cover and cook for 25 - 30 minutes. Stir occasionally. At the end of cooking you may add for additional flavor a little sea salt or tamari. Allow to set 1 minute and serve.

TOFU EGGSALAD

1 Cake of tofu, boiled 5 - 10 minutes and
    drain
2 Scallions, chopped
½ Onion, diced
1 Stalk of celery, diced
1 - 2 TBS. fresh squeezed orange juice
1 TBS. tamari
¼ Cup of mayonnaise (optional)
¼ Tsp. dry mustard (optional)

Boil the tofu for 5 - 10 minutes, drain and squeeze off all excess liquid. Allow to cool. Place the chopped scallions into a suribachi bowl, add the cooled tofu and mix together using a wooden pestle. This should now look like "real" egg salad. Add the orange juice and tamari and mix together thoroughly. Stir in the onion and celery. Add the mayo if desired. Serve on lettuce or in sandwich form. Top with chopped tomatoes and/or sprouts.

TOFU SANDWICH MIX

½ Pound tofu (boiled for 10 minutes,
    drain and place in a bowl)
¼ Cup Sesame butter or tahini
1½ TBS. tamari
1 TBS. onions, minced
2 TBS. celery, minced
1 TBS. scallions, sliced

Crumble the tofu into small pieces. If you have a suribachi bowl use the wooden pestle to break up the tofu. Mix all other ingredients together and mix thoroughly into the tofu. Chill and serve.

TOFU SPREAD

1 Square tofu, steam 5 minutes, squeeze
    out excess liquid
¼ Cup fresh squeezed lemon
2 Cloves garlic, minced
½ Tsp. Sea salt
¾ Tsp. dried dill weed or chives
2 TBS. corn oil
¼ Cup water

Place all ingredients in a suribachi bowl or blender and blend until creamy and smooth. Chill and serve.

SAVORY TOFU

1 Square tofu, steam 5 minutes, squeeze
    out excess liquid
1 Onion, minced fine
1 Clove garlic, minced fine
¼ Cup sesame butter or tahini
1 TBS. rice vinegar
¼ Tsp. chives
3 TBS. tamari
½ Tsp. Sea salt
¼ Tsp. sage
¼ Tsp. thyme

Place all ingredients in a suribachi bowl or blender and blend until creamy and smooth. Chill and serve.

TOFU SLOPPY JOES

1 Square of tofu, boil for 10 minutes,
    drain, squeeze out excess liquid
1 Onion, chopped fine
2 Cloves of garlic, minced
¼ Green pepper, chopped fine
¼ Tsp. Sea salt
½ Tsp. Italian seasoning
1 TBS. sesame oil
1 Cup butternut squash, pureed (or mock
    tomato sauce)
Mozzarelli cheese

Heat the sesame oil in a cast-iron skillet and saute garlic, onions and pepper. Add crumbled tofu and sea salt. Stir all ingredients together. Add Italian seasoning and stir well, cook for 5 minutes. Add the pureed squash and simmer for 5 minutes more. Place on muffins or whole wheat bread, add the cheese on top and broil until the cheese is brown.

TOFU BURGERS

1 Square of tofu, boil for 10 minutes,
    drain, squeeze out excess liquid
½ Cup bulghur
1 Cup of water
1 Clove garlic, minced
1 Onion, minced
½ Tsp. basil
½ Tsp. oregano
½ Tsp. cumin
½ Tsp. Sea salt
¾ - 1 Cup whole wheat flour
Freshly grated romano cheese

Bring the water to a boil, add the bulghur and sea salt. Lower the flame and simmer for 5 - 10 minutes. Mix all ingredients together in a separate bowl. Add the cooked bulghur to all the ingredients. Allow to cool then add the flour. Moisten hands and form patties. Heat a skillet and add a little sesame oil and fry the burgers on both sides.

ONO CHEESE

3 TBS. rice vinegar
¼ Tsp. garlic powder
1 Square tofu
Onozaki Miso (unpasteurized rice miso)
* For a different flavor use barley miso.

In a separate bowl mix together the rice vinegar and garlic powder. In another bowl, place the square of tofu and pierce it with a wooden skewer or toothpick. Pour the rice vinegar mixture over the tofu, drain the liquid off and repeat this process until most of the liquid has been absorbed into the tofu. Place a thick layer of miso around the entire square of tofu. Place the miso coated tofu into a crock, cover and place in a cool area. Store for 3 - 4 days. If you live in a hot climate place the crock in the refrigerator. The longer you allow the tofu to ferment, the cheesier the flavor will become. After 4 days, wash and remove the miso from the tofu. Slice and serve. Store in an air tight container in the refrigerator.

FRESH SHRIMP SPREAD

½ Pound shrimp, cooked and chopped
4 Ozs. tofu, steamed and drained, then
    mashed
1 Tsp. freshly squeezed lemon juice
1 Clove garlic, minced
Dash of paprika

Mix all the ingredients together either in a suribachi bowl or blender. Allow to cool and serve with crackers.

SAUTEED ONIONS AND TEMPEH

Saute onions in a cast-iron skillet, place tempeh patties on top and cook for 5 minutes on each side. Add tamari to taste. Place in a sandwich or serve as is with the rest of your meal. Use in a sandwich with sauerkraut.

You can crumble the tempeh after it has been steamed and sautee it with onions, garlic, carrots, and cabbage to make a stew. Use a little tamari to taste.

See Spread Section

** One of the most versatile spreads is miso, used in combination with other natural ingredients. When you have unexpected guests and need to serve something delicious in a hurry, miso will form the basis for the perfect solution.

MISO SPREAD

1 TBS. miso
4 TBS. sesame butter or tahini
3 TBS. of water
1 Tsp. orange peel, grated
¼ Tsp. dried basil

Put tahini in saucepan and toast for 2 - 6 minutes. Add miso diluted in water and mix. Allow to cook for 5 minutes, stirring constantly. Add basil and orange peel. Simmer for 2 minutes more. Serve.

BEAN BURGERS

2 Cups aduki or pinto beans, cooked
    (or ½ & ½)
1 Clove garlic, minced
3 Scallions, minced
1 Carrot, grated
½ Tsp. Sea salt
1/8 Tsp. dry mustard
1 Cup whole wheat flour
2 TBS. tamari
Sesame oil for frying

Combine all ingredients and add the flour a little at a time, mix thoroughly. Form patties approximately 3" in diameter and ½ inch thick. Fry in a little sesame oil, make sure the oil is hot before putting the patties in the skillet. Drain on paper towels before serving. Will yield 10 - 12 burgers.

LENTIL BULGHUR BURGERS

½ Cup green lentils, to 1½ cups of water
¼ Cup bulghur
½ Tsp. Sea salt
1 Clove garlic, minced
1 Medium onion, minced
½ Tsp. sage
¼ Tsp. celery seed
1 Fertile egg
¼ Cup freshly grated romano cheese
1 Cup whole wheat flour

Place lentils, garlic and onions in a pot with water. Bring to a boil, lower flame and simmer for 20 minutes. Add the sea salt, bulghur and all seasonings to the lentil mixture, allow to simmer for 5 - 7 minutes or until the water is evaporated. Remove from the pot and allow to cool. When cooled add the egg, flour and cheese. Be sure to mix the flour into the mixture thoroughly. Moisten your hands and form into patties, fry in a skillet with a little sesame oil. Serve.

RICE BURGERS
(Yields 5 - 7 patties)

1 Cup brown rice, cooked
¼ Cup rolled oats
¼ Cup corn meal
¼ Cup wheat germ
1 Small onion, diced
1 Stalk celery, diced
1 TBS. tamari
2 TBS. corn oil
1 Fertile egg, beaten well

Combine in a separate dish:
2 TBS. rice flour
2 TBS. wheat germ

Combine the brown rice, oats, corn meal and wheat germ with the vegetables, egg and tamari. Form into patties, then dust with the rice flour and wheat germ mixture. Place the oil in a skillet, when the oil is hot, brown the patties on both sides. Serve.

MILLET BURGERS

3 Cups millet, cooked
1/3 Cup lentils, cooked
2/3 Cup sunflower seeds
1 Onion, minced
½ Small carrot, grated
¼ Tsp. Sea salt
2/3 Cup whole wheat flour
¼ Tsp. oregano

Combine millet, lentils, sunflower seeds, onion, and carrot in a bowl. Mix thoroughly, then add sea salt, oregano and if the mixture is too dry sprinkle with a little liquid. Form mixture into burgers or any shape you like. Put 1/3" of sesame oil or corn oil into a cast-iron skillet. Pan fry over a medium heat. Serve plain or with a sauce.

BENZ PATTIES

2 Cups buckwheat groats, cooked
¾ Cup unbleached white flour
1 Medium onion, diced
1 Carrot, diced
7 - 10 Fresh mushrooms, sliced thin
1 Ear corn, kernels removed from cob
½ Green pepper, chopped
1 Tsp. sesame oil
1 TBS. tamari, diluted in ¼ cup water
1 Cup bread crumbs or corn meal
Pinch of Sea salt

Saute all vegetables and set aside to cool. Combine vegetables with groats, add tamari and a few drops of water. Mix thoroughly. Add enough flour to hold mixture together. Form patties and set aside. Combine the remaining flour, add salt and water to form a thin batter.

In a cast-iron skillet, pour ½" oil and heat to 360°. Dip patties into the batter, roll in the bread crumbs until completely covered. Place in the hot oil and fry 3 - 4 minutes or until golden brown. Place the patties on a paper towel to remove excess oil. Serve.

POWER SHIFT BURGERS

2 Cups barley, cooked
2 Small onions, minced
2 Scallions, sliced thin
1½ TBS. Miso, diluted in ½ cup hot water
1 TBS. sesame butter
Sesame oil for frying
Flour, as needed

Combine all the ingredients in a large bowl and mix together well. Add flour as needed to thicken the mixture. Form into patties. Heat the sesame oil in a skillet and fry the patties on both sides. Serve on whole wheat rolls, along with lettuce, pickle, relish, etc.

MACARONI SALAD

1 Cup whole wheat elbow macaroni,
    cooked and drained
½ Cup cooked aduki beans
1 Onion, diced
1 Scallion, sliced thin
2 Stalks of celery, diced
2 Small carrots, grated
½ Tsp. Sea salt
Mayonnaise to taste

Toss all ingredients together, mix in mayonnaise dressing. Garnish with parsley, chill and serve.

SALAD GRANADA

2 Cups fresh shrimp, lobster or crab meat,
    cook and cut into small pieces
2 Small onions, diced
1 Carrot, diced thin
1 Cup celery, diced
5 Red radishes, sliced
1 Head lettuce, chopped in small pieces

Mix all ingredients together and toss gently. Add your favorite dressing. Lemon-tamari dressing is an excellent choice. (See dressing chapter)

FRUIT FERRARI

1 Pint strawberries, wash, remove stems
3 Apples, peeled and cut into 8ths
3 Peaches, peeled and cut into 8ths
1 Pear, peeled and cut into quarters
¼ Cup raisins
¼ Cup toasted almonds, slivered
¼ Cup sunflower seeds

DRESSING:

1/3 Cup rice syrup
Juice of 1 lemon
Pinch of Sea salt

Place all the fresh fruit in a large bowl. Sprinkle lightly with sea salt. In a separate bowl, mix together the rice syrup and lemon juice. Pour the dressing over the fruit, chill and serve.

CONTINENTAL BROWN RICE SALAD

2 Cups cooked brown rice (hot)
2 Medium onions, chopped fine
¼ Green pepper, chopped fine
2 TBS. lemon juice
1 Tsp. Sea salt
¼ Cup corn oil
¼ Tsp. oregano
Ripe olives
Freshly chopped parsley
1 small pint of feta cheese

Add the salt along with the chopped onions and pepper to the freshly cooked brown rice. Blend together the oil and lemon juice and pour over the rice. Toss the ingredients together. Sprinkle with oregano and garnish with olives, freshly chopped parsley and feta cheese.

KIDNEY BEAN SALAD

1 Cup cooked kidney beans
1 Clove garlic, minced
5 Scallions, sliced
1 Small green pepper, chopped fine
2 Stalks celery, chopped

Place the kidney beans in a bowl, add the garlic, scallions, celery and green peppers. Gently toss together and set aside.

NISSAN DRESSING

½ Cup sesame oil
¼ Cup rice vinegar
¼ Tsp. Sea salt
1/8 Tsp. paprika
1 TBS. rice syrup
1 TBS. tamari
2 TBS. chopped parsley

Place all ingredients in a bowl and mix together. Chill for 1 hour before using. Pour over the kidney beans, toss and serve. Top with sunflower seeds.

THREE BEAN SALAD

1½ Cups green beans, cut 1½" diagonals
1½ Cups yellow wax beans, cut 1½"
    diagonals
½ Cup cooked garbonzo beans
2 Medium onion, sliced in thin half moons
2 Hardboiled fertile eggs, sliced
2 Potatoes, peeled, boiled and sliced thin
½ Tsp. Sea salt

Place beans in a steamer basket with 1" of water and a pinch of sea salt, steam until tender. Drain and put in a large bowl. Remove steamer basket, using the same water boil onion slices for 1 minute. Add to green beans along with cooked garbonzos. Toss all ingredients, add sea salt and rice vinegar dressing. Allow to stand for one hour in the dressing, then toss again before serving. (See dressing chapter for rice-vinegar) Garnish with sliced hardboiled eggs. Serve.

RICE CURRY SALAD

1 Cup cooked brown rice
½ Cup cooked wheatberries
1 Cup Ono cheese, (See recipe this section)
2 Onions, chopped
3 Stalks celery, chopped
1 Tomato, sliced
Sea salt to taste

EAST INDIAN DRESSING:

1 Clove garlic, minced
½ Cup raisins
1/3 Cup rice vinegar
¼ Cup corn oil
2 TBS. lemon juice
3 TBS. barley malt syrup
2 Tsp. curry powder
¼ Tsp. Sea salt

In a saucepan heat the oil, add the curry powder and garlic. Simmer for 1 minute. Then add the barley malt syrup, lemon juice, raisins, rice vinegar and sea salt. Simmer for 5 minutes. In a separate bowl, combine the brown rice and wheatberries. Mix together well. Add the onions and celery, crumble the cheese, add in tomatoes and toss together with grain. Pour the warm East Indian Dressing over the grain and toss together. Refrigerate for 1 hour and serve.

GREEK SALAD

Assorted green lettuce: bib, romaine,
    iceberg
5 - 6 Scallions, diced
1 Onion, diced
10 - 15 Fresh mushrooms, sliced
½ Green pepper, sliced
Feta cheese
3 Greek peppers
A few Greek olives
Sea salt to taste
Rice vinegar to taste
Corn oil

Lightly toss the salad ingredients together, add the sea salt, oil and vinegar to taste. Garnish with oregano, chill and serve.

d'ELEGANCE SALAD

1 Cup of bulghur, soaked in 4 cups of
    water for approximately 2 hours
    or until the bulghur is soft
1 Onion, diced
2 Stalks of celery, diced
1 Carrot, diced
½ Cucumber, peeled and sliced
¼ Green pepper, diced
4 - 5 Red radishes or daikon radish, sliced
Handful of freshly chopped parsley
¼ Tsp. Sea salt

Dressing:
¼ Cup corn oil
1 TBS. rice vinegar

Drain off the liquid from the bulghur.
Mix the bulghur and vegetables together
in a large wooden salad bowl. Prepare the
dressing and blend well with the bulghur
and vegetables, chill and serve.

CORVETTE CHICKEN AND RICE SOUP

2 Cloves garlic, minced
2 Onions, diced
2 Stalks of celery, diced
2 Small potatoes, diced
1 Carrot, diced
¼ Butternut squash, diced
¼ Tsp. Sea salt
¼ Tsp. sage
2/3 Cups brown rice
6 Cups chicken soup stock

Place 3 TBS. of chicken soup stock in a
soup pot. Saute the garlic, onions then add
the remaining vegetables and rice. Mix
together well. Add the sage and sea salt,
along with the remainder of the chicken
stock. Bring to a boil, lower the flame and
simmer for 25 - 30 minutes or until the
rice is tender. If you desire further seasoning, add 1 TBS. of tamari at the end of
cooking.

ROCKET RICE SOUP

1 Onion, diced
1 Carrot, diced
1 Turnip, diced
1 Stalk of celery, diced in ½" pieces
½ Cup brown rice, rinsed and drained
6 Cups water or soup stock
Pinch of Sea salt
1 TBS. tamari

Layer all vegetables in the order given,
along with the brown rice. Gently and
slowly pour liquid down the sides of the
pot. Add sea salt, bring to a boil and
cover. Lower flame and cook for 25 minutes or until the rice is tender. Add tamari,
stir and serve.

HIGH CAM MILLET SOUP

7 Cups of water or soup stock
1 Cup tempeh, diced (Cook tempeh first
    in water seasoned with tamari, 3 -
    5 minutes)
½ Cup millet, rinsed and drained
2 Onions, diced
1 Carrot, diced
½ Cup green beans, ½" pieces (add 10
    minutes before end of cooking)
¼ Tsp. Sea salt
1 Bay leaf/or pinch of thyme
Tamari to taste

Layer all ingredients in the following order:
onions, carrot, tempeh, millet and a pinch
of sea salt. Gently and slowly pour enough
liquid down the sides of the pot to cover
ingredients. Cover and bring to a boil,
lower flame and simmer. When the millet
expands, add enough water to cover. This
is repeated until the millet is done. Now
add 3 cups of cold liquid, salt, and bay
leaf, allow to simmer for 10 minutes.
Add green beans, bring to a boil, lower and
simmer for 10 minutes more. Add tamari
to taste. Serve.

G.T. MUSHROOM BARLEY SOUP

7 Cups of water or soup stock
2 Cloves of garlic, minced
2 Onions, diced
1 Carrot, diced
½ LB. of fresh mushrooms, sliced
½ Tsp. Sea salt
½ Cup barley, rinsed and drained
Sesame oil
3 TBS. tamari
Freshly chopped parsley for garnish

Bring barley to boil in 2 cups of liquid, add a pinch of sea salt. Cover and lower flame, cook for 30 minutes. In a cast-iron skillet, add sliced mushrooms to the DRY skillet, sprinkle on sea salt, cover and cook dry over a medium flame. Pour off excess liquid and set aside. Now lightly coat the skillet with sesame oil, saute vegetables, beginning with garlic, onions, etc. including mushrooms. Add all sauteed vegetables to the barley, plus the additional liquid. Cook for 10 - 15 minutes. Season with tamari at end of cooking. Serve with parsley as a garnish.

SUPRA VEGETABLE SOUP

2 Onions, diced
2 Stalks of celery, diced fine
½ Butternut squash, cubed
½ Acorn squash, cubed
3 - 4 Pieces of Crescent pumpkin, cubed
7 Cups of water or soup stock
½ Cup brown rice or millet, rinsed and
    drained
2 TBS. of Miso, diluted and pureed

Layer all vegetables in a heavy soup pot, in the order given, EXCEPT celery (which will be added 10 minutes before end of cooking time). Gently pour the liquid down the sides of the pot to avoid disturbing vegetables. Place grain on top. Cover and bring to a boil, reduce flame and simmer for 25 minutes or until grain is tender. Add celery, and miso puree and allow to simmer for 5 minutes. Serve.

MARQUIS CLAM CHOWDER

1 Dozen fresh clams
2 Quarts of water (8 cups)
1 Cluster broccoli stems, sliced
2 Onions, diced
½ Butternut squash, peeled and cubed
2 Potatoes, unpeeled and diced/or
    rutabago, peeled and diced
2 Stalks of celery, diced
¼ Cup wakame, cut into tiny pieces
    (soak, discard water)
Pinch of thyme
Pinch of oregano
1 Bay leaf

Clean and scrub clams thoroughly. Bring clams and water to a boil, cook clams until the shells open. Pour off liquid in a fine strainer, except for the last inch, which will contain sand. Reserve the liquid for soup stock. Add onion, carrots, squash and wakame to the clam broth. Bring to a boil and cook for 4 minutes. Remove the clams from their shells, place on a cutting board and mince very fine. Add potatoes, celery, minced clams, bay leaf and oregano to the soup. Simmer over a low flame for 20 minutes, add broccoli. Be sure to remove the bay leaf before serving. Add miso or tamari to taste at the end of cooking.

ELECTRA 225 SOUP

2 Onions, diced
3 Stalks of celery, diced
1 Cup of oats
1/3 Cup lentils, rinsed and drained
¼ Tsp. Sea salt
6 Cups of water or soup stock

Layer all ingredients in a soup pot in the order given. Gently pour the liquid down the sides of the pot. Cover, and bring to a boil, lower flame and cook for 25 - 30 minutes. Add sea salt and simmer for 10 minutes more. Serve garnished with scallions.

MILAN MINESTRONE SOUP

7 Cups of water or soup stock
1/3 Cup wakame, cut into tiny pieces
    (soak, discard water)
½ Cup garbonzo beans, 80% cooked
2 Onions, cut into 1/16th
1 Carrot, diced
2 Scallions, sliced
¼ Green pepper, diced
1 Turnip, cut into matchsticks
1 Stalk of celery, sliced
1 Zucchini, cut 1" thick slices
1 Clove garlic, minced
¼ Tsp. oregano
½ Tsp. Sea salt
½ Cup fresh romano cheese, grated
¼ - ½ Cup red Chianti wine
1 Bay leaf
1 TBS. parsley, chopped
2 TBS. tamari
1 Cup whole wheat elbow macaroni

Lightly saute all vegetables in 2 Tsp. of sesame or corn oil. Saute garlic and onions separately and place sauteed vegetables in a bowl. Bring soup stock to a boil. Add partially cooked beans and all vegetables to the stock. Lower flame, add bay leaf, oregano and cover. Simmer for 25 minutes. Add elbow macaroni and salt, bring to a rapid boil stirring constantly, lower flame, cover and simmer for 15 minutes. Stir occasionally. Add wine, simmer for 5 minutes, add tamari. Serve with grated cheese.

NOODLES AND BROTH

1 Package of soba or udon noodles
5 Cups of water
Pinch of Sea salt
1½ Tsp. of bonita flakes (optional)
3 TBS. of tamari
1 Sliced scallion

Cook noodles in salted water, rinse and drain. Place 2½ cups of noodle broth in a pot. Add the bonita flakes and bring to a boil. Lower the flame and simmer for 3 minutes. Add tamari and place the noodles back into the pot. Stir and let set for one minute, covered. Garnish with sliced scallions and serve.

CASSEROLE MONTE CARLO

1 Cup cooked brown rice/or leftover grain
2 Onions, diced
¼ Green pepper, diced
1 Tomato, sliced thin then quartered
Mix ¼ cup tamari with ¾ cup of water
Thin slices of cheddar cheese, camembert,
    brie or tofu

Place grain in the bottom of a glass baking dish. Spread evenly, then top with onions, pepper and tomatoes. Pour the tamari/water mixture evenly over the casserole. Bake at 350° for 20 minutes. Then add the tofu or slices of cheese on top of the casserole. Bake for an additional 10 minutes or until cheese has melted.

BROWN RICE STUFFED PEPPERS

2 Cups brown rice, cooked
6 Green peppers, pre-salted
¼ Cup peas, uncooked
1 Stalk celery, chopped
1 Carrot, shredded
½ Cup caulifloweretts, chopped
3 Scallions, chopped
2 Hardboiled eggs (fertile), chopped

DRESSING:

2 TBS. rice vinegar
2 TBS. corn oil
1 TBS. lemon juice
1 Clove garlic, minced
½ Tsp. dry mustard

In a small bowl, combine all the dressing ingredients and set aside. Cut off the tops of the green peppers and remove the seeds. In a large bowl combine the rice and vegetables. Mix together well, then add the eggs and mix again. Add the dressing to the rice and vegetable mixture. Allow this mixture to set for 3 hours. You may refrigerate. Salt the interiors of the peppers and stuff with the rice mixture. Place the peppers in a casserole dish and add a little water to the bottom. Bake at 325° for 20 minutes or until done.

POTATO STEW

5 Medium potatoes, peeled and diced
3 Cloves garlic, minced
3 Onions, diced
2 Stalks celery, diced
2 Tsp. Sea salt
½ Tsp. marjoram
¼ Tsp. dill weed
¼ Tsp. paparika
1 Cup soya or almond milk
1½ Tsp. corn oil
1 Cup soup stock
1 TBS. tamari

Lightly coat a large cast-iron saucepan with oil. Saute the onions, garlic, carrots, celery and potatoes for 3 - 4 minutes. Add the soup stock, salt and spices. Bring to a boil, lower the flame to medium and cook for 20 minutes. Add the almond milk and cook an additional 25 minutes. Add the tamari at the end of cooking and simmer for 3 - 4 minutes.

ONION DELIGHT

4 Large onions
Leftover rice or millet delight
Corn oil
3 TBS. tamari
½ Cup white wine

Cut the tops off the onions, peel and scoop out the center meat of the onion. Pour a drop of oil in the core of the onion, then rub the inside and outside of the onion with the oil. Stuff the onion with the leftover grain. Mix together the white wine and tamari, put the onions in a deep bowl, pour the liquid over the onions and marinate for 30 minutes. Place the onions in a casserole dish along with the remaining liquid, cover and bake at 325° for 20 minutes. Remove the cover, baste and cook an additional 25 minutes or until the onions are tender.

TABOULY-BO A cold summer meal

4 Ears of corn, uncooked, kernels removed from cob
1 Carrot, medium, diced
2 Onions, chopped fine
1 Turnip, diced
1 Cup broccoli, floweretts
1 Scallion, sliced
1 TBS. corn or sesame oil
2 TBS. tamari diluted in ¼ cup of water
1 Package of tofu
Juice of 1 orange
Pinch of Sea salt
Handful of freshly chopped parsley

Saute lightly in a cast-iron skillet in this order: onion, carrot, turnip, broccoli, corn. As each vegetable is done, set aside and when all are sauteed combine again in the skillet. Add tamari and water, mixing with vegetables for 1 minute. Turn into a casserole dish and add scallion, mixing gently. Allow to cool and refrigerate. Cream the tofu with a little broth or water in a suribachi bowl with a wooden pestle. Add juice of one orange and sea salt to taste. When mixture is smooth spread on top of vegetables as you would if icing a cake. Top with chopped parsley. Refrigerate again and serve cold.

* PERSONAL NOTES

173

Exit 14
NOODLES

Grains In Their Modified Class

Although made from one or more types of flour, noodles are the easiest flour product to digest. This makes them an excellent quick meal and a popular one with young children.

Noodles come in many types and sizes. Some, like the Japanese "soba" noodle, which is made mostly from buckwheat flour, are thinner and shorter. Another category, called "udon", are made from whole wheat and unbleached white flours and are thicker and chewier. Other noodles will list ingredients such as artichoke, corn, and even potato flours. Some products like "soba" noodles have been made with salt and none need be added in cooking. Others, like "udon", need a pinch of sea salt in the cooking water to bring out their flavor. Always check the package label.

There are so many ways noodles can be served in addition to simple soups and broths. They adapt to many casserole and pasta recipes and make a main course as well. They can be deep fried after cooking for a crunchy snack or served over other vegetable dishes, as in chow mein.

The Chinese people are believed by historians to have originated noodles, and according to some reports, explorers such as Marco Polo may have carried the idea back to the European countries where it was developed into various macaroni and spaghetti products.

Today, there are many of these whole grain products in North America and Europe which are excellent for occasional use. They include: rigatoni, lasagna, ziti, shells, elbows, spirals, and other shapes of many kinds. Most of these are made from a blend of whole wheat and white flours, however, we prefer to avoid those products which indicate "enriched" flours have been used. Look instead for the ones which have whole grain flours without preservatives.

There are a few basic ways to cook noodles. The first is to bring the water to a boil, simply add the dry noodles and when the water boils again, reduce the flame and cook until the center is the same color as the inside. Do not overcook.

Another cooking method is to boil the water, add noodles, bring to a boil again and then add a little cold water to stop the boiling action. When the water begins to boil the next time, again add a little cold water, repeat this 3 times.

When noodles are done, remove from pot, place into a strainer and rinse by running cold water over them. This will prevent the noodles from sticking together.

Another method for testing the noodles to see if they are done, is to toss a strand of noodle or spaghetti against a smooth surface. If it sticks, it is usually done.

Do not throw away the cooking water when draining the noodles. You can use the broth to serve them in. This broth can also be used later in many ways, such as sour-dough starter for unyeasted bread, if allowed to ferment slightly. Or, add it to muffins, pancakes, or any bakery product where natural methods of raising the dough are desired. It also makes a good soup stock, be sure to refrigerate so that it stays fresh.

HOMEMADE WHOLE WHEAT NOODLES

1 Cup whole wheat flour
3 Cups unbleached white flour
1 Tsp. Sea salt
1 Tsp. corn or sesame oil
1 Cup water

Mix dry ingredients in a wooden mixing bowl. Work in oil with your hands until blended. Add water a little at a time, until the dough which forms is stiff but able to be kneaded. Knead dough, working from the center and pushing towards the edges, folding it to the center and working out again. After kneeding 15 minutes cover the dough with a damp cloth, allow to set 15 minutes, then knead it for another 15 minutes, or until smooth. Add water as needed.

Roll the dough on a floured board in a rectangular shape if possible, one side being nearly the size of the noodle length you desire. Then, when the dough has been stretched as much as possible in the other direction, and is approximately 1/10th inch thick, cut a straight line in two places, dividing the dough into three pieces. Work one section of the dough at a time. If the edges are too irregular you can cut away a little dough to form the sides. Use a straight edge (any box will do) and cut the noodles as thin or thick as you wish. I recommend a 1/8" width for a standard noodle for use in broth but you can cut fettucine width, which is slightly wider, or lasagna, which is 1½". They will only expand slightly when cooked. If the knife sticks, use extra flour to dust the pasta as you work. As strips are cut away from the dough, lift them with your fingers and let them fall in a natural twist onto a lightly floured piece of wax paper where they can remain undisturbed until they are dry.

They will harden in the shape they fall. When completely dry, (about 4 hours) they may be stored in a glass jar or plastic bag. They can also be cooked immediately after cutting, if you prefer not to store them for later use.

NOODLES AND BROTH

1 Package of soba or udon noodles
5 Cups of water
Pinch of Sea salt
1½ Tsp. of bonita flakes (optional)
3 TBS. of tamari
1 Sliced scallion

Cook noodles in salted water, rinse and drain. Place 2½ cups of noodle broth in a pot. Add the bonita flakes and bring to a boil. Lower the flame and simmer for 3 minutes. Add tamari and place the noodles back into the pot. Stir and let set for one minute, covered. Garnish with sliced scallions and serve.

FETTUCCINE ALA VEGETABLES

2 Cloves garlic, minced
1 Onion, diced
5 Scallions, diced
1 Carrot, cut into matchsticks
2 Small zucchini, cut into matchsticks
½ LB. fresh mushrooms, sliced
Corn oil
½ Tsp. Sea salt
¼ Tsp. oregano
¼ Tsp. basil
1 Fertile egg yolk
1 lb. Homemade fettuccine noodles
1 Cup oat or rice milk, or you may use
    fresh raw milk
½ Cup freshly grated Parmesan cheese

Saute the garlic, onions, carrots, zucchini and mushrooms in corn oil in a large skillet, add the spices and sea salt. Mix well and set aside. Cook the noodles in a separate saucepan and when they are done combine the vegetables and noodles, tossing together gently. Place the ingredients on a low flame and simmer until hot.

Beat the egg yolk and milk until foamy. Add to the fettuccine and vegetables ½ Tsp. sea salt, stirring gently. Add ¼ cup of cheese and toss. Place on a serving platter and sprinkle with the remaining parmesan cheese. Serve with a tossed salad and steamed broccoli.

SPAGHETTI AND CLAM SAUCE
(Serves 4)

1 Package spaghetti, (1 lb.)
1 Dozen fresh clams
2 Cloves garlic, minced
3 TBS. Sesame oil
1 Onion, chopped fine
2 Scallions, sliced
1/8 Green pepper, diced fine
1 Lemon
1 TBS. tamari
¼ Cup grated romano cheese
Handful of fresh parsley

Cook spaghetti in boiling, salted water and drain well. Scrub clams thoroughly and cook in 1 quart of water. Boil clams until clams open, remove from the shells and mince. Place minced clams in a bowl and squeeze the juice of a lemon over them. Using a fine strainer, pour off clam broth, save for sauce. (Avoid bottom inch which will be very sandy.)

In a heavy cast-iron skillet, saute garlic, pepper, onions and scallions in sesame oil, over a medium flame for about 5 minutes. Add 2 cups of the strained clam juice and bring to a boil. Lower the flame and simmer for 5 minutes, stirring occasionally. Add minced clams, tamari, parsley and mix thoroughly. Cook for 2 minutes, then combine clam sauce with spaghetti and toss. Place in a serving bowl and top with grated romano cheese.

NOODLES AND LEEKS

1 Package of noodles
5 Cups of water
3 TBS. of tamari
2 Leeks, chopped
10 - 12 Drops of fresh grated ginger juice

Cook noodles, rinse and drain. Place 2½ cups of noodle water in a pot. Add chopped leeks and ginger. Bring to a boil, lower flame and simmer for 1 - 2 minutes. Add tamari, stir and let set for one minute. covered. Place noodles into the broth to warm them and serve.

NOODLE AND SHRIMP BAKE

1 Package udon or ramen noodles (cook
    and set aside)
½ lb. Fresh small shrimp, deveined and
    peeled
¾ Cup bread crumbs (Use stale toasted
    bread)
½ Cup sharp raw cheddar cheese, grated
1 Clove garlic, minced
1 Onion, diced
½ Green pepper, diced
Corn oil
1 Cup of water or vegetable soup stock
1 TBS. arrowroot
Sea salt

Lightly coat a skillet with corn oil and
saute the garlic, onions and pepper. Dilute
the arrowroot in cold water or soup stock
and add to vegetables, stirring constantly.
Bring to a boil, when the mixture thickens,
lower the flame, add the cheddar cheese,
stir until melted. Add the shrimp and
allow to cook for 2 - 3 minutes, add the
sea salt and mix. Add the previously
cooked noodles and toss gently. Place
all the ingredients into a casserole dish,
allow to cool, cover and place in the
refrigerator for 1 hour. Remove and place
in a pre-heated 350° oven and cook for
30 minutes. Top with the bread crumbs
and cook 15 more minutes, uncovered.
Serve.

NOODLES AND MUSHROOMS

1 Package of noodles
5 Cups of water
2 Shiitake mushrooms, soak for
    30 minutes, remove stems, slice
3 TBS. tamari
10 - 15 drops of fresh grated ginger juice
2 Scallions, sliced

Cook noodles, rinse and drain. Place 2½
cups of noodle water in a pot. Add previously soaked mushrooms, bring to a
boil, lower flame and simmer for 5 minutes. Add ginger, scallions and tamari
and simmer three minutes more. Place
noodles back in the broth to warm and
serve.

CHOW MEIN

1 Package soba noodles
1 Cup mung bean sprouts
1 Onion, diced
1 Carrot, diced
½ Cup celery, thinly sliced
½ Cup Chinese cabbage, thinly sliced
1 Cup tofu, cubed and fried
1 Leaf of mustard green, sliced
3 Shiitake mushrooms, soak and slice
    (remove stems)
1 TBS. arrowroot, diluted in 1/3 cup of
    water
Sesame oil for deep frying
4 Cups of noodle water
2 TBS. of tamari

Cook and drain noodles. Cut them in half.
Heat a skillet with the oil and deep fry
noodles. In a separate pot bring the reserve
noodle water with tamari added to a boil.
Lower the flame, add onions, carrots and
mushrooms. Simmer for 5 minutes. Add
arrowroot to thicken, stirring continuously.
Bring to a rapid boil, reduce heat and
simmer for 10 minutes. Add bean sprouts,
cabbage, and celery and simmer for 3 - 5
minutes. Place over deep fried noodles
and garnish with fried tofu and serve.

RAMEN NOODLES WITH VEGETABLES

1 Package ramen noodles
1 Cup snow pea pods, rinsed and snipped
½ Green or red pepper, chopped
2 - 3 Cup of vegetable soup stock or water
1 Onion, chopped
2 - 3 TBS. of tamari or to taste
5 - 6 Drops of freshly grated ginger juice
1 TBS. umeboshi vinegar
1 Cup fresh mushrooms, sliced

Bring the water or vegetable soup stock to
boil, add the ramen noodles and cook
about 5 minutes. Add the snow pea pods,
onions, pepper and mushrooms, lower
heat and cook until the pea pods are
tender. Add tamari, ginger juice, umeboshi
vinegar. Garnish with scallions and serve
hot.

Exit 15
BEAN POWER

When Better Bodies Are Built
Beans Will Build Them!

Protein is a chemical compound that is an essential part of every cell. Man and animals synthesize proteins from the foods they eat. Plants can make their proteins from **non**-organic elements using energy that came originally from sunlight in a process called "photosynthesis."

Protein is available from many sources for modern man, but the **quality** of the protein is the important factor. Modern nutritionists tend to over-emphasize the importance of protein ingestion, without regard to the dynamics of the constant interchange between protein, carbohydrates, and fat within our body. Food is used for the formation of body cells, but also for the energy of daily activity. Carbohydrates are required in greater volume for this need.

A history of the opinions on protein requirements shows many changes throughout past years. It was believed in the 19th century that for an average person, 118 grams of protein daily was sufficient. For a person doing heavy labor, their daily protein needs should be 145 grams. This however, was not the only opinion. Dr. Russell Chittenden of Yale University, in 1901, believed that the daily protein requirement should be reduced. Experiments done at that time, with athletes, teachers, and soldiers, led him to conclude that a person could maintain good health on a low-protein diet by consuming only 36 grams of protein daily.

This was modified by an American nutritionist in 1912, McCay, to 125 grams, suggesting that this would contribute to a stronger race of people having more muscular strength and fighting spirit.

Scientists today are still not in agreement as to the need of protein. According to the National Cancer Institute, in their 1977 "Status Report," a lower protein intake can inhibit the development of spontaneous or chemically induced tumors. Comparisons of rats eating 5% and 20% casein diets, (cow's milk) showed rats on the high protein diet had a 50% greater incidence of cancer, and **all of the test rats developed tumors or precancerous lesions. None of the rats eating the lower protein intake developed lesions.**

The food value of a protein depends on the type and amounts of amino acids it contains, **not** on the total amount of protein in a serving. Scientists have found over 20 amino acids in plant and animal cells and have termed ten of these "essential." They are: tryptophan, theonine, isoleucine, lysine, methinnine, leucine, thistine, phenylanine, tryosine and valine. Some foods high in protein have fewer usable acids, and these foods may produce excretion of a percentage of their protein in body wastes. For example, a **BREAST-FED BABY** eliminates no protein. Yet a baby fed cow's milk will eliminate up to 50% of the available protein, due to the composition of the amino acids. Since protein cannot be stored in the body, this creates a strain on an immature infant's kidneys. Children can transmute their own protein from carbohydrates; therefore, it is not recommended that they eat large volumes of meat.

We note that in charts showing the breakdown of amino acids, animal foods typically contain only **four** out of the essential ten. Further, two of these four amino acids, leucine and lysine, are related to body growth. Adults who are no longer developing skeletally do **not** need much of these amino acids. Vegetable food, on the other hand, characteristically contains **six** of the amino acids, and two of these are related to body maintenance and metabolism. These are the real needs of an adult.

Probably the most ideally **BALANCED** protein, with respect to the composition of amino acids, is to be found in **BROWN RICE. Miso,** (fermented soybean paste) **tamari,** (naturally fermented soysauce), and **sesame salt,** (roasted sesame seeds and sea salt) also have almost all of the essential amino acids.

Proteins are digested in the stomach and small intestines and absorbed into the blood as amino acids. They are then carried to all organs and tissues, where they begin to produce body construction and body energy for activity. Vegetable proteins are more flexible than animal proteins in their ability to successfully fluctuate between these two functions. In addition, animal protein overworks and clogs the pores of the kidney. This is caused by the residue produced when meat ferments in the intestines. These same toxins damage the heart, arteries and nervous system. Animal protein also produces many allergies and causes overacidity. Vegetable proteins never produce these effects, because they break down more slowly in the intestines.

In conclusion it seems clear that:

1. Diets built on a **BALANCED** consumption of whole cereal grains, beans, and vegetables, along with a small amount of animal products, provide a **better source of protein** than diets high in meats, eggs or dairy products.
2. The body's requirement for construction and energy need not necessarily come from protein itself, but may be supplied by complex carbohydrates.
3. Excess protein in the body wastes energy and creates toxins by fermenting in the intestines.
4. Excess protein cannot be stored in body tissues.

BEANS - PROTEIN AND AMINO ACIDS

Beans are related to the pea family and are very high in protein, carbohydrates, iron, vitamins and minerals. Bean plants have the ability to enrich the soil with nitrogen and bacteria taken from the air. This makes them especially liked by farmers and home gardeners. They are among the most nourishing vegetables eaten by man, supplying per 100 grams the following:

	PROTEIN	CARBOHYDRATES	IRON	VIT.A	VIT. B
Aduki	21.5 gm.	58.4 gm.	4.8 mg.	6 IU	2.5 mg.
Lentils	24.7 gm.	60.1 gm.	6.8 mg.	60 IU	2.0 mg.
Chick Peas	20.5 gm.	61.1 gm.	6.9 mg.	6.9 IU	2.0 mg.
Soybeans	34.1 gm.	33.5 gm.	8.4 mg.	80 IU	2.2 mg.
Black Beans	22.9 gm.	—	7.9 mg.	—	2.2 mg.

Among the many varieties of beans cultivated throughout the world, some are eaten after they have become fully ripe and these are called "dry beans." They are the most contracted beans such as adukis, lentils and chickpeas. These are to be preferred in our daily diet along with pinto, navy and red kidney beans. To be used less often, are the varieties which are picked when full grown but before they have ripened and turned hard. These are called green shell beans and include some varieties of kidney and string beans. Other kinds of "stringless" or "snap" beans are picked at a still younger stage and both the half-formed seeds and juicy pods are eaten. These are the most expanded types of beans and should be used occasionally.

Some beans can be eaten dried or green, like lima beans. These are very similar to soybeans but are not recommended for frequent use due to their digestion inhibiting enzyme, triptin. It is sometimes felt that all beans are difficult to digest and create intestinal gas and stomach problems. Actually the factors influencing their digestability are more likely to be proper preparation and cooking methods, **thorough chewing,** reasonably chosen amounts (usually a tablespoon or two per meal is sufficient), and the time of day eaten.

We suggest beans be avoided late in the day and that their preparation include a piece of Kombu sea vegetable about three inches long and placed on the bottom of the pot to help prevent flatulence. A few more tips on how to prevent flatulence: Soaking beans overnight will help break down the very starchy components (stachose and raffinose) into sugars. Bring your beans to a fast hard boil with a 3" piece of kombu and cook for 20 minutes . (Prepare according to recipe) Another suggestion would be to boil the beans for 5 minutes, then soak them in ice cold water for 20 minutes. Then, rub them gently until the hulls float freely off, then prepare them according to your recipe.

Be sure to cook beans as long as needed to ensure softness and never add salt to the cooking water until the end of the cooking time, since this will keep the beans from softening and affect digestability. To prevent the beans from breaking, limit your stirring to a minimum and use a low flame.

In general, the best way to cook beans is in a pressure cooker. It saves time, water, and the beans emerge softer without pre-soaking. First, rinse the beans in a strainer. Use 3 **CUPS** of water to each cup of beans and bring to full pressure over a high flame. Lower the flame and cook most beans for one hour, with the exception of lentils, which only require 12 minutes, and chickpeas, which need a full hour and a half. Bring the pressure down quickly under cold running water and remove the cover. Add the appropriate amount of salt to the beans and simmer for 2 - 3 minutes or until the excess liquid is evaporated. You also may add a little water at this time if needed.

Black beans should not be pressure cooked because their skins may come off and clog the pressure gauge. For this same reason it is best to avoid trying to cook too many beans at one time. A pressure cooker should be no more than half full including the amount of liquid.

When cooking beans in a pot, wash them in a strainer and soak for 2 - 3 hours before cooking. Lentils do not need soaking and chickpeas, ideally, are soaked overnight. Reserve the soaking liquid for soup stock or just use it as part of the amount of cooking water. For one cup of beans, using this method, you will want four cups of cold water. Bring beans, kombu and water to a boil, lower flame leaving the lid slightly open and cook for two hours for most types of beans. Again, the exceptions are for lentils, which need only 35 minutes to cook, and chickpeas, which may take as long as four hours. Add ¼ teaspoon sea salt for each cup of beans near the end of cooking time while there is still some liquid in the pot.

Another method called "shocking" method; Place kombu sea vegetable and beans in a pot. Add enough water to cover. Bring to a boil, lower flame and cover. When water has evaporated, add enough cold water to cover. Repeat this 3 - 4 times until the beans are 80% done. Add ¼ teaspoon sea salt per 1 cup of beans. Remove cover and allow to simmer until soft. When beans are tender raise flame to medium until excess water is removed.

Beans are sometimes used medicinally, for example, aduki beans are excellent for kidney disorders. Black beans are useful in treating conditions of the sexual organs, as in cases of irregular menstruation, infertility, or low sexual appetite. Navy and lima beans are sometimes suggested for liver problems due to their lower oil content.

BEAN RECIPES

LENTIL SHRIMP GUMBO

1½ Cups lentils, rinsed
½ Cup millet, rinsed
2 Carrots, diced
2 Large onions, diced
½ Green pepper, thinly sliced
1 Stalk celery, sliced
1 Small butternut squash, cubed
1 TBS. corn oil
4 Cups of water
1 Pound fresh shrimp, cleaned and
    deveined
10 Drops fresh grated ginger juice
3 TBS. tamari

Saute all vegetables lightly in corn oil and set aside. Bring water to a boil, add lentils and millet and return to a boil. Lower the flame and cook for 35 minutes. Add the vegetables and cook for 15 minutes, adding water as needed to prevent drying out, stir occasionally. Clean and devein shrimp, add to gumbo 5 minutes before removing from heat. Add ginger juice and tamari to flavor at the end of cooking. This is one of the easiest recipes to prepare and ideal for the working person.

ADUKI BEANS WITH SQUASH OR PUMPKIN

1 Cup aduki beans, rinsed
1 2" piece kombu, wipe clean
3½ Cups of water
½ Pound pumpkin or squash, cubed
1 TBS. tamari

Place beans, water and kombu in a pressure cooker. Bring to full pressure over high heat. Reduce the flame to low and cook for 30 minutes. Bring pressure down under cold running water. Add squash or pumpkin. Bring pressure back to full pressure, reduce flame to low and cook for 12 minutes more. Allow pressure to return to normal, uncover and add tamari. Garnish with sliced scallions.

PINTO BEANS

1 Cup pinto beans, rinsed and soaked
    for 4 hours
1 Carrot, diced
1 Onion, diced
1 Turnip, diced
¼ Tsp. Sea salt
4 Cups of cold water
Tamari to taste

Place pinto beans in a pot with water. Bring to a boil, lower the flame and simmer until 80% cooked, (approximately 1 hour). Add sea salt and vegetables, cover and simmer until tender. Add tamari to taste.

ADUKI, CHESTNUTS AND RAISINS

1 Cup aduki beans, rinsed and soaked for 2
    hours
1 Cup dried chestnuts, rinsed and soaked
    for 15 minutes
2/3 Cup raisins
1 - 6" Strip kombu, wipe clean
4 Cups of water
Pinch of Sea salt

Place the kombu in the bottom of the pressure cooker, add the aduki beans, chestnuts and raisins. Gently pour the water down the sides of the pressure cooker. Bring to full pressure, lower the flame and simmer for 1 hour. Allow pressure to return to normal. Remove the cover, add a pinch of sea salt and let set for a few minutes. Serve over brown rice or use as a side dish.

WIDETRACK LENTIL

1½ Cup lentils, cooked and pureed
1 Cup winter squash, diced
2 Onions, diced
1 Carrot, diced
1 Cup turnip, diced
1 Fertilized egg
¼ Cup lemon juice in ¾ cup water (Total
    1 cup)
1 6" piece of kombu, wipe clean,
    place in bottom of pot
2 TBS. tamari
1 TBS. sesame oil

Place kombu in pressure cooker. Saute vegetables in oil for 10 minutes, then place on top of kombu. Add diluted lemon juice, cover and bring to full pressure over a high heat. Reduce flame to low and cook 15 minutes. Remove from heat and bring pressure down under cold running water. Combine cooked lentils with all remaining ingredients and mash together with the vegetable mixture. Place in a casserole dish and bake for 30 minutes at 350° .

ADUKIS AND COMPANIONS

1½ Cups aduki beans, pressure cooked
    in 4 cups of water (Strain and save
    liquid)
2 Onions, chopped
2 Carrots, diced
1 Parsnip, diced
1 Small turnip, chopped
1 TBS. corn oil
½ Tsp. Sea salt
¼ Cup tofu
1 Cup bechamel sauce (See sauces)
Pinch of thyme

In a cast-iron skillet saute all vegetables. Saute tofu in corn oil separately and set aside. Combine beans, bean juice, and all sauteed vegetables, cover and simmer for 20 minutes. Add tofu, sea salt, bechamel sauce, and thyme. Cover and simmer for 15 minutes. Serve.

FRUIT-BEAN CASSEROLE

1½ Cups cooked aduki beans
1 Apple, thinly sliced (option, a mandarin
    orange in sections)
2 Medium size onions, chopped
½ Green pepper, chopped
2 Bay leaves
1 TBS. corn oil
½ Tsp. Sea salt
1 Stalk of celery, sliced
¼ Cup of raisins

Saute the onions in the corn oil, add green pepper and celery, then the apple and raisins. Mix all the sauteed ingredients with the cooked aduki beans, add sea salt and blend together. Place in a casserole dish, add bay leaves on top of beans and bake ½ hour at 350° , covered. Before serving, remove the bay leaves.

BEAN BURGERS

2 Cups aduki or pinto beans, cooked
   (Or ½ & ½)
1 Clove garlic, minced
3 Scallions, minced
1 Carrot, grated
½ Tsp. Sea salt
1/8 Tsp. dry mustard
1 Cup whole wheat flour
2 TBS. tamari
Sesame oil for frying

Combine all ingredients and add the flour a little at a time, mix thoroughly. Form burgers approximately 3" in diameter and ½ inch thick. Fry in a little sesame oil, make sure the oil is hot before putting the patties in the skillet. Drain on paper towels before serving. Will yield 10 - 12 burgers.

LENTIL BULGHUR BURGERS

1½ Cups of water
½ Cup green lentils
¼ Cup bulghur
½ Tsp. Sea salt
1 Clove garlic, minced
1 Medium onion, minced
½ Tsp. sage
¼ Tsp. celery seed
1 Fertile egg
¼ Cup freshly grated romano cheese
1 Cup whole wheat flour

Place lentils, garlic and onions in a pot with water. Bring to a boil, lower flame and simmer for 25 minutes. Add the sea salt, bulghur and all seasonings to the lentil mixture, allow to simmer for 5 - 7 minutes or until the water is evaporated. Remove from the pot and allow to cool. When cooled add the egg, flour and cheese. Be sure to mix the flour into the mixture thoroughly. Moisten your hands and form into burgers, fry in a skillet with a little sesame oil.

LIMAS AND CABBAGE

1 Cup limas, cooked in 4 cups of water
¼ Cup dulse or wakame, soak and
   sliced fine (Discard soaking water)
1 Clove garlic, minced
1 Carrot, diced
½ Head cabbage, chopped fine
¼ Tsp. Sea salt
½ Tsp. sesame oil
2 TBS. tamari
2 Small onions, diced

When beans are 80% done, lightly coat a cast-iron skillet with sesame oil and heat the skillet. Saute garlic and onions first, then add carrots and cabbage. Do not over-cook your vegetables. Add the dulse or wakame and saute vegetables with the beans. Bring to a boil, add sea salt, lower the flame, cover and simmer until done. Add tamari, stir and simmer 2 minutes before serving.

TRIPLE CARB SPECIAL

1 Cup of aduki beans, rinse and soak
   for 4 hours
3   6" pieces of kombu, soak 30 minutes;
   cut into 1" squares
1 Butternut squash, cubed into 2" pieces
Tamari to taste

Place the kombu squares in the bottom of a pot, add the aduki beans and cover with water. Bring to a boil, lower the flame and simmer for 30 minutes. Add the cubed squash, sprinkle with sea salt, cover and cook for an additional 25 - 30 minutes or until the beans and squash become soft. If the water evaporates, add enough to ensure moisture. Add tamari to taste, at the end of cooking. Turn off the heat and let vegetables and beans set for several minutes. Serve.

MOCK MEAT LOAF OR BEAN BURGERS

1½ Cups aduki beans, rinsed
½ Cup pinto beans, rinsed
1 3" piece of kombu (wipe clean)
3½ Cups water
¾ Tsp. sage
½ Tsp. dry mustard

Place all ingredients in a pressure cooker. Bring to pressure, lower the flame and cook for 1 hour. Allow pressure to come down, drain off the liquid, cool and then mash the beans. Set aside.

In a separate pot place:
1 Cup boiling water
½ Cup bulghur
Pinch of Sea salt

Bring all the ingredients to a boil, lower the flame and simmer for 15 minutes. Set aside to cool.

In a skillet, lightly saute the following and set aside:

2 Cloves, garlic, minced
2 Scallions, diced
1 Onion, diced
1 Carrot, grated
½ Tsp. sage

In a large wooden or stainless steel bowl, combine all the beans, bulghur and sauteed vegetables. Add ¾ Tsp. sea salt and 2 TBS. tamari. Blend together. Add into the mixture, 2 - 2½ cups of unbleached white flour. Knead the mixture as you would bread, until all the flour and ingredients have been blended well. Then add ½ cup of parmesan cheese. (You may also add 1 fertile egg to this mixture.)

Form into patties and saute in a skillet with a little sesame oil, on both sides. Or, form into a meat loaf and turn into a lightly oiled meat loaf pan or casserole dish and bake in a 325° oven for 25 - 30 minutes. You may serve the meat loaf with the mock tomato sauce.

REFRIED BEANS

1 Cup pinto beans, cooked*
1 Cup aduki beans, cooked*
*Mash the pinto beans and aduki beans
    together.
1 Onion, chopped
2 Cloves garlic, minced
½ Red pepper, minced
2 Scallions, minced
Sesame oil
1 TBS. tahini or sesame butter
2 TBS. miso, diluted in 1 cup of water
2 TBS. parsley
1 Tsp. chives
1/8 Tsp. corriander
½ Tsp. chili powder
2 Slices of homemade bread soaked in
    1 cup of water

Have all your ingredients arranged on your counter. Soak the bread in 1 cup of water. In a sauce pan or skillet saute the onions and scallions for 2 minutes, then add the garlic and red pepper and saute for a few minutes more.

Add the bean puree and all other ingredients, adding the bread and water last, to the sauteed vegetables. Mix well breaking the bread into small pieces. Cook for 10 minutes, stirring constantly. Pour the mixture into an oiled baking dish or casserole. Bake at 350° for 30 minutes or until the top browns slightly. Serve with rice, or in chapati to make burritos, or use as a dip with corn chips.
*(See the sauce section for hot sauce recipe.)

* PERSONAL NOTES:

BRONCO BEANS

½ Cup aduki beans, rinsed
½ Cup pinto beans, rinse and soak
    for 1 - 2 hours
1 3" piece kombu (wipe clean)
1 Large onion, minced
1 Carrot, diced
2 TBS. Miso, dilute in ¼ cup water
Sesame oil
3 Cups of water

Pressure cook beans with the kombu, bring to full pressure over high flame. Lower flame and simmer for 45 minutes. Allow pressure to return to normal. Lightly coat a cast-iron skillet with oil and saute onions and carrots. Place beans, onions and carrots, along with the diluted miso, in a baking dish. Mix well and bake 2 hours at 300°.

KIDNEY BEANS AND SQUASH

1 Cup kidney beans, rinsed
3½ Cups of water
¼ Tsp. Sea salt
1 - 2 " strip of kombu, wipe clean
1 Cup butternut squash, cubed
1 TBS. miso-pureed

In a cast-iron pot place the kombu on the bottom add the kidney beans and water next. Pour the water gently down the sides of the pot. Bring to a boil then reduce the heat and cover. Cook until the beans are 80% done. Add the squash and additional water if needed. Add the sea salt and simmer until tender. Add the miso at end of cooking and allow to simmer for 3 - 5 minutes. Serve.

SWEET BAKED BEANS

1 Cup aduki beans, rinsed
1 3" strip of kombu (wipe clean)
1 Onion, ¼" rounds
1 Carrot, ¼" cuts
3 Cups of water
¼ Tsp. Sea salt
1/3 Cup rice syrup

Place kombu, onion and carrots along with the beans in pressure cooker. Bring to full pressure, lower flame and simmer for 60 minutes. Bring pressure down by placing under cold running water. Remove cover and add sea salt and mix well. Place in a baking dish, stir in the rice syrup and mix well. Bake for 1 hour at 300°.Serve.

GARBONZO BEAN DELIGHT

1½ Cups garbonzo beans, cooked (save
    cooking liquid)
2 Onions, diced
1 Carrot, diced
3 Stalks celery, finely chopped
2 TBS. almond butter
2 TBS. tamari
1 Tsp. corn oil

Heat corn oil in a skillet and saute onions and carrots for 3 minutes, add celery and cook 2 minutes more. Add the cooked beans and their juice. Mix tamari and almond butter together and stir into the the ingredients. Cover and allow to simmer for one hour. Serve.

Exit 16
SPROUTS AND SPROUTING

The Assembly Line

There are many books on the subject of sprouting; they make a complicated endeavor of an innocent budding of life. I believe the following method of sprouting will be the easiest one to use. Besides, if a thing is too difficult, it does not get done regularly, and the eating of home-grown sprouts is an experience I hope you will enjoy often.

Sprouts add so much appeal to the top of a simple salad. They are great in sandwiches, in fact they may garnish any grain or vegetable dish, and you will think of many new uses, I am sure. Indeed, my only problem is keeping enough on hand.

Our favorite seeds for sprouting are alfalfa seeds and mung beans, but wheat berries and lentils or any whole, unprocessed seeds or beans may be sprouted. Wheat berries produce a larger sprout that has a more fibrous taste and if allowed to grow too long, they become coarse and unappetizing.

All that is really needed is a clean glass jar of 1 quart size with a wide mouth. Cover the bottom of the jar with seeds, depending on the size seeds. Mung beans are larger than alfalfa so use more of them. Fill the jar with water, and cover the mouth with a piece of cheesecloth, or a set of plastic lids with holes. Soak overnight, in the morning drain off the water and rinse again in cold water, you need not remove the lid. Drain off the excess water and turn the jar upside down or at a 45 degree angle. Put the jar in a dark place such as a kitchen cupboard and don't forget they are there. Repeat the rinsing **every morning** and again in the evening, if this is convenient. I frequently rinse only once a day and they grow just fine. Soon the sprouts will have developed to an edible size. This may take about 3 days. Then put the jar on a sunny window ledge for another day or two before rinsing. You will soon notice that they will get some green color to their tiny tops, which were white when they were in the dark place. This is the production of chlorophyl, which plants can make only when exposed to sunlight. At this point in their growth you may stop the growing process by rinsing them in a bowl and floating their hulls to the top to remove them, then refrigerate. I know you will enjoy adding sprouting to your skills.

SPROUTS AND CABBAGE
(Serves 4)

1 Cup mung bean sprouts
2 Cups cabbage, shredded
1 Onion, cut into 16th
1 TBS. rice vinegar
1 TBS. sesame oil
1 TBS. tamari

Lightly coat a cast-iron skillet with oil. Saute the onions first, then add the cabbage and saute for 4 minutes. Add the sprouts and saute for an additonal 2 minutes. Add the rice vinegar and tamari and gently mix. Simmer for 3 minutes. Serve.

SAUTEED SPROUTS

2 Onions, diced
1 Clove garlic, minced
1 TBS. tamari
3 Cups mung bean or lentil sprouts

Lightly coat a skillet with sesame oil and saute the garlic and onions, for 3 - 4 minutes. Add the sprouts and saute for 1 - 2 minutes. Add the tamari and serve.

*PERSONAL NOTES:

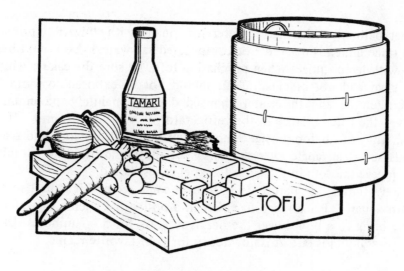

Exit 17
TOFU

The Covertible Bean

What is it? It isn't a dairy product, although it looks like cheese. It's not meat, although the protein quality is approximately the same as found in beef and poultry. It isn't new, having been invented some two thousand years ago. It is believed to have originated in China and then taken to Japan. It has now become popular in Europe and the United States. Tofu is a complete source of protein made from soybeans. Tofu's texture is similar to farmer's cheese and, if eaten raw or uncooked, has a very bland taste. Yet, when seasoned right and prepared properly it makes a delightful dish.

Tofu is an adaptable food that may be prepared in many different ways. It may be deep-fried, boiled, baked, steamed or broiled and in the hot summer, occasionally may be eaten raw.

Some will say, "Why bother eating tofu when there are real cheeses and meats?" One reason is economy. Tofu sells for as little as $1.29 per pound, which is far less than the cost of animal protein. But the main reason for using tofu is YOUR HEALTH. Tofu has **no** cholesterol and is very low in saturated fat. For you calorie watchers, an eight ounce serving has a mere 150 calories. Compare this to eight ounces of eggs which contains three times as many calories, not to mention the cholesterol question. Steak has five times the number of calories.

Four ounces of tofu sells for 30 cents, it contains 75 calories, and provides us with ten grams of protein. Tofu is rich in calcium, phosphorus, iron and B vitamins. It is easy to digest and may be enjoyed by children and grandparents alike. Tofu is available at natural food stores and in the produce department at some supermarkets. It may also be found in oriental food stores, but the quality is often inferior due to the use of vinegar, alum and chemicals as solidifying agents. The difference between the tofu sold in natural food stores and some supermarkets and the oriental stores is the type of coagulant used. Make sure you

189

read the label before purchasing. I prefer tofu made with "nigari", (primarily magnesium chloride and trace minerals derived from evaporated sea water). Your next best choice is tofu that is made with lemon juice. When purchasing tofu, be sure the cake is whitish in color and the water is clear and not brackish. Tofu should not be exposed to warm temperatures. It should be refrigerated and the water changed **daily** to maintain maximum freshness. You need not cover the tofu to store in the refrigerator, it will keep from 3 - 10 days. You may want to drain the tofu before using. Simply wrap it in a clean cloth and place between two cutting boards set at an angle over the sink. Let the liquid drain for 30 minutes or longer, or you may squeeze the tofu in the cloth to expel excess liquid.

We have found that before using tofu in some recipes, it is best to steam or boil the tofu. Cut into squares. Place the tofu either in a pot with 2 inches of water or in a steamer basket, cover, bring to a boil, lower the heat and cook for 5 - 7 minutes. Drain in a strainer until all the excess liquid is out. It is now ready for your favorite recipe.

TOFU RECIPES

TOFU BURGERS

1 Square of tofu, boil for 10 minutes,
    drain and squeeze out excess liquid
½ Cup bulghur
1 Cup of water
1 Clove garlic, minced
1 Onion, minced
½ Tsp. basil
½ Tsp. oregano
½ Tsp. cumin
½ Tsp. Sea salt
¾ - 1 Cup whole wheat flour
Freshly grated romano cheese

Bring the water to a boil, add the bulghur and sea salt. Lower the flame and simmer for 5 - 10 minutes. Mix all ingredients together in a separate bowl. Add the cooked bulghur to all the ingredients. Allow to cool then add the flour. Moisten hands and form burgers. Heat a skillet and add a little sesame oil and fry the burgers on both sides.

*PERSONAL NOTES:

TOFU SLOPPY JOES

1 Square of tofu, boil for 10 minutes,
    drain and squeeze out excess liquid
1 Onion, chopped fine
2 Cloves of garlic, minced
¼ Green pepper, chopped fine
¼ Tsp. Sea salt
½ Tsp. Italian seasoning
1 TBS. sesame oil
1 Cup butternut squash, pureed
    (or mock tomato sauce)
Mozzarelli cheese

Heat the sesame oil in a cast-iron skillet and saute garlic, onions, and pepper. Add crumbled tofu and sea salt. Stir all ingredients together. Add Italian seasoning and stir well, cook for 5 minutes. Add the pureed squash and simmer for 5 minutes more. Place on a muffin or whole wheat bread, add the cheese on top and broil until the cheese is brown.

TOFU AND SAUCE

1 Cake tofu
½ Tsp. Sea salt
2 Cups soup broth or water
1 TBS. tamari
1 TBS. arrowroot, dissolved in 1 TBS.
    water
2 Scallions, sliced thin
1 Tsp. grated ginger juice or lemon juice

Slice the tofu into 2" cubes. Bring soup broth to a boil. Add sea salt and place tofu cubes into the pot. Bring back to a boil, lower the flame and cook long enough for the tofu to warm. Carefully lift out the tofu with a slotted spoon. Bring the stock back to a boil and add tamari and ginger juice. Mix in diluted arrowroot and simmer for a few minutes until the mixture thickens, stirring constantly. Cover the tofu cubes with the sauce and sliced scallions and serve.

TOFU TEMPURA

1 Cake tofu, drained and cut into 1½"
    cubes
1 Cup whole wheat flour
2/3 Cup of water
½ Tsp. Sea salt
2 TBS. tamari
20 Drops of freshly grated ginger juice
3 TBS. grated daikon or white radish
Corn oil for deep frying

Place the oil in a cast-iron skillet or deep fryer and heat to approximately 350°. Combine the sea salt, flour and water to form the batter. Place the tofu cubes in the batter. Drop the tofu into the hot oil and fry for 3 - 5 minutes or until golden and crisp. Place on paper towels to drain off excess oil. Heat the tamari and ginger juice and place in a bowl for dipping. Place a small amount of grated radish on top of each cube and serve.

STROGANOFF TOFU

1 Pound of tofu, steamed for 10 minutes,
    drain off excess liquid, cut into
    ½" x ½" pieces
2 Cloves of garlic, minced
1 Onion, minced
2 - 3 Cups of freshly sliced mushrooms
½ Tsp. Sea salt
½ Cup red wine
½ Cup of yogurt, plain
¼ Tsp. basil
¼ Tsp. cumin
¼ Cup sesame oil
½ Cup tamari

Place the tofu in a large bowl and marinate for 30 minutes in the tamari, cumin, basil, and 2 Tsp. of sesame oil.

Lightly saute the onions, garlic, in the remaining oil. Then add the mushrooms and saute for an additional 5 - 7 minutes, stirring constantly. Add the tofu and sea salt and allow to cook for 10 minutes. Add the liquid from the marinate to the mixture as needed to prevent burning.

Add wine and yogurt, mix well. Taste and if more seasoning is required add a little more of the marinade. Allow the mixture to simmer for a few minutes. Serve over a bed of brown rice.

SPICED TOFU

1 Cake tofu
2 Scallions, sliced thin
Fresh grated ginger juice
Tamari

Slice the tofu into squares and sprinkle scallions on top. Squeeze one or two drops of ginger juice on each square. Add a few drops of tamari to each square and serve.

TOFU EGGSALAD

1 Cake of tofu, boiled 5 - 10 minutes
    and drained
2 Scallions, chopped
½ Onion diced
1 Stalk of celery, diced
1 - 2 TBS. fresh squeezed orange juice
1 TBS. tamari
¼ Cup of mayonaisse (optional)
¼ Tsp. dry mustard (optional)

Boil the tofu for 5 - 10 minutes, drain and squeeze off all excess liquid. Allow to cool. Place the chopped scallions into a suribachi bowl, add the cooled tofu and mix together using a wooden pestle. This should now look like "real" eggsalad. Add the orange juice and tamari and mix together thoroughly. Stir in the onions and celery. Add the mayo if desired. Serve on lettuce or in sandwich form. Top with chopped tomatoes and/or sprouts.

ONO CHEESE

3 TBS. rice vinegar
¼ Tsp. garlic powder
1 Square tofu
Onozaki miso (unpasteurized rice miso),
    use barley miso for a different flavor

In a separate bowl mix together the rice vinegar and garlic powder. In another bowl, place the square of tofu and pierce it with a wooden skewer or toothpick. Pour the rice vinegar mixture over the tofu, drain the liquid off and repeat this process until most of the liquid has been absorbed into the tofu. Place a thick layer of miso around the entire square of tofu. Place the miso coated tofu into a crock, cover and place in a cool area. Store for 3 - 4 days. If you live in a hot climate place the crock in the refrigerator. The longer you allow the tofu to ferment, the cheesier the flavor will become. After 4 days, wash and remove the miso from the tofu. Slice and serve. Store in an air tight container in the refrigerator.

TOFU AND SHRIMP DELIGHT

1 Cake of tofu, steamed for 5 minutes,
    drained, squeeze out excess liquid
    cut into 1" cubes
1 Pound fresh shrimp, peeled and deveined
2 Cloves garlic, minced
3 Medium onions, cut into 8th
2 Scallions, cut into ¼" diagonals
1 TBS. sesame oil
½ Tsp. freshly squeezed ginger juice

Prepare cooking sauce and set aside:

1 TBS. arrowroot
¼ Tsp. Sea salt
1 TBS. light miso, diluted in ½ cup of
    water

Stir all the ingredients together and set aside.

Lightly coat a cast-iron skillet with sesame oil and when the oil is hot saute the garlic and onions for 3 minutes. Add the shrimp and ginger juice and saute for 2 minutes more. Place these ingredients in a separate bowl. Lightly coat the skillet again with sesame oil and saute the tofu and scallions for 5 minutes, then add the shrimp and vegetables along with the sauce. Bring to a boil, stirring constantly, until the mixture thickens, about 2 - 3 minutes. Serve over a bed of rice.

PANTERA TOFU

1 Cake tofu, drained and mashed
2 Medium onions, minced
1 Small carrot, diced
1 Small turnip, diced
¼ Tsp. Sea salt
3 TBS. tamari
1 Tsp. sesame oil

In a cast-iron skillet over a medium flame saute onions, then add the carrots and turnips and cook for 10 minutes. Add the sea salt and tamari and mix in the mashed tofu. Lower the flame and simmer for 15 minutes, stirring constantly. You may add one or two drops of water if necessary.

BAKED TOFU

1 Cake tofu, sliced lengthwise, 3" long
    and ¼" thick
1 Tsp. almond butter or sesame butter
    (toasted)
1 TBS. fresh orange juice
1 TBS. Cold Mountain red miso
2 TBS. fresh chopped parsley

Place slices of tofu at a 45 degree angle in a lightly oiled baking dish leaning against each other like dominoes. Puree the miso, orange juice and almond butter together to make a creamy sauce, adding just enough water to give it a smooth consistency. Pour the sauce over the tofu and bake at 350° for 20 minutes. Garnish with parsley and serve.

FRIED SPICY TOFU

1 Pound of tofu, boil for 5 minutes, drain
    and squeeze out excess liquid
    cut into ½" cubes
2 Cloves of garlic, minced
2 TBS. onions, minced
¼ Tsp. Sea salt
¼ Tsp. basil
¼ Tsp. thyme
1/8 Tsp. cumin
½ Tsp. curry powder
3 - 4 TBS. tamari, with a little water
1/3 Cup grated romano cheese
Sesame oil for sauteing

Heat a cast-iron skillet and coat with a little sesame oil. Saute the garlic and onions, then add the tofu to the mixture. (You may add a little more oil so the tofu does not stick to the skillet.) Saute both sides of the tofu, approximately 7 - 8 minutes. Mix all the spices with the tamari and water and then add to the skillet. Raise the heat and mix well, then lower and sprinkle on the cheese. When the cheese has melted, serve.

STUFFED TOFU ALA CRAB OR FISH

1 Package of tofu
2 Onions, diced
Fish stuffing, (see stuffing recipe)
1 - 2 Small cloves of garlic, minced
2 Cups of cabbage, shredded
Shiitake mushrooms, soaked for 30 min-
    utes, sliced fine (remove the stems)
1 TBS. yellow miso, diluted in 8 ozs. of
    water
2 Tsp. arrowroot or kuzu
1 TBS. tamari
Sesame oil

Cut the tofu square in half, diagonally, to make 8 triangles. Let the tofu drain in a collander for 10 minutes. Place between paper towels and gently press out the excess liquid. On the widest side of each triangle, cut a pocket to within a ½" of the edges. Fill each pocket with 1½ Tsp. of fish stuffing. Pour sesame oil into the skillet, approximately 1" and heat to 350°, add several tofu triangles and fry. Turn once until golden on all sides, 3 - 5 minutes. Remove from the oil and allow to drain on paper towels. Bring a skillet to a high heat and add a Tsp. of sesame oil, when the oil is hot saute garlic and onions for 30 seconds, add the cabbage and stir fry till it starts to wilt, then add the mushrooms. Place the stuffed tofu on top of the vegetables.

In a separate bowl mix together arrowroot, tamari, and diluted miso, pour the broth over the tofu mixture and cover. Allow to simmer for 3 - 5 minutes. Stir carefully so as not to break the tofu. Bring to a boil, when the sauce thickens lower the flame and simmer for 1 minute. Serve.

TOFU ELAN

5 - 7 Cups of water
1 TBS. tamari
2 Cakes of tofu, cut into 2" cubes
3 TBS. miso, pureed in a little water
3 Scallions, sliced thin

Place water and tamari in a pot and bring
to a boil. Lower the flame and simmer
for 2 minutes. Add tofu, cover and bring
to a boil, lower the flame and simmer for
3 minutes. Turn off the flame, add the
miso and scallions. Cover and let set for
2 minutes more. Serve hot.

TOFU SANDWICH MIX

½ Pound tofu (boiled for 10 minutes,
      drained and placed in a bowl)
¼ Cup sesame butter or tahini
1½ TBS. tamari
1 TBS. onions, minced
2 TBS. celery, minced
1 TBS. scallions, sliced

Crumble the tofu into small pieces. If
you have a suribachi bowl use the wooden
pestle to break up the tofu. Mix all other
ingredients together and mix thoroughly
into the tofu. Chill and serve.

TEMPEH

Tempeh is a delicious, cultured food consisting of tender, cooked soybeans, and is usually formed into ¾" to 1" thick square patties or long rolls. It achieves its firmness and nutritional enhancements through the process of fermentation. The same process is used in making cheeses, yogurt, beer, wines, miso and tamari, as well as many other foods. The presence of a mold is required to achieve the end product. The beneficial mold of "rhizopus" culture is combined with cooked soybeans.

The fermentation process creates a dense cottony mycelium which binds the beans into a firm, textured food, easily sliced and possessing great versatility. The mycelium gives the flavor and aroma of sauteed mushrooms. More important the mold creates enzymes which predigest the protein, fats and carbohydrates in the tempeh, making them easy for you to digest.

Flatulence causing factors found in whole beans are virtually eliminated, an important consideration for many people. The potency of numerous vitamins, such as B-12, B-6, B-3 and folic acid are increased by a factor of four or more. As you can see, a complete transformation occurs. But, there is more! Fresh tempeh contains 19.5 percent protein, about as much as chicken or beef and is a complete protein containing all the essential amino acids.

Furthermore, it has the highest quality protein found in any soyfood, as measured by the Protein Efficiency Ration (PER). It is also one of the richest known vegetal sources of vitamin B-12. A typical 3½ ounce portion provides between 133 and 293 percent of the adult recommended daily allowance of B-12.

Tempeh differs from most other protein foods in that it is entirely free of cholesterol, is low in fats, especially saturated fats, contains only 157 calories per 3½ ounce serving and has only trace amounts of sodium. No salt is added in the production.

Tempeh is a whole food, possessing the essence of wholeness and natural dietary fiber. Digestability ranks high, as a quality of tempeh. During the fermentation process, the "Rhizopus" culture produces enzymes that partially break down the soy proteins and oils, improving their assimilation by the body.

You may wonder where tempeh originated and why it has such low marketability at the present time. Although there are no known records of its origin, researchers look to Java as its source, as far back as 2500 years ago. However, it was only recently (1962) that the first tempeh shop opened in this country. The editor of *Prevention* magazine, Robert Rodale, wrote in a feature article, *"Tempeh Is On Its Way Up.* Before long it will be widely acclaimed across this land of ours . . . I'm convinced that tempeh is just sitting there waiting for the lightning of discovery to strike, the way it hit yogurt. All the signs point to that happening, and soon."

Remember that raw, fresh tempeh should be cooked before using the tempeh in a recipe. Steam the tempeh for 15 minutes, then use in various ways. Once you have tried some of these recipes, don't be afraid to experiment and create your own. Tempeh can be baked, boiled, broiled, steamed, fried, sauteed or barbecued. You may use it in soups, stews, sandwiches, cooked with all vegetables, sea vegetables, or you may use it as a side dish. Tempeh can be frozen up to 4 weeks. When using tempeh or tofu, remember to eliminate your bean consumption for the day.

SAUTEED ONIONS AND TEMPEH

Saute onions in a cast-iron skillet, place tempeh patties on top and cook for 5 minutes on each side. Add tamari to taste. Place in a sandwich or serve as is with the rest of your meal. Used in a sandwich with sauerkraut.

You can crumble the tempeh after it has been steamed and sautee it with onions, garlic, carrots, and cabbage to make a stew. Use a little tamari to taste.

TEMPEH STEW

4 Oz. tempeh
1 Cup water
3 - 4 Onions, chopped
1 Carrot, chopped
½ Green pepper, chopped
2 Stalks celery, chopped
3 Potatoes, diced
1 Cup fresh mushrooms, sliced in half
1 Tsp. sage
½ Tsp. basil
½ Tsp. thyme
1 TBS. tamari, diluted in ½ cup of water
1 TBS. corn oil

Place the oil in a baking dish, crumble the tempeh and cover the bottom of the dish. Sprinkle the sage, basil and thyme evenly over the tempeh. Layer half the diced onions, half the potatoes, add the celery, peppers, carrots and mushrooms. Top with the remaining onions and potatoes. Add the tamari and water. Bake at 350° for 2½ hours. Check occasionally to see if there is moisture. If not, add more water.

TEMPEH SCRAMBLE

4 Ozs. tempeh, cut into small cubes
1 Onion, diced
¼ Green pepper, diced
2 Fertile eggs, beaten well
¼ Tsp. basil
¼ Tsp. chives
1 TBS. corn oil
Sea salt
1 Oz. chedder cheese, grated

Lightly coat a cast-iron skillet with oil. Fry tempeh on both sides until golden brown. Add the onions, peppers, chives and basil. Saute for 4 - 5 minutes. Add the beaten eggs and scramble. Salt to taste, add the cheese on top and allow to melt. Serve.

TEMPEH ALFETTA

½ Package tempeh, steamed for 15 - 20 minutes
1 Stalk of celery, chopped
1 Onion, chopped
½ Tsp. dry mustard, dilute in ¼ cup water
1 Scallion, diced
Tamari to taste
1½ Cups water
1 TBS. bonita flakes

In a saucepan, place the onions, celery, water and bonita flakes. Bring to a boil, lower the flame to medium and cook until the vegetables are tender. In a separate bowl mix the cooked tempeh and all other ingredients. Then add the tempeh mixture to the cooked vegetables and cook for 20 minutes or until the water has evaporated. Remove from the saucepan and allow to cool. Serve on a bed of lettuce or use in a sandwich.

Exit 18
VEGETABLES

The Power Accessories

The land grown vegetables are among the most creative and versatile food categories that you have, so spike your diet with originality. There are so very many to choose from, and the range of taste sensations is so much more dramatic than the combinations found in grain dishes. Anyone who has ever gone on a total grain diet for a few days can confirm that the addition of vegetables to the plate is an explosive treat to the taste buds. The proper choices, combined with correct cooking methods, can enhance all the other dishes on your plate and either excite or soothe your palate, as desired.

Vegetables are simply defined as foods obtained from the leaves, stems, buds, roots, tubers, seeds, or fruits of plants. Each kind of vegetable has its own particular nutritive quality, however, you shall learn how to use specific ones for your particular health needs. For this purpose, we will make a distinction between fruits and vegetables, even though there is one group of **vegetables** in which the part **botanists** term "fruit" is the only part that is eaten. These " fruit vegetables " include tomatoes, eggplants, peppers, cucumbers, melons and squashes. ALL of these **except** squashes, which are the most contracted of this group, are avoided on a daily consumption basis and are to be enjoyed occasionally. This is because of their greatly expanded qualities; high potassium content, fast-growing, softer, more liquid content. For the same reason, we have suggested avoiding **over-consumption** of **fresh** fruits on a daily basis, reducing most diets to smaller amounts. We have a need for fresh fruits for a specific type of physical condition, such as when a person has been eating animal products, chemicalized processed foods, or has already become ill and needs fresh fruits in the daily diet as a **cleanser**. This is one function fresh fruit does well, but as it cleanses the bloodstream many nutrients are also washed away with the toxins. This creates a vicious cycle, which automatically causes a weak feeling and an urge to resume the consumption of fast energy producing meats, sugars, dairy products and processed foods. This in turn creates more predisposition to illness.

To establish sound building blocks for truly healthy body and mind cells, this entire group of fruits and the "vegetable masqueraders" mentioned above are used with awareness and care.

The vegetables which are important because of the food value of their leaves or stems include the following: cabbage, kale, endive, parsley, mustard greens, collard greens, watercress, lettuce and many more. All groups contain a variety of wild vegetables found in nature. These are frequently sold in specialty stores and favored by those who prefer to avoid all possibility of man's intervention in food production. Some familiar names are dandelion, milkweed and cattails.

To insure thorough washing when preparing green leafy vegetables, or the stems of vegetables, always cut them from the root, just above the point where the stem or stems separate. Rinsing them in cold, salted water keeps them bright, crisp and colorful.

Vegetables bearing edible seeds have already been discussed in the grain and bean chapters, so we will only mention that corn was included previously as a grain, since it has many of those characteristics. Please refer to the grain chapter for its many food uses.

Our last food group is the root vegetables, which include all underground stems and tubers. This general group has the most contracted forms of all and includes all types of potatoes, onions, salsify, carrots, beets, turnips, rutabaga and parsnips. Wild vegetables in this group include burdock, jinenjo, and taro potato. Once a potato is peeled and boiled in a volume of water, it is virtually left minerally deficient and becomes acidic.

If you are truly interested in the health and welfare of your body and mind, you will want to shop for only **fresh** fruits and vegetables as opposed to frozen, canned or packaged. Although home canning is an acceptable method of preserving a supply of foods since it employs no preservatives, it is always **preferred** that foods be eaten in season. On a daily basis however, you will benefit the most from searching out a farmer's market outlet or a good roadside stand. We cannot repeat often enough that the processing of food causes some degree of deterioration to their life-giving energy force. Besides, if we cannot convince you scientifically, you have only to listen to your inner ear - that intuitive part of you which responds to the joy of nature itself by lifting your spirits when you smell unpolluted air, freshened by a rain-soaked forest, or warming your heart when you walk through freshly-tilled gardens. How can you quiet the urge to create life through living substances? Not by nurturing your loved ones with dying bits of once growing greens, wrapped in plastic and packaged in waxed boxes, like little coffins for plants, all lined up on the supermarket freezer. I am sure many of you remember when the produce we ate came from a store called the "Green Grocer's" instead of a "Quick Stop." Today's fast pace has forced many people to accept frozen and canned foods, loaded with preservatives and artificial enrichment, but "convenience" was never the road to health. For some of us, the day of decision is here. We will either refuse to yield to the demands made on our time by an indifferent world and return to the richer values of proper food selection and preparation or we will pay the price, as does one out of every four Americans who die of cancer.

We try to shop for our fresh produce on a frequent schedule so food does not need to be stored longer than necessary. Leafy greens are the most fragile and it is best to purchase them daily. Some items, of course, must be kept for periods of time at home. In our climate, (Florida) we refrigerate most items in brown paper bags. Corn is bought in the husk and it is not removed until used. Only badly spoiled leaves or parts are removed before storing - even dirt is left on - the idea is to avoid wetting the vegetable, which causes rotting. They can be cleaned with a vegetable brush and cold water just prior to cooking.

We store some vegetables such as turnips, onions and pumpkins in a well ventilated vegetable basket. We also leave out our squashes and apples, but you will judge from your climate and room conditions whether or not to refrigerate. Our suggestion is to avoid it when possible. If you are lucky enough to have a cold cellar, you can take advantage of it by buying in quantity and storing for longer periods.

We have acquired another habit. We must ignore the brightly beckoning colors of dyed food, waxed, gleaming fruits and vegetables. Apples and cucumbers in particular are deceptive. But other items have also been "dressed up" to tempt the unwary shopper.

I am reminded of one of my favorite childhood riddles, told with glee and giggled over when the audience fully understood the implication.

Question: "What's worse then finding a worm in an apple?"

Answer: "Finding only half a worm."

Today I see this little joke somewhat differently, since finding a worm would be an unlikely occurrence in our over sprayed, insecticide treated, chemically-fertilized fruits and vegetables.

When organically grown, the possibility of finding a worm **does** exist, but, Oh! the rewards of the risk. Flavor returns to the product once again. Genuine sweetness flows from a humble carrot and the true meaning of "freshness" can be experienced by even the most dulled palate. When it is not possible to get naturally fertilized, organically grown produce, the wise shopper will still select fresh, locally grown items that are in season and as a second choice buy fruits and vegetables grown in a climate similar to their own.

Sometimes a limp, forlorn, drooping product is the best buy. Remember, the loss of moisture content alone does not harm a vegetable. Often we remove the liquid by cooking just to create **BALANCE** through contraction. Vegetable flavor is not lost, but sometimes even enhanced. In addition, the smaller sizes are not necessarily inferior products either. Frequently you will find that the faster the food handling or cooking becomes, the more acidity is being produced. Longer, slower methods of preparing foods produce a more alkaline result and leaves us feeling calmer, more relaxed and tranquil.

In a hot climate with long summer days, (contracted conditions) you will want to use shorter cooking times and to use smaller pieces of vegetables cut more finely. The quick sauteing method is ideal for this purpose, along with matchstick cuts, pencil cuts, slivering, shredding and grating, as well as steaming and boiling.

In cold weather, particularly in more northern locations, a wise cook will use longer cooking methods with larger pieces of vegetables cut into chunks or cubes. Baking or roasting methods are preferred under these conditions and the longer method of sauteing. In deciding for yourself which vegetables to select for your specific physical needs, remember that all green leaves absorb carbon dioxide and through photosynthesis creates oxygen, which they release. This is the very opposite of the function of our lungs which take in oxygen and give off carbon dioxide. In plants, the chlorophyll bonds the carbon dioxide with life fluid (sap) and, in the human body, hemoglobin does the same task, bonding oxygen with blood. The two are much alike in their function, the plants' chlorophyll contains magnesium and our hemoglobin contains iron. In the interplay created when we consume plants, the magnesium is replaced by iron from our bloodstream and hemoglobin is produced, thus assuring us of an energetic "porter" to carry a healthy supply of oxygen to all parts of our body and brain.

Increasing your use of fresh vegetables is the first step to good health. Leafy greens, as we have seen, improve circulation and oxygenation. Root vegetables, on the other hand, benefit the intestinal and digestive organs through a number of ways. They create the proper enzyme and bacterial conditions and act as a contracting force to **BALANCE** an expanded organ.

To create **BALANCE** we should eat all sections of a vegetable. There are many shapes in which to cut your vegetables for cooking, and a variety of shapes are suitable for different methods of preparation. It is advisable to vary your cooking methods to prevent becoming bored and to reflect the changes in temperature, weather, physical activity or condition. Try cutting your vegetables diagonally, rather than horizontally, so that each piece will have an even **BALANCE** of each force. Here is a basic description of eight types of cuts which may be used.

1. **Slicing** - This may be thick or thin, diagonal or straight across. Common sense will advise that a harder vegetable like a carrot may need to be cut thin to cook with a thicker cut of a softer vegetable such as a summer squash.
2. **Dicing** - is cutting into small squares approximately ¼ inch in size.
3. **Cubing** - is the same square cut, only larger, ½ inch or more.
4. **Chunks** - are larger cubes ranging from one inch to two-inch pieces.
5. **Mincing** - is very fine chopping and usually done with a square ended vegetable knife 2" wide with the tip held in place and a rapid up-down motion of the knife handle. **Chopping** is the same method but the vegetable is left more coarse.
6. **Shredding** - is a long thin cut or strip. Leaves may be stacked on top each other, rolled up then shredded by slicing thin strips 1/8th inch in width.

7. **Matchsticks** - cuts are like the French "julienne" cuts. The vegetable is sliced lengthwise or diagonally into one to three-inch pieces, then stacked up and cut the opposite direction in 1/8th - inch strips to form matchstick shapes.

8. **Pencil cuts** - are exactly like sharpening a pencil, slivering is a finer smaller version of the same basic shape (resembling irregular triangular wedges). This may be accomplished to perfection with long root vegetables, such as carrots and burdock, by making one cut on the angle starting at the tip end, and then rolling the carrot a quarter turn and making the next angle cut halfway up the previously cut edge.

SAUTEING - QUICK WAY

Cut vegetables into small pieces. Lightly coat a cast-iron skillet with oil and bring to medium heat. Always avoid free-pouring oil at any time and use the minimum amount possible to prevent sticking or burning. Usually a total amount of **one teaspoon** will do a skillet full of vegetables. Our bodies obtain adequate oil from our frequent use of seeds and grains, therefore we need not cover up the taste of our vegetables nor add to our daily consumption. Add the vegetables separately, beginning always with onions, if used. Turn them with a clockwise motion with wooden spatulas until they change color and become clear. Then set the onions aside in a bowl and proceed to saute the remaining vegetables, using the same technique, beginning with the most **contracted** vegetables and **finishing** with the most **expanded** ones. These will usually be the softer vegetables, containing more liquid, or which grow faster and generally grow the furthest from the ground. At the end, mix all the vegetables gently together in the skillet and cook them an additional few minutes, adding whatever seasonings desired at that time. This method is sometimes called stir-frying and is the simplest way of producing a very **BALANCED** vegetable dish. We use it perhaps more often than any other way. The vegetables retain most of their crispness and are never over-cooked.

SAUTEING - LONGER METHOD

This method **BALANCES** the contracting effect of a longer cooking time with the expanding influences of adding water to the vegetables. It may also be used entirely free of the addition of oil, although it then would technically resemble simmering.

Cut the vegetables into larger pieces than the shorter method, using the more coarse cuts given earlier. Lightly oil a large pot or cast-iron skillet and bring to medium heat. Place the onions in first and stir them as before until clear in color. This will cook all the oxalic acid and insure that it does not affect the remaining vegetables. Then add all of the firm (contracted) vegetables at once. Put just enough water in to cover the bottom of the pot, cover tightly, reduce the heat to low and cook until the largest pieces have just begun to soften. Now add all the expanded or more liquid bearing vegetables, such as summer squash, zucchini, celery, broccoli, chard, bok choy, cabbage, and continue cooking covered for about 2 - 4 minutes. At the end of cooking add the desired seasonings and if the pot contains any excess liquid, leave the cover off until it has evaporated.

BOILING

As simple as this method of cooking sounds, boiling and steaming, the most expansive of preparations, require just as much attention to detail to produce a flavorful result. Over-boiled vegetables lack the color they should have and can taste flat, dull and mushy. Even root vegetables, which have the longest cooking times, will eventually break down and lose their appeal. Greens, of course, suffer the most from careless timing and in general need only a little more time than for blanching to be properly boiled. Remember that vitamin C is destroyed in eight minutes at boiling temperature. Let your palate have a chance to be re-educated to the fresher flavors contained in crispy vegetables. The hazards of destroying food value by over-cooking are so great as to be worthy of repeating.

Even covering your vegetables after cooking should be avoided since they will continue to cook. Although a pinch of sea salt or tamari can be added to boiling water, try serving vegetables with a side dish of tamari diluted with a little hot water from which the vegetables were boiled, or garnish with sesame salt or umeboshi plum juice. (See chapter on condiments) Save any additional water for soup stock.

STEAMING

Another excellent way to prepare vegetables is by using a stainless steel steamer. These foldable items, which fit any pot, may be purchased in a natural food store or any household section of a department store. It makes good sense, however, to buy the best one available since they are very inexpensive items. If poorly made they will be hard to clean, and they are useless if the legs which hold them away from the boiling water are poorly attached and break. When steaming vegetables, place ½" of water in your pot and bring to a boil. Place vegetables in the steamer with a pinch of salt, as desired. Cover, lower the flame and steam until done. We have found this method to be just as fast a method as boiling, since the live steam permeates very quickly and there is practically no loss of food value. All the vitamin content is preserved within the vegetable, however, you will have a little broth for soup stock remaining. Either boiling or steaming can be used on a daily basis since excess oil in the diet should be avoided.

BAKING

An ideal cooking method for fall and winter seasons is baking. You will be **BAL-ANCING** your food to the environment. Winter is an expanded climate (cold, perhaps wet, short days) and baking is a longer cooking method. This style is used mostly for root vegetables or ground fruits, such as squash, pumpkin and, on occasion, potatoes. Oil is not needed in our method if you wish to prepare squash and pumpkin prepare as follows: Cut the vegetable in half and remove seeds, saving for use later as a delicious snack. Turn the vegetable upside down and place in a shallow baking dish with about 1/8th inch of water in the bottom. The concave shape of the vegetable keeps most of the meat away from the liquid and it will steam cook in the oven in less time than in the usual dry method. If a dryer flavor is preferred, however, you can still begin in this manner and turn it upright when it is 75% cooked and then brush the surface with a little tamari or malt syrup. Return to the oven to bake until soft. To prevent a burned pan bottom, which would occur with the addition of the syrup, just put a little more water in the pan, if it dries before done.

Some vegetables will, of course, need an oiled pan and their skins may also be rubbed with a little oil to prevent splitting.

We mentioned that the pumpkin and squash seeds may be saved for snacking and here is how you go about making them taste unique. First, wash them, removing all vegetable matter. They will squirt through your fingers and detach easily. Rinse them thoroughly in a strainer and then spread them evenly in a shallow glass, clay, or stainless steel pan. Dry them in a 350 degree oven for about 15 minutes or until they crunch all the way through when you bite one in half. No moisture should remain in the seeds, but you will know if they will be empty shells inside when you eat them. A little experimenting with the conditions in your kitchen will guide you to good results. Remove them from the oven and sprinkle them with a little tamari or salt. Stir them to coat all sides, then put them back in the baking dish and bake at 300 degrees for 5 minutes. They should be brown and ready to eat.

TEMPURA

Tempura cooking is a delightful treat, but because of the amount of oil needed we do not have it too often. It is especially restricted for people who suffer from liver, gallbladder and intestinal problems. For those persons it is best not to enjoy it until their health has been restored. But for those who are in good health, I know you will enjoy tempura cooked fish, shellfish and vegetables dipped into a very light batter and deep-fried until golden brown. Our favorite is onion rings and trout or flounder fingers, and we are so fortunate to have a family member who spends many patient hours catching fresh fish. There are no more delicious seafood dishes anywhere than those prepared with careful attention to freshness and a loving, sharing spirit.

Sesame oil is the best for tempura, and a cast-iron skillet, wok, or deep saucepan plus the recipe for the batter (see chapter on seafood) is all that you need. Pour the oil in your skillet or pot, heat it to 340 - 360 degrees. If the oil is at a lower temperature when you add your tempura it will tend to be moist and soggy, and if it is higher you may burn your tempura. It is possible to use a deep-fryer technique with more oil, but we have found that the pieces can be turned over once, and the same result is obtained with far less oil. Also, we prefer not to reuse any oil that has been used to cook fish or seafood. The shallower amount of oil makes it possible to discard the remainder.

Have your cut-up pieces of food ready to go and lightly floured before dipping in the batter. If the pieces are dried thoroughly before flouring they will be lighter in their finished texture. When pieces have browned, it is wise to keep them in a wire basket in a warm oven until served. If they are drained on paper towel they sometimes lose their crispness due to the heat being unable to escape and subsequently the coating becoming moist.

PRESSURE COOKING

Generally this method of preparation is reserved for grains and beans since few vegetables require long cooking times. However, squash, pumpkin, and burdock root are the exceptions and we have enjoyed some delicious results. The vitamin loss is minimal, the convenience for the person with a difficult schedule is great, and if there is broth remaining in the pressure cooker, it makes a wonderful soup stock.

Vegetables to be used on a **regular** basis are as follows: broccoli, Chinese cabbage, chives, collard greens, watercress, dandelion greens, kale, leeks, mustard greens, turnip greens, brussel sprouts, corn on the cob, onions, cabbage, rutabago, acorn squash, butternut squash, hubbard squash, pumpkin, radish, carrots and carrot tops, dried daikon, daikon, lotus root, parsnips and salsify. Vegetables to use OCCASIONALLY are: fresh beans and peas, snap beans, wax or yellow beans, jinenjo, cucumber, endive, escarole, mushrooms, romaine lettuce, shiitake mushrooms, alfalfa sprouts, summer squash, head lettuce and string beans. AVOID daily consumption of the following (occasional use is advised): asparagus, bamboo shoots, dock, fennel, ferns, okra, avocado, eggplant, green and red peppers, artichokes,potato and ginseng.

MUSHROOMS

When preparing fresh mushrooms, wash them clean. Place them on a cutting board and slice them into pieces. Place the pieces in a cast-iron skillet, lightly sprinkle with sea salt, cover and dry roast over a medium heat for 20 - 30 minutes. Drain off the excess dark liquid. You have just added salt, time and fire to a vegetable which is very expansive, it grows rapidly, sometimes overnight and contains lots of liquid. You have changed the mushroom from being very expansive to a contracted, edible vegetable. You may now season the mushrooms and enjoy them.

VEGETABLES

THOSE WE EAT MOST OFTEN:

Broccoli	Turnips	Turnip Greens
Cauliflower	Parsnips	Beets
Chinese Cabbage	Kale	Celery
White Cabbage	Escarole	String Beans
Burdock or gobo	Endive	Swiss Chard
Dandelion	Lettuce	Sprouts
Salsify	Brussel Sprouts	Kohlrabi
Watercress	Parsley	Jinenjo Potatoes
Coltsfoot	Onions	Yellow Summer Squash
Carrots	Leeks	Zucchini
Acorn Squash	Scallions	Rutabagas
Butternut Squash	Radish	Romaine Lettuce
Buttercup Squash	Daikon Radish (white radish)	Collards
Pumpkin	Red Radishes	Mustard Greens

Occasional use if living in the South (or in hot summer months):

Green and Red Peppers	Mushrooms	Tomatoes
Green Peas	Cucumber	Sweet Potatoes
White Potatoes		

Those vegetables that we seldom eat:

Bamboo Shoots	Asparagus	Eggplant
Artichokes		

Living in Florida, we occasionally eat vegetables such as green or red peppers, tomatoes, cucumbers, mushrooms, green peas, sweet potatoes, and, when consuming those vegetables, we combine them with the vegetables that we eat more often. This achieves **BALANCE**. The climate in Florida is much hotter and more humid. For those living in a cooler climate, it is suggested for BETTER HEALTH that you limit your consumption of those vegetables to moderate use, and in the summer months. If in the winter you eat raw salad daily, you will always feel cold. The time for salads is the summer (or move to Florida). We do not reject anything with strong rigidity. Everything in moderate **BALANCE**.

VEGETABLE RECIPES

GLAZED CARROTS

8 Medium size carrots, cut into quarters
    lengthwise
¾ Cup of water
2 TBS. fresh squeezed orange juice
1 TBS. sesame butter
½ Cup barley malt syrup
½ Tsp. Sea salt

Place the quartered carrots in a heavy saucepan with water and ¼ cup of the barley malt syrup. Cover and cook until the carrots are almost tender. Remove from the pan. Combine ¼ cup of the carrot liquid with the remaining ingredients. Boil for 5 minutes. Add the carrots and simmer for 5 minutes, basting occasionally. Serve.

CARROTS A LA SESAME

5 Medium carrots, diagonal cut, ¼"
2 TBS. toasted sesame seeds

Steam the carrots until they are tender. Place in a serving dish and top with the toasted sesame seeds.

SWEET AND SOUR CARROTS

1 Lb. of carrots, cut diagonally
1 Small green pepper, cut into small strips
4 - 5 Ozs. of dried fruit (Dried peaches or
    apricots. Reconstitute the fruit using
    ½ cup of water. Drain off and reserve
    the liquid.)
1/3 Cup barley malt syrup
¼ Tsp. Sea salt
2 TBS. rice vinegar
1 TBS. tamari
2 Tsp. arrowroot

Place carrots in a heavy saucepan. Cook with a small amount of water, approximately 15 - 20 minutes, or until tender. Add the green pepper and cook for an additional 3 minutes. Drain off and reserve the liquid (about 1/3 cup). Allow the liquid to cool, when cooled add the arrowroot and cooled liquid in a saucepan, mix well. Add the sea salt, barley malt syrup and 1/3 cup of vegetable broth, mix well. Add the vinegar and tamari and the reserved fruit liquid. Bring to a boil, stirring constantly until the mixture thickens. Add the fruit and sauce to the carrots. Serve hot or chilled.

CREAMED CARROTS AND ONIONS

2 Cups of carrots, diced
1 Cup of onions, diced·
Corn oil
Sea salt
2 Cups of cold water
¼ - ½ Cups of rice flour

Lightly coat a cast-iron skillet with corn oil, add the onions and carrots and a pinch of sea salt. Saute for 2 - 3 minutes over a medium flame. Reduce the flame to low, cover and cook until the carrots are 80% done. Mix cold water and the rice flour together and gradually add the mixture to the carrots and onions. Be sure to stir constantly to prevent lumping. Bring to a boil, reduce flame to low, cover and simmer 15 - 20 minutes. Stir occasionally. Season to taste with sea salt and cook for a few minutes more. Garnish with chopped parsley and serve.

CARROTS AND GREEN BEANS WITH TOFU

2 Small carrots, cut into matchsticks
20 Green beans
½ Cake tofu, drained and cut into 2" x 1" pieces
½ Tsp. sesame oil
¼ Tsp. Sea salt
2 TBS. tamari

Place the green beans in a pot, adding enough water to cover. Bring to a rapid boil and add salt. Cook for 5 minutes. When beans are bright green, place them in cold water and drain. This will prevent them from further cooking and will preserve their color. Place them on a cutting board and slice them diagonally. Using a cast-iron skillet, heat the oil and saute the carrots, stirring for about 5 minutes, over a medium flame. Add the beans and tofu and mix together. Add tamari and a few drops of water if necessary. Serve hot.

CARROTS AND TURNIPS

3 Turnips, diced
2 Carrots, cut into matchsticks
Pinch of Sea salt
Tamari to taste
1/3 Cup of water
1 TBS. chopped parsley

Lightly coat a cast-iron skillet and saute carrots and turnips for 3 - 4 minutes, adding a dash of sea salt. Add the water and cover, simmer for 10 minutes. Add tamari to taste and simmer for 3 minutes more, uncover allowing the water to evaporate. Garnish with parsley and serve.

SAUTEED ONIONS, CARROTS AND CABBAGE

1 Clove garlic, minced
2 Onions, diced
1 Carrot, diced
¼ Head of cabbage, shredded
1 TBS. of tamari, diluted in 3 TBS. water
1 Tsp. sesame oil

Lightly coat a cast-iron skillet with oil. Saute garlic and onions for 1 - 2 minutes. Add the carrots and saute for 3 - 4 minutes. Add the cabbage and saute for 1 -2 minutes more. Season with the diluted tamari and cook for another 1 minute. Serve.

CARROT AND CABBAGE SAUTE

5 - 6 Leaves of a cabbage, sliced in ¼" cuts
1 Small carrot, slivered
¼ Tsp. Sea salt or 1 TBS. tamari
¼ Tsp. sesame oil

In a cast-iron skillet heat the oil and saute the cabbage, stirring constantly for 2 minutes, over a medium flame. Add the carrots and saute for another 2 minutes. Lower the flame, cover and simmer for 10 minutes more. Season with sea salt or tamari. Serve.

ONION DELIGHT

4 Large onions
Leftover rice or millet delight
Corn oil
3 TBS. tamari
½ Cup white wine

Cut the tops off the onions, peel and scoop out the center meat of the onion. Pour a drop of oil in the core of the onion, then rub the inside and outside of the onion with the oil. Stuff the onion with the left-over grain. Mix together the white wine and tamari, put the onions in a deep bowl, pour the liquid over the onions and marinate for 30 minutes. Place the onions in a casserole dish along with the remaining liquid, cover and bake at 325° for 20 minutes. Remove the cover, baste and cook an additional 25 minutes or until the onions are tender. Serve.

FUEL INJECTED POWER VEGETABLES

1 - 5" piece of kombu
5 Shiitake mushrooms, soaked and stems
    removed
1 Onion, cut into quarters
½ Butternut squash, cubed
1 Thick carrot, cut in ½" diagonals
7 Daikon rounds, cut ½" thick
1 Lotus root or turnip rounds, cut in ½"
    slices
1 Burdock root, also (aka) gobo, sliced
    diagonally in ¼" pieces
2 TBS. tamari
1½ Cups of water

In a pressure cooker, layer all vegetables starting with the kombu and adding by layers according to the order given. Gently pour water down the sides of the pressure cooker in order not to disturb the layers. Add the tamari. Bring to full pressure over high heat, using a wire trivet or heat dispersing pad. Then lower the flame and cook for 15 minutes. Allow pressure to return to normal. Mix and serve. This is a very hearty dish and excellent to make when you feel a loss of energy or are fatigued.

BROCCOLI PARMESAN

1 Head of broccoli flowerettes
1 Onion, chopped
1 Clove of garlic, minced
2 Cups of fresh mushrooms, prepared and
    cooked with the dry method
¼ Cup of sunflower or pumpkin seeds
¼ Cup of water
¼ Tsp. Sea salt
1 TBS. tamari
¼ Cup grated parmesan cheese

Heat a cast-iron skillet with sesame oil and saute the onions and garlic first. Add the mushrooms, sea salt and seeds and saute for a few more minutes. Then add the water and tamari. Place the broccoli floweretts on top and lower the flame. Cook covered for 10 minutes. Do not over-cook the broccoli. Remove from the stove, sprinkle with the grated cheese and serve over a hot bed of rice or noodles.

POTATO STEW

5 Medium potatoes, peeled and diced
3 Cloves garlic, minced
3 Onions, diced
2 Stalks celery, diced
2 Tsp. Sea salt
½ Tsp. marjoram
¼ Tsp. dill weed
¼ Tsp. paprika
1 Cup soya or almond milk
1½ Tsp. corn oil
1 Cup soup stock
1 TBS. tamari

Lightly coat a large cast-iron saucepan with oil. Saute the onions, garlic, carrots, celery and potatoes for 3 - 4 minutes. Add the soup stock, salt and spices. Bring to a boil, lower the flame to medium and cook for 20 minutes. Add the almond milk and cook an additional 25 minutes. Add the tamari at the end of cooking and simmer for 3 - 4 minutes. Serve.

VEGETABLE STEW

1 Tsp. corn oil
1 Cup whole wheat flour
3 TBS. tahini
¼ Tsp. Sea salt
3 Cups vegetable broth
¼ Cup tamari

Have the following vegetables sauteed and ready:

1 Medium turnip, quartered
3 Medium onions, cut in 1/8ths
2 Medium carrots, cut in ½" diagonals
1 Small butternut squash, cubed
2 Stalks celery, diced ½"
1 Cup cauliflowerettes
1 Bay leaf
Pinch of thyme
3 - 1" pieces of orange peel
½ Cup green beans
½ Cup mushrooms

In a large pot, add the oil and heat over a medium flame. Then add the flour and mix in the oil, forming a paste, cook together for 5 minutes. Add the tahini, sea salt and vegetable broth. Stir the mixture until it forms a gravy, then add all the sauteed vegetables. Add enough water to cover the vegetables and bring to a rapid boil. Lower the heat, cover and cook for 30 minutes. At the end of cooking add the tamari and simmer for 3 - 4 minutes. Serve over a bed of brown rice.

SQUASH AND CHEESE BAKE

1 Large onion, chopped
½ Lb. cheese, grated
1 Cup homemade bread crumbs
½ Tsp. Italian seasoning
5 - 6 Medium summer yellow squash

Cube the summer squash into ½ inch pieces. Steam the pieces for 5 minutes. Layer squash, onions and cheese in a lightly oiled baking dish. Top with bread crumbs and Italian seasoning. Bake uncovered for 35 - 40 minutes at 350 degrees. Serve.

STIR FRY BROCCOLI

1 Head of broccoli, flowerettes
1 TBS. sesame oil
SAUCE:
2 Tsp. tamari
2 Tsp. kuzu, diluted in ½ cup of cold water
5 - 7 Drops of freshly squeezed ginger root
Pinch of Sea salt

In a small saucepan combine the sauce ingredients and bring to a boil, stirring constantly until the mixture thickens. Remove from the flame and set aside. Then heat 1 tablespoon of sesame oil in a cast-iron skillet or wok, add the broccoli flowerettes and stir fry for 2 minutes. Lower the heat, cover and simmer for 2 minutes. Pour the sauce over the broccoli and serve.

MASHED SWEET POTATO AND SQUASH

2 Onions, diced
1 Carrot, diced
1 Small butternut squash, peeled and diced
2 Medium sweet potatoes, peeled and
    cubed
½ Tsp. Sea salt
Handful freshly chopped parsley

Place all ingredients in a heavy pot. Add just enough water to cover, add sea salt. Bring to a boil and cook until tender. Drain off excess liquid and save for soup stock. Whip the mixture with a mixer or hand beater until smooth and garnish with parsley. Serve.

PRESSURE COOKED PUMPKIN OR SQUASH

1 Small pumpkin, seeds removed, cut in
    1½" pieces (or use squash)
Pinch of Sea salt
Water

Place enough water in a pressure cooker to just cover the bottom. Add pumpkin or squash and sea salt. Bring to full pressure over a high heat using a wire trivet or heat dispersing pad. Reduce the heat to low and cook 3 - 4 minutes. Allow pressure to return to normal, remove cover and serve.

CHILLED BROCCOLI WITH DRESSING

1 Head of fresh broccoli, flowerettes
1/3 Cup of fresh lemon juice
1 Clove garlic, minced
1 TBS. onion, diced
1 TBS. barley malt syrup
1/8 Tsp. paprika
¼ Cup corn oil
1 Hard boiled fertile egg, chopped

Steam the broccoli until tender, 2 - 3 minutes. Submerge in a bowl of ice water. Drain and set aside. Mix together the remaining ingredients, add the broccoli flowerettes and toss gently. Chill for 1 - 2 hours. Top with chopped egg and serve.

SIMPLE SUMMER SQUASH

3 Small summer squash, (yellow, crook-necked) cut into ½" slices
2 Medium onions, cut in 1/8ths
2 Tsp. Cold Mountain red miso, diluted in 1/3 cup of warm water
¾ Tsp. sesame or corn oil

Using ¼ Tsp. of oil, saute the onions in a cast-iron skillet, over a medium flame until the onions are clear. Add the remaining oil and squash, stirring and mixing the vegetables for 3 minutes. Now add the diluted miso to the vegetables. Reduce the flame to low and simmer until the water evaporates. Serve hot.

STEAMED SQUASH

1 Unpeeled acorn squash, scrubbed clean and cut into 1½" cubes
Pinch of Sea salt

In a heavy pot, place ½" of water and sea salt. Insert a steamer basket in the pot. Place the squash in the basket. Bring the water to a boil, reduce the flame and simmer for 10 - 12 minutes, or until tender. Serve hot.

EBONY MISO

1 Eggplant, medium size, cut into thick rounds (½")
1 TBS. sesame oil
2 - 3 TBS. miso, diluted in a little water

Sprinkle the eggplant rounds with a little sea salt on both sides and allow to set for 3 minutes, then pat dry with a paper towel to help remove the excess liquid. Saute in oil over a low flame for 3 minutes. Add enough water to cover half the thickness of the eggplant. Bring to a rapid boil, lower the flame and cook for 15 minutes. Add the diluted miso and simmer until water evaporates. Serve.

ITALIAN STYLE GREEN BEANS

½ Pound fresh green beans cut into 1½" diagonals
2 Cloves garlic, minced
1 Onion, diced
Handful freshly chopped parsley
1 TBS. corn oil
¼ Tsp. oregano
¼ Cup freshly grated parmesan cheese
¼ Cup water

Lightly coat a cast-iron skillet with corn oil. Saute the onions and garlic, then add the green beans and water. Cook for an additional 5 minutes or until the beans are tender. Pour all the ingredients into a casserole dish, sprinkle with the oregano and cheese. Place in the oven and bake at 350° for 10 minutes. Serve garnished with fresh parsley.

BOILED SQUASH WITH TAMARI

2 Unpeeled acorn squash, remove seeds
¼ Cup of tamari

Cut the squash into 8 - 10 crescents. Cover with water and bring to a boil, then lower the flame. Cook for 15 minutes. Add the tamari and cook for 15 minutes more or until tender. Serve.

SQUASH ITALIANO

2 Onions, cut in 1/10ths
2 Summer squash, or 1 zucchini, cut in ½"
    rounds
Pinch of Sea salt
Sesame oil
1 TBS. miso, diluted in 1/3 cup of water
¼ Cup fresh grated romano cheese
¼ Tsp. oregano

Lightly coat a cast-iron skillet with oil. Add squash and a pinch of sea salt. Stir fry over a medium flame for 10 minutes. Add the onions and oregano, saute for another 3 minutes. Combine ingredients in a casserole dish, pour the diluted miso over the vegetables, sprinkle with grated cheese and bake in the oven at 350^c for 15 minutes. Serve.

ALMOND VEGETABLE SAUTE

1 Onion, sliced thin
1 Carrot, sliced thin
1 Handful green beans, cut in half
1 Cup cauliflowerettes
½ Cup slivered toasted almonds
Sesame oil

SAUCE

1 Clove garlic, minced
2 TBS. vegetable soup stock
2 TBS. tamari
2 Tsp. arrowroot
1 Cup cold water

In a bowl, dilute the arrowroot in the cold water. Add the garlic, tamari and soup stock. Set aside for later use.

Lightly coat a large cast-iron skillet with oil, saute the onions, carrots and green beans for 3 minutes, over a medium high flame. Add the cauliflowerettes and saute an additional 1 - 2 minutes longer. Add the sauce and cook until the mixture thickens. Top with the toasted almonds and serve.

VICTORY SPECIAL

3 Small sweet potatoes, peeled, cut in ½"
    pieces
2 TBS. nut butter; almond, cashew or sesame
Pinch of Sea salt
1 TBS. tamari

Bring sweet potatoes to a boil in a heavy pot with just enough water to cover, add salt and bring to a boil. Cook uncovered for 20 - 30 minutes or until tender. If the water has not evaporated, drain and save the liquid for soup stock. Mix the nut butter with tamari and brush over the potatoes. Serve hot or cold.

KALE KLUTCH

1 Bunch of kale, washed and chopped
1 - 2 Small carrots, slivered
1 Cake of tofu, drained and cubed
Pinch of Sea salt

In a heavy pot add ½" of water. Insert a steamer basket and place the chopped kale into the basket. Place the carrots and tofu on top of the kale. Sprinkle the vegetables with a pinch of sea salt. Bring the water to a boil, reduce the flame, cover and cook until the kale is crisp and bright green in color. Serve.

PARSNIPS WITH BLACK-EYED PEAS

½ Pound parsnips, sliced ¼"
1 Onion, chopped
2 Cups black-eyed peas, shelled
2 Tsp. sesame oil
Sea salt to taste

Lightly coat a cast-iron skillet with oil. Saute the onion for 3 minutes. Add the parsnips and peas, lower the flame and simmer for 30 - 40 minutes or until tender. Season to taste with sea salt. Serve.

CANDIED SWEET POTATOES

3-5 Sweet potatoes or yams, peeled and cut
　　into 1" rounds
Pinch of Sea salt
Sprinkle of cinnamon
Barley malt syrup

Place the sweet potatoes in a heavy sauce-pan and add enough water to cover. Cook uncovered for 15 - 20 minutes. Drain off the excess liquid and place the cooked sweet potatoes in a casserole, pour evenly the barley malt syrup over the top, sprinkle with a little cinnamon and place the casserole dish in a pre-heated oven at 325° and bake for 10 minutes or until tender. Serve.

LAYERED VEGETABLES

5 Potatoes, sliced
½ Green pepper, diced
2 Onions, diced
1 Zucchini, sliced
2 Carrots, diced
1 Ear of corn, sheared off the cob
¼ Tsp. Sea salt
2 Cups mock tomato sauce

Lightly coat a casserole dish with corn oil. Layer all the vegetables in the order given above. Sprinkle with sea salt. Pour the mock tomato sauce over the vegetables. Cover and bake at 350° for 1½ hours. Serve.

EAST INDIAN VEGETABLES

1 Clove of garlic, minced
2 Onions, chopped
½ Pound broccoli flowloweretts
½ Pound cauliflowerettes
¼ Cup of raisins
1 TBS. sesame oil
Pinch of Sea salt
¼ Tsp. curry powder

Lightly coat a cast-iron skillet and saute the garlic, onions, cauliflower and broccoli. Add the sea salt and curry powder, then the nuts and raisins. Gently stir until tender. Serve on a bed of brown rice.

SWEET AND SOUR VEGIES

2 Cloves garlic, minced
2 Parsnips, diced or/ 2 carrots, diced
　　(or use both)
2 Small onions, diced
¼ Head of green cabbage, shredded
1/3 Cup raisins
2 TBS. ume vinegar or rice vinegar
Sesame oil for sauteeing
1½ Cups of water

Lightly coat a saucepan and saute the garlic, onions, cabbage, parsnips and carrots. Add raisins, rice vinegar and sprinkle on a little sea salt. Pour the water in and mix well. Bring to a boil, lower the flame and simmer for 35 minutes. Serve.

STEAMED CARROTS, CAULIFLOWER AND BROCCOLI

1 Carrot, cut diagonally, 1/8"
Handful caulifloweretts
Handful broccoli flowerettes

Place ½" of water in a pot, along with a steamer basket. Add the carrots, cover and bring to a boil. Lower the flame and steam for 3 - 4 minutes. Add the cauliflower, steam for 2 minutes. Add the broccoli and steam an additional 1½ minutes. Season and serve hot.

ORIENTAL VEGETABLES

4 Stalks of bok choy
½ Cup butternut squash, diced
2 Medium onions, cut in 1/8ths
1 Stalk of celery, diced
1 Clove garlic, minced
¼ Tsp. Sea salt
1 Tsp. sesame oil

Lightly coat a cast-iron skillet with oil and saute the garlic and onions until clear. Add the squash, celery and stalks ONLY of bok choy, stirring constantly. Add ½ cup of water, sea salt or tamari and bok choy leaves. Cover and simmer for 15 - 20 minutes　over a low heat. Serve.

ROLLS-ROYCE PEPPERS

1 Cup cooked lentils
½ Cup cooked millet
2 - 3 Cabbage leaves, shredded
1 Carrot, diced
1 Onion, diced
1 Stalk of celery, diced
2 TBS. tamari, diluted in water
6 Green peppers, remove tops and
    hollow out center, salt insides

Saute the vegetables in a little sesame oil and combine with the cooked lentils and millet. Mix well in a large bowl. Add the diluted tamari and mix again. Stuff the presalted peppers and place in a casserole dish. Add a little water to the bottom and bake at 325 degrees for 15 - 20 minutes or until done. Serve.

SHIITAKE MUSHROOMS, ONIONS AND SNOW PEAS

1 Medium onion, cut in 1/8ths
3 Shiitake mushrooms, soak for 30 min-
    utes, remove stems and slice
1 Pound snow peas, strings removed
Sesame oil
Tamari to taste

Lightly coat a cast-iron skillet with oil and saute the onion for 3 minutes over a medium flame. Add the shiitake mushrooms, stir, cover and lower the flame for 3 - 5 minutes. Add snow peas and tamari, stir, cover and cook over a low flame for 2 - 3 minutes. Serve.

LEEKS AND MISO

2 Leeks, sliced crosswise in ¾" cuts
½ Tsp. sesame oil
½ Cup almond miso sauce (see recipe in
    sauce chapter)

Saute the leeks in a lightly coated cast-iron skillet until browned. Add the almond miso sauce and simmer for 2 - 3 minutes and serve.

STIR FRIED CHINESE STYLE

1 Pound Bok Choy, cut diagonally, ¼"
2 Stalks of celery, cut diagonally, ¼"
1 Clove garlic, minced
1 Slice ginger root, 1" long
1 TBS. sesame oil
¼ Tsp. Sea salt
1 Tsp. barley malt syrup
1 TBS. tamari
3 TBS. soup stock or water

Mix together the barley malt syrup, tamari and water and set aside. Heat the oil in a cast-iron skillet or wok. Place the 1" piece of ginger root in the hot oil, cook until brown and then discard the root. Add the garlic, bok choy and celery, stir fry for 2 - 3 minutes, sprinkle the sea salt over the vegetables, then add the barley malt mixture. Cover and cook for an additional 1 minute. Serve topped with sesame seeds.

ORANGE - GREEN - & WHITE

1 Carrot, pencil cut
2 Onions, cut in 1/8ths lengthwise
1 Clove garlic, minced
Handful snow pea pods
Tamari to taste

Lightly coat a cast-iron skillet with oil and saute the garlic, onions and carrots for 5 - 7 minutes over a medium flame. Add snow pea pods and saute for 2 minutes more. Add tamari to taste and serve.

GLAZED ONIONS

4 Large yellow onions, cut in half
1 TBS. yellow miso, diluted in 1 cup hot
    water
4 Tsp. barley malt syrup
1/8 Tsp. paprika
1 Tsp. tahini

Place the halved onions in a heavy saucepan or skillet with a tight fitting lid. Combine remaining ingredients and pour over the onions. Cover and simmer for 1 hour or until the onions are tender. Serve.

PUMPKIN OR ACORN SQUASH WITH MISO

2 Pounds pumpkin or 1 acorn squash, peeled and cubed
2 Onions, cut in 1/8ths
1 Tsp. corn oil
3 TBS. miso, diluted in a little water
1 Cup of water

Lightly coat a cast-iron skillet with oil and saute the onions over a medium flame, gently stirring for 4 minutes. Add the pumpkin or squash and saute for 4 minutes more. Add enough water to cover, bring to a rapid boil, cover, lower the flame and simmer for 30 minutes. You may add a little more water if necessary to prevent burning. Add the diluted miso to the mixture and simmer until dry. Serve.

MOONROOF BEETS

2 Beets, sliced "julienne," chop leaves
2 Onions, medium size cut in 1/8ths
1 Tsp. sesame oil
¼ Cup of water
1 TBS. miso, diluted in ¼ cup of water
1 Turnip, cut lengthwise in 1/8ths

Lightly coat a cast-iron skillet with oil, saute onions for 3 minutes, over a medium flame. Saute the beets and turnips along with the onions for 5 minutes more. Add ¼ cup of water, cover, lower flame and simmer for 5 minutes. Add chopped beet leaves and simmer for 3 minutes more. Add the diluted miso to the mixture, and simmer for 3 minutes. Serve.

STEAMED GREENS

You may use the following greens alone or in combinations: turnip, kale, mustards, collard, radish, daikon, watercress. Wash and slice the greens and place in a pot with a small amount of water, or place in a steamer basket. Leave in 5 - 7 minutes, sprinkle lightly with tamari or sea salt. Serve hot.

TOFU VEGETABLE CHEESE BAKE

½ - 1 Cup of leftover grain (rice, barley millet or any combination)
1 Pound of tofu, drained, chopped in small pieces
2 - 3 Summer squash or zucchini, sliced
1 Large tomato, sliced
2 Onions, sliced thin
1/3 Cup of coarsely ground parmesan cheese

MARINADE

1 Clove of garlic, minced
1 Tsp. green pepper, minced
½ Tsp. rosemary
¼ Tsp. sage
1 TBS. lemon juice
3 TBS. tamari
½ Tsp. Sea salt
1 Cup of water

*Mix all the above ingredients in a bowl.

Place the tofu in the marinade for 20 minutes. Lightly oil a casserole dish. First layer the grain, then the onion, squash and tomato. Pour the marinade and tofu over the top of the casserole. Top with the grated cheese. Place in a pre-heated oven and bake, covered, for 45 minutes to 1 hour. Serve hot.

HOT TURNIPS

5 - 6 Turnips, cut into quarter moons
1 TBS. lemon juice
1 TBS. corn oil
1 TBS. parsley, chopped

Cut the turnips into half then quarters. Place them in a steamer basket and steam until tender. In a sauce pan, heat the oil, lemon juice and parsley for 1 minute. Pour over the turnips and serve.

LAYERED VEGETABLES
(Waterless cooked vegetables)

3 - 6" Pieces of kombu, wiped clean
2 Medium onions, cut in quarters
1 Acorn or butternut squash, cubed
5 Pieces of daikon radish, ½" rounds
1 Tsp. Sea salt
Tamari to flavor
You may add additional choices of vegetables such as: carrots, cabbage, turnips, green beans, lotus root, etc. - Always placing the kombu in first, then the onions, etc.)

Soak the kombu for approximately 1 - 1½ hours. Cut all vegetables and set aside. Using a cast-iron pot with a heavy lid or a pot that has been made for waterless cooking, place the kombu (cut into 1" squares) in the bottom first. Add the rest of the vegetables in the order given. Add enough water just to cover the kombu. Sprinkle with sea salt. Cover and bring to a boil, lower the flame and allow to steam for 20 - 25 minutes. Check the pot occasionally to see if the water has evaporated. If the water has evaporated before end of cooking time, add a little water to the pot. When each vegetable is soft, flavor with tamari to taste, stir gently and cover for another 2 - 3 minutes, until there is no steam. Serve.

DAIKON, GREENS AND KOMBU

2 6" Pieces of kombu, soak for ½ hour
     and cut into 1" pieces
8 Rounds of daikon radish - cut 1" thick
Greens, (collards, kale, turnip, etc.),
     washed and chopped

Place the pieces of kombu in the bottom of a pot. Place the daikon on top, add ½" water, cover and let cook on a medium heat for 25 - 30 minutes. Check periodically to make sure the water has not evaporated. Add the greens at the end of cooking and steam for 3 - 4 minutes. Serve hot.

DAIKON AND CARROT

1 Carrot, slivered
1 Cup daikon, slivered
Pinch of Sea salt
1 Tsp. lemon rind

SAUCE

4 TBS. tamari
½ Cup of water
2 Tsp. lemon juice

Sprinkle the carrot and daikon with sea salt. Place the vegetables in a strainer and blanche in a pot of boiling water. Squeeze out excess liquid and place in a bowl, mix and toss with the lemon rind. Add sauce ingredients and serve.

GREEN BEANS AND ALMONDS

2 Cups green beans, washed and snipped
¼ Cup toasted almonds, chopped
Sesame oil
Tamari to taste

Lightly coat a cast-iron skillet with oil. Add beans and a pinch of sea salt and saute for 3 - 4 minutes, adding just enough water to cover the bottom of the skillet. Cover, lower the flame, and simmer until the beans are almost done. Add tamari to taste and allow to cook until done. Add almonds, stir and serve. The color of the beans should be bright green.

PARSNIPS AND BARLEY MALT

6 Medium parsnips, cut into ½" diagonals
½ Tsp. Sea salt
½ Cup barley malt syrup

Place the parsnips into a pan. Add boiling water to cover. Sprinkle with the sea salt and cook until tender (approximately 20 minutes). Drain and add the barley malt syrup, cover and cook over a low flame for about 5 minutes. Serve.

213

SAUTEED MUSTARD GREENS
DAIKON AND CARROT

1 Bunch of mustard greens, washed and cut
      in 1" diagonal slices (rolled)
1 Cup daikon, cut into thin rounds
1 Carrot, sliced diagonally
Sesame oil
Tamari to taste
¼ Cup of water

Lightly coat a cast-iron skillet with oil and saute the daikon and carrot, add a pinch of sea salt. Saute for 3 minutes over a medium flame. Add water, cover, lower the flame and cook until the daikon is 80% done. Add the mustard greens and tamari, stir, cover and cook for 2 - 3 minutes. Take off the cover and let the water evaporate before serving.

ENDIVE

7 - 8 Endive leaves, cut into half
2 Cloves garlic, minced
1 Onion, sliced 1/8ths
2 Tsp. rice vinegar
2 TBS. tamari, diluted in ¼ cup water
2 Tsp. sesame oil
1 Hardboiled fertile egg, sliced in quarters

Lightly coat a cast-iron skillet with oil Saute the onions and garlic, then add the endive leaves and saute until the leaves become transparent. Add the rice vinegar, and tamari, simmer for 3 - 4 minutes. Serve hot, garnish with sliced hardboiled egg.

Exit 19
SALADS

Automatic Transmission — To Smooth The Road

Salads that are prepared raw or lightly boiled are relatively expanded and are excellent companions when serving fish or fowl, especially during the hot summer months. Salad also aids the body in the discharge of stored animal protein, animal fats and salts. Raw salad should be eaten in season, mid-spring and summer are the ideal times. Eating salad helps **BALANCE** the body temperature which is often raised by hot weather. If you should choose to eat raw salads in the winter months, don't be surprised to find yourself having chills and feeling less energetic.

A very useful way of satisfying the desire for raw salads, but with the advantages of cooked greens, is to serve "Boiled Salad." This method is actually a form of blanching and utilizes a fast immersion in boiling water to destroy any organisms or parasites on the vegetables, with an immediate end to the cooking process by plunging them into icy water.

To prepare, simply place 2 inches of water in the bottom of a heavy pot and bring to a boil, adding a pinch of sea salt. Place the cut vegetables or sliced greens in the water for 1- 2 minutes and do each vegetable separately, starting with the mildest flavored ones first. Then, using a pair of tongs, remove from the boiling water and plunge into ice water before putting them in a colander to finish draining. Some fragile greens like watercress need less than 1 minute to boil.

THE POWER GLIDE - Boiled Salad

Choosing from a selection of greens such as collards, mustards, kale, turnip, radish, watercress, daikon and chinese cabbage, wash and slice the greens. Add 2 carrots, that have been cut into matchsticks, 1 onion, cut into 1/16ths and ¼ cabbage. (this is optional) Place a few inches of water into a pot with a little sea salt. Bring to a boil, drop several vegetables into the pot and boil 2 - 3 minutes. Immediately remove from the pot and squeeze out the excess liquid. Eat plain or serve with a condiment or dressing.

THE DYNAFLOW - Boiled Salad

½ Cup onions, cut in 1/8ths
½ Cup carrots, slivered
½ Cup radish, daikon, red or white, slivered
½ Cup celery, cut thin
Sprinkle of sunflower seeds
Pinch of Sea salt

Boil vegetables in the following order: Onions, 1 minute, carrot, 1½ minutes, radish, 1½ minutes, and celery, 1 minute. Rinse in cold water, drain and place in a bowl. Serve with dressing and garnish with sunflower seeds.

BOILED BROCCOLI-CARROT SALAD

2 Cups broccoli, floweretts
1 Cup carrots, matchstick cuts
Pinch of Sea salt

Boil carrots for 1½ minutes and broccoli for 1 minute. Plunge into cold water and drain. Arrange carrots in the center of a dish and surround with green broccoli floweretts in a circle. Add your favorite dressing and serve.

KALE SALAD

1 Cup of cabbage, shredded
¼ Cup celery, cut diagonally
1 Cup kale, cut diagonally
½ Cup carrots, cut into matchsticks
½ Cup onions, cut into 1/8ths
2 - 3 Red radishes, sliced thin
1 Sprig of parsley, chopped for garnish
Pinch of Sea salt

In a pot, place approximately 3" of water. Bring the water to a boil, add a pinch of sea salt. Starting with the cabbage, kale and then celery boil each of these vegetables separately for 1 - 1½ minutes. Boil the carrots, onions and radishes for 1 minute. Rinse in cold water and drain. Place the vegetables in a bowl, add your favorite dressing and serve. Garnish with parsley.

MACARONI SALAD

1 Cup whole wheat elbow macaroni,
    cooked and drained
½ Cup cooked aduki beans
1 Onion, diced
1 Scallion, sliced thin
2 Stalks of celery, diced
2 Small carrots, grated
½ Tsp. Sea salt
Chopped parsley for garnish

Toss all ingredients together with the sea salt. Mix in mayonnaise dressing. Garnish with parsley and serve chilled.

ITALIAN SALAD

1 Cup garbonzo beans, cooked
3 ozs. vermicelli noodles, cooked
1 Small carrot, cut into thin half moons
1 Tsp. minced onions
1 Clove garlic, minced
1 Medium size unwaxed cucumber, sliced
    thin
Juice of one fresh orange
2 TBS. corn oil
1 Tsp. Sea salt

Cut vermicelli into 1" lengths. Set aside. Bring 2" of water and a pinch of sea salt to a boil. Cook carrots for 2 minutes, rinse in ice water, drain and set aside. Place minced onions and garlic in a large bowl with oil and remainder of salt, along with the orange juice. Mix and let stand for 10 - 15 minutes. Add vermicelli, carrots, cucumber and garbonzos. Toss all ingredients and serve.

CABBAGE SALAD

1 Medium cabbage, finely cut
3 Stalks of celery, finely diced
Cabbage salad dressing (see dressings,
    Exit 22)

Toss the cabbage and celery together in a bowl. Add the cabbage dressing and mix thoroughly. Serve.

WINDJAMMER SALAD

½ Cup cooked arame, cut into 2" pieces
    (refrigerate 30 minutes before using)
1 Head lettuce, chopped
1 Small cucumber, sliced thin
4 Red radishes, sliced thin
1 Small onion, cut in 8ths
½ Cup shredded carrots
½ Cake tofu, cut into 1" pieces
Brown rice vinegar dressing (see dressings,
    Exit 22)
Place all ingredients in a bowl, toss lightly and serve with vinegar-tamari dressing.

CUCUMBER-WAKAME SALAD

2 Cucumbers, sliced thin
1½ Ozs. wakame, rinse and soak 15
    minutes, cut into ½" pieces
    (discard water)
Pulp of one orange
¼ Cup ume vinegar
Pinch of Sea salt
¼ Cup of water

Slice the cucumbers and sprinkle lightly with sea salt, allow to set for 10 minutes. Using a paper towel, press off the excess liquid. Combine all the ingredients and serve.

BEAN SALAD

1 Cup cooked aduki beans
½ Cup cooked garbonzo beans or 1 cup
    kidney beans
2 Cups cooked green beans, cut diagonally
1 Onion, minced
1 Carrot, cut in matchsticks
1 Tsp. Sea salt
Brown rice vinegar dressing (see
    salad dressings, Exit 22)

Place all ingredients in a bowl. Add sea salt and toss together. Allow to marinate for 30 minutes in rice-vinegar dressing.

SALAD GRANADA

2 Cups shrimp, lobster, or crab; cooked
    and cut in small pieces
2 Small onions, diced
1 Carrot, diced thin
1 Cup celery, diced
5 Red radishes, sliced in thin rounds
1 Head lettuce, iceberg, chopped in small
    pieces

Mix all ingredients together and toss with your choice of dressing, mayonnaise or lemon tamari is an excellent choice. (See dressings, Exit 22)

THREE BEAN SALAD

1½ Cups green beans, cut 1½" diagonals
1½ Cups yellow wax beans, cut 1½"
    diagonals
½ Cup cooked garbonzo beans
2 Medium onions, sliced in thin half
    moons
2 Hardboiled fertile eggs, sliced
2 Potatoes, peeled, boiled and sliced thin
½ Tsp. Sea salt
Brown rice vinegar dressing (see
    salad dressings, Exit 22)

Steam beans in 1" of water with a pinch of sea salt in a steamer until tender. Drain and put in a large bowl. Remove steamer and use same water to boil onion slices for 1 minute. Add to green beans along with cooked garbonzos. Toss all ingredients with sea salt and rice vinegar dressing. Allow to stand for one hour in the dressing, then toss again before serving. Garnish with sliced hardboiled eggs.

GARBONZO SALAD

2 Cups cooked garbonzo beans
1 Pound of ramen or vermicelli noodles,
    cooked, cut 1" then cooled
1 Cucumber, sliced thin
¾ Cup fresh squeezed orange juice
2 TBS. corn oil
1 Clove garlic, minced
1 Onion, minced
1 Small carrot, sliced thin, cut into
    flowerettes

Bring 1" of water to a boil, add ¼ Tsp. sea salt and cook carrots until tender. Drain carrots and dip in a bowl of ice water to keep bright orange color. In a larger bowl, add garlic, onions, oil, salt and orange juice. Mix. Allow to set for 15 minutes. Now add the remaining ingredients and toss. Chill 15 minutes and serve.

AUTOBAHN SALAD

¼ Head of lettuce, chopped
1 Stalk celery, chopped
¼ Carrot, diced
2 Scallions, sliced
3 Red radishes, sliced
1 TBS. raisins

Toss all ingredients in a bowl. Serve with choice of salad dressing.

KIDNEY BEAN SALAD

1 Cup cooked kidney beans
1 Clove garlic, minced
5 Scallions, sliced
1 Small green pepper, chopped fine
2 Stalks celery, chopped

Place the kidney beans in a bowl, add the garlic, scallions, celery and green peppers. Gently toss together and set aside. Then prepare Nissan Dressing.

NISSAN DRESSING

½ Cup sesame oil
¼ Cup rice vinegar
¼ Tsp. Sea salt
1/8 Tsp. paprika
1 TBS. rice syrup
1 TBS. tamari
2 TBS. chopped parsley

Place all ingredients in a bowl and mix together. Chill for 1 hour before using. Pour over the kidney beans, toss and serve. Top with sunflower seeds.

CAESAR SALAD

1 Head of Romaine lettuce, rinsed
See salad dressing chapter for the caesar
    dressing

Serve immediately.

FRUIT FERRARI

1 Pint strawberries, cleaned and stemed
3 Apples, peeled and cut into 8ths
3 Peaches, peeled and cut into 8ths
1 Pear, peeled, cut into quarters
¼ Cup raisins
¼ Cup toasted almonds, slivered
¼ Cup sunflower seeds

DRESSING:

1/3 Cup rice syrup
Juice of 1 lemon
Pinch of Sea salt

Place the fresh fruit in a large bowl. Sprinkle lightly with sea salt. In a separate dish, combine the rice syrup and lemon juice, mix well. Pour the dressing over the fruit. Chill and serve.

d'ELEGANCE SALAD

1 Cup of bulghur, soaked in 4 cups of
    water for approximately 2 hours
    or until the bulghur is soft
1 Onion, diced
2 Stalks of celery, diced
1 Carrot, diced
½ Cucumber, peeled and sliced
¼ Green pepper, diced
4 - 5 Red radishes or daikon radish, sliced
Handful of freshly chopped parsley
¼ Tsp. Sea salt

Drain off the liquid from the bulghur. Mix the bulghur and vegetables together in a large wooden salad bowl. Prepare the following dressing and blend well with the bulghur and vegetables, chill and serve.

DRESSING

¼ Cup corn oil
1 TBS. rice vinegar

GREEK SALAD

Assorted green lettuce, bib, romaine
    iceberg
5 - 6 Scallions, diced
1 Onion, diced
10 - 15 Fresh mushrooms, sliced
½ Green pepper, sliced
Feta cheese
3 Greek peppers
A few Greek olives
Sea salt to taste
Rice vinegar to taste
Corn oil

Lightly toss the salad ingredients together, add the sea salt, oil and vinegar to taste. Serve chilled.

CONTINENTAL BROWN RICE SALAD

2 Cups cooked brown rice (hot)
2 Medium onions, chopped fine
¼ Green pepper, chopped fine
1 - 2 TBS. lemon juice
1 Tsp. Sea salt
¼ Cup corn oil
¼ Tsp. oregano
Ripe olives
Freshly chopped parsley
1 Small pint of feta cheese, crumbled

Add the salt along with the chopped onions and pepper to the freshly cooked brown rice. Blend together the oil and lemon juice and pour over the rice.

Toss all the ingredients together. Sprinkle with oregano and garnish with olives, freshly chopped parsley and feta cheese.

RICE CURRY SALAD

1 Cup cooked brown rice
½ Cup cooked wheatberries
1 Cup ono cheese, (See Exit 17)
2 Onions, chopped
3 Stalks celery, chopped
1 Tomato, sliced
Sea salt to taste

EAST INDIAN DRESSING

1 Clove garlic, minced
½ Cup raisins
1/3 Cup rice vinegar
¼ Cup corn oil
2 TBS. lemon juice
3 TBS. barley malt syrup
2 Tsp. curry powder
¼ Tsp. Sea salt

In a saucepan heat the oil, add the curry powder and garlic. Simmer for 1 minute. Then add the barley malt syrup, lemon juice, raisins, rice vinegar and sea salt. Simmer for 5 minutes. In a separate bowl, combine the brown rice and wheatberries. Mix together well. Add the onions and celery, crumble the cheese and tomatoes and toss together with grain. Pour the warm East Indian Dressing over the grain and toss together. Refrigerate for 1 hour and serve.

LENTIL SALAD

1 Cup of lentils, cooked
¼ Tsp. Sea salt
1 Clove of garlic, minced
¼ Tsp. thyme
2 TBS. rice vinegar
2 TBS. freshly chopped parsley
1 Medium onion, diced

Toss all the ingredients together in a large bowl. Allow to cool in the refrigerator and serve on a bed of fresh lettuce.

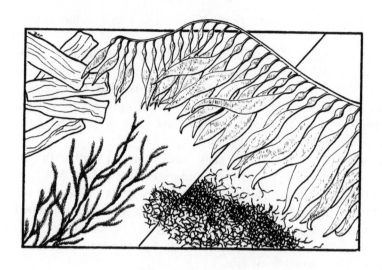

Exit 20
SEA VEGETABLES

High Detergent Power

When you experience your first taste of a sea vegetable, you may find it has an unusual flavor. To best enhance the palatable qualities of these very desirable food sources, we suggest you prepare them carefully with regard to the rinsing and soaking instructions. For example, all sea vegetables must be soaked or rinsed before cooking, except for kombu, which is wiped with a dry cloth to remove excess sea salt residue. In the beginning, use sea vegetables in soups and in combinations with beans and land vegetables, such as carrots, onions, daikon or radishes. They will gradually become familar to you. It is easy to learn to relish the somewhat distinctive flavors with a little repetition, as we do. Include them on a plate which has **BALANCED** amounts of grains and land vegetables and among other benefits you will notice **healthier hair** and an improved **nervous system.**

Although any plant in the sea can be called a seaweed, when I speak of sea vegetables I usually mean a seaweed of the larger, red, or brown algae types. Algae are usually divided into four groups: blue-green, green, brown or red. Kombu, kelp, and wakame, are types of brown algae and have structures which resemble leaves, stems, and roots. Brown algae are found in salt water, unlike the simple-celled blue-green algae which sometimes form slimy growths in the bottom of stagnant fresh water pools or the green algae which also grow mostly in fresh water and requires light to develop.

Sea vegetables I use, such as dulse, Irish moss, and others from which agar-agar is obtained, are of the red algae type, usually grown in the sub-tropical seas. They sometimes co-exist with coral to form reefs. Agar-agar is a gelatin substance obtained from seaweeds of various types. It is frequently used in the preparation of foods in oriental countries. I use it as a base for desserts and in other recipes to thicken and hold the other ingredients, in much the same way as gelatin. In scientific fields it is used as a base in laboratories and as a culture in which to grow bacteria.

Irish moss is also called carrageen and is used commercially in many ways. We use it as the basis for some soups and desserts, however, kombu and wakame are easily found in natural food stores and we use them on a more regular basis. Hiziki, dulse and nori are also easily found and, because of their distinctive appearance, create a dramatic effect on the plate. Arame is a cousin to hiziki, but has a milder flavor and is quite easy to obtain. Both can be used in cooked form or served in cold salads.

Giant kelps, which sometimes grow 200' long in the Pacific, are used in commercial ways, such as the manufacture of fertilizer and explosives during W.W. I. Chemists can also extract large quantities of iodine and algin from kelp. Algin is useful commercially because it can hold several different liquids together. For example, in ice cream it keeps the water in the milk from forming crystals. It is used in salad dressing and chocolate milk. The word kelp is also used to mean an alkaline ash made by burning the seaweed itself. It contains as much as fifteen pounds of iodine to a ton of ash.

With the exception of certain kinds of fish, sea vegetables are the only natural source of iodine in our diet, since we use a non-iodized form of sea salt. Learning to use them is important to your health.

Kombu, wakame and other forms of kelp are the highest sea vegetables in calcium content. Dulse and nori are the highest in iron. All sea vegetables are rich in vitamins A and C as well as, thiamin, (B-1), riboflavin, (B-2) and niacin. Sea vegetables are an important source of minerals which are not found so abundantly in land vegetables. Below is a chart showing the composition of the mineral content of those most commonly used.

SEA VEGETABLES (per 100 grams):   Note: A dash indicates insufficient information is available

	Protein	Fat	Carbohydrates	Calcium	Potassium	Sodium	Magnesium	Phosphorus	Iron	Iodine
Kombu	7.3	1.1	54.9	800	—	2500	—	150	—	—
Wakame	12.7	1.5	51.4	1300	—	2500	—	260	13	—
Kelp-powder	—	1.1	—	1100	5300	3000	760	240	—	150
Nori	35.6	0.7	44.3	250	—	600	—	510	12	—
Hiziki	5.6	0.8	42.8	1400	—	—	—	56	29	—
Dulse	—	3.0	—	570	8100	2100	220	22	6.3	8
Kanteen	—	—	—	450	—	—	—	—	—	0.2
Irish Moss	—	—	—	880	2850	2900	—	160	9	—

The higher concentration of minerals and the specific enzymes found in sea vegetables actually aid the body in discharging the effects of animal food and help the system in adapting to vegetable quality food. In addition, sea vegetables help the body expel radioactive wastes which have permeated body tissues from the atmosphere. Alginic acid, which is an important element found in brown algae like wakame, kombu and hiziki, acts on the metallic elements which accumulate in the intestine and converts them into insoluble salts which are then discharged safely.

Sea vegetables can be combined and cooked with brown rice, millet and barley as well as your favorite beans, tofu and tempeh. They can also be used in making vegetable grain pies, which are excellent for traveling.

Nori is easy to prepare and great for a snack. It may be used as a garnish for grains and soups. For pregnant women who are concerned about their iron levels, this is a must. Green nori flakes are the highest in protein and iron. Another use for this versatile sea vegetable is rice balls, which make a great snack and a good traveling companion.

222

RICE BALLS

Leftover grain can be formed into
    balls if left at room temperature
Leftover vegetables, (optional)
Leftover sea vegetables, (optional)
Sheets of nori
Umeboshi plums, pit removed

You may want to mix together leftover vegetables and/or sea vegetables into the grain. This adds a nice variety and tasty change to the rice balls. Next take several sheets of nori and holding the nori by the corners, heat the sheet over a flame. Move the nori continuously over the flame until it turns green. Then cut the nori into quarters. Wet your hands, take the rice and form a ball about the size of a large golf ball. Insert into the middle a ½ Tsp. umeboshi paste or plum, use your finger or chop stick. Wet hands again and wrap two pieces of nori around the rice ball, completely covering it. Press firmly. The rice balls can be left out or refrigerated, depending on your climate.

HIZIKI AND BEANS

1 Cup hiziki or arame, soak,
    discard water
½ Cup pinto beans or soybeans, soaked
    overnight
Water
Tamari to taste

Place the pinto beans in a pot. Place the arame or hiziki on top, DO NOT mix. Add enough water to cover the arame. Bring to a boil, cover, reduce the flame to low. Simmer until the beans are 80% done. Remove the cover, raise the flame slightly and cook until almost all the liquid evaporates, add the tamari at the end of cooking and serve.

ARAME AND LOTUS ROOT

1 Cup arame or hiziki, soak,
    discard water
1 Cup lotus root, sliced into matchstick
    cuts or quarters
Sesame oil
Water
Tamari to taste

Chop the arame or hiziki, then lightly coat a cast-iron skillet with sesame oil and heat. Place the lotus root in the skillet and saute for 5 - 7 minutes. Add the arame and water to cover. Bring to a boil, cover and lower the flame, simmer for 30 - 35 minutes. Season with tamari to taste and cook for another 10 minutes. Remove cover and cook until all excess water has evaporated. Serve.

ARAME-DAIKON-CURRY

1 Cup arame, soak, discard
    water
1 Clove garlic, minced
2 Carrots, matchstick cut
5 Slices daikon, ¼" diagonal cuts
2 Tsp. sesame oil
½ Tsp. curry powder
1 Medium onion, sliced
3 TBS. tamari

Rinse and soak the arame for 15 minutes. Drain off the liquid. Saute vegetables beginning with the onion and garlic then adding the carrots and daikon.

Set aside vegetables and saute the arame for 2 - 3 minutes. Then combine the arame and vegetables and stir gently, add the curry powder and ½ cup water. Cover and simmer for 15 - 20 minutes. Add tamari just before removing from the flame.

ARAME AND DRIED DAIKON

1 Cup arame, rinse and soak
    discard water
½ Package dried daikon, soaked in water
    to cover, discard soaking water
2 Cloves garlic, minced
Sesame oil
Tamari to taste

Soak the arame and daikon for 15 minutes, drain off the liquid. Saute the garlic and daikon in a lightly coated cast-iron skillet. (Use just a small amount of sesame oil.) Add the arame and saute for 3 - 4 minutes, add ½ cup water and tamari, stir. Cover, lower the flame and allow to simmer for 15 minutes. Serve.

DRIED DAIKON AND KOMBU

1 4" piece kombu, soak for 1 hour
½ Package shredded dried daikon. soak
    for 10 minutes

Chop the presoaked kombu into small pieces and also cut the daikon. Boil both ingredients in the soaking water for about 30 minutes. Add tamari to flavor and simmer for 2 - 3 minutes or until there is very little liquid left. Serve.

HIZIKI AND SESAME SEEDS

4 - 6 Ozs. hiziki, rinse and soak,
    discard water
1½ Tsp. sesame oil
3 TBS. tamari
3 TBS. sesame seeds

Rinse and soak hiziki for 10 minutes. Drain and rinse again. Cut into 2" pieces. Lightly coat a cast-iron skillet with sesame oil and saute hiziki for 5 minutes. Cover with water, bring to a boil, lower and simmer for 30 minutes. Then toast the sesame seeds in a dry cast-iron skillet over a medium flame for 5 minutes, stirring constantly. Seeds will turn light brown and give off a nutty fragrance. Remove from the heat, grind the seeds in a suribachi bowl and sprinkle over hiziki. Add tamari and serve.

ARAME-DRIED DAIKON-CARROTS AND ONIONS

1½ Cup arame, rinse and soak in water,
    cover for 15 minutes (discard
    water)
½ Package dried daikon, soak in water
    cover for 15 minutes (discard
    water)
1 Carrot, cut in matchstick cuts
1 Medium onion, sliced
1 Tsp. sesame oil
2 Cloves garlic, minced
3 TBS. tamari

Rinse and soak arame and daikon for 15 minutes. Heat a cast-iron skillet and coat with sesame oil. Saute onion and garlic then add the daikon and saute, then add the carrots and saute. Set vegetables aside. Saute the arame for 3 - 5 minutes, then add the vegetables, ¼ cup of water and tamari. Simmer for 15 - 20 minutes. Serve.

HIZIKI AND VEGETABLES

4 - 6 Ozs. dry hiziki, soak, discard
    water
2 Cloves garlic, minced
2 Onions, sliced in 8ths
1 Carrot, cut in matchsticks
2 Tsp. sesame oil
3 TBS. tamari

Rinse the hiziki in cold water and allow to soak for 10 minutes in enough water to cover. Rinse again and drain. Cut the hiziki into 2" pieces. Lightly coat a cast-iron skillet with sesame oil and saute the onions, garlic and carrots, set aside. Place a little more sesame oil in the skillet and saute the hiziki with the garlic, for 5 minutes. Add enough liquid to cover and bring to a rapid boil, stirring constantly. Lower the flame, add the vegetables and tamari. Simmer uncovered for 35 minutes or until most of the liquid has evaporated.

WAKAME-ONION
(Looks Like Spinach)

6 Pieces wakame, approximately 5" each,
    soak in water or bancha tea
1 Large onion, sliced
Sea salt
1 Fresh lemon

Soak the wakame, and drain off the liquid. In a cast-iron skillet saute the onion in a little sesame oil. After the wakame has soaked for 5 minutes cut it into ½" strips. Add to the onion, cover with water or bancha tea, sprinkle on a little sea salt, cover and simmer for 40 minutes. Squeeze the juice of a fresh lemon over the mixture and serve.

VEGETABLES WRAPPED IN KOMBU

1 Piece of kombu, 7" x 3", soak for
    10 minutes.
1 Carrot, sliced in ¼" pieces
1 Turnip, sliced
Tamari to taste
Sesame oil
Dried gourd, (found in a natural food
    store and oriental store)

Lightly coat a cast-iron skillet with sesame oil and saute the carrot and turnip on a medium flame for 10 minutes. Place the pre-soaked kombu on a cutting board. Place the vegetables in the center. Roll and tie tightly with gourds at the ends and the middle. Place in a pot, add a ¼ cup of water, kombu should be covered half way and bring to a rapid boil. Cover, lower the flame, and simmer for 40 minutes. Uncover, add the tamari and simmer for 20 minutes more. Remove from the pot, slice and serve.

ARAME AND FRIED TOFU

4 Ozs. arame, soak 15 minutes, discard
    water
2 Tsp. sesame oil
3 TBS. tamari
1 Cake of tofu, drained, sliced into ½"
    rectangular pieces

Before slicing the tofu, squeeze out the excess liquid. In a skillet, lightly coated with sesame oil, fry the tofu on both sides until the pieces are golden brown and set aside. Slice the arame into small pieces, saute in a little oil. Combine the tofu and diluted tamari. Add enough liquid just to cover. Simmer, uncovered, until the liquid has evaporated. Serve.

WAKAME, ONIONS, AND CARROTS

4 - 6 Ozs. wakame, soak and slice in
    ¼" pieces, discard water
2 Onions, sliced in 8ths
2 Carrots, cut in matchsticks
Sesame oil
2 TBS. tamari
1 TBS. rice vinegar

Lightly coat a cast-iron skillet with sesame oil and saute the onions and carrots over a medium heat for 5 minutes. Add the pre-soaked (drained) wakame and cover with water. Bring to a boil, cover and simmer over a low flame for 15 - 20 minutes. Add the tamari and rice vinegar. Simmer for 10 minutes and serve.

WAKAME in soups . . . see Soup Exit 10

WAKAME use in condiments . . . see
    Condiment Exit 23

NORI use in condiments . . . See
    Condiment Exit 23

AGAR-AGAR or KANTEN . . . See
    Dessert Exit 24

KOMBU STOCK . . . See Soup Exit 10

NORI, FRIED TOFU AND SESAME SEEDS

3 sheets of nori, cut in 4ths, soak
    in water, drain and discard liquid
1 TBS. tamari
Sesame oil
1 TBS. sesame seeds, toasted
½ Cake tofu, drained, dried and cut into
    rectangles

Lightly coat a cast-iron skillet with sesame oil and saute the nori. Lower the flame and add ¼ cup of water and simmer covered for 10 minutes. Add the tamari and tofu and simmer for 5 minutes more, uncovered. Serve and garnish with sesame seeds.

LAND AND SEA

4 Medium potatoes, diced
2 6" Pieces kombu, soak for 30 min-
    utes, chop into 1" pieces
2 TBS. barley malt syrup
3 TBS. tamari
1 TBS. rice vinegar
2 TBS. corn oil
½ Cup water

Mix the barley malt syrup, tamari and rice vinegar in a small bowl and set aside. Coat a sauce pan with the corn oil and saute the potatoes until browned on all sides. Add the kombu and saute for 2 minutes. Pour the barley malt mixture over the potatoes and kombu, stir gently, coating the vegetables. Add the water, bring to a boil. Cover, lower the flame and simmer until the potatoes are tender. Serve.

ARAME AND LENTILS

½ Cup of lentils, partially cooked
    (70% done)
½ Cup of arame, soak in water, discard
    water and chop
2 Cloves of garlic, minced
2 Onions, diced
¼ Cup of butternut squash, peeled
    and cubed
¼ Cup acorn squash, peeled and diced
2 TBS. rice vinegar, diluted in ¼ cup of
    water
2 TBS. tamari
Corn oil for sauteeing

Saute the garlic, onions and then the squash, set aside. Saute the arame, and combine the lentils and vegetables, with the arame. Dilute the vinegar in water and add to the mixture. Bring to a boil, lower the flame and simmer until water is almost evaporated. Add tamari and simmer for 3 - 4 minutes. Serve.

ARAME AND HERBS

½ Cup arame, soak in water, cover for
    15 minutes. Discard water and
    chop into 1" pieces
2 Onions, sliced
1 Head broccoli floweretts
2 TBS. corn oil
1 Bay leaf
1 Tsp. basil
2 Tsp. celery seeds
3 TBS. tamari
Water

Lightly coat a saucepan with corn oil and saute the onions and broccoli flower-etts for 3 minutes. Set aside. Use the remaining oil and saute the arame for 3 - 4 minutes. Add the sauteed onions and broccoli to the arame, along with the bay leaf, basil and celery seeds. Mix well, add enough water to cover and simmer for 20 minutes. Add the tamari at the end of cooking and serve.

DULSE AND VEGETABLES

4 - 6 Ozs. dulse, rinse, slice and soak,
    discard liquid
1 Onion, sliced in 8ths
1 Carrot, pencil cut
5 - 7 Drops of freshly grated ginger juice
Sesame oil
Tamari to taste

Lightly coat a cast-iron skillet with sesame oil and stir fry the vegetables over a medium flame for 10 minutes. Add the dulse, tamari and ginger juice with a little water. Lower the flame and simmer for another 10 minutes. Serve. Use just enough tamari to taste.

CANDIED KOMBU

1 Cup barley malt syrup
½ Cup water
2 - 6" Pieces of kombu, soak for 30 minutes, chop into 1" pieces

Place the barley malt syrup and water in a saucepan, mix together. Bring to a boil, stirring constantly. Add the kombu pieces, lower the flame and simmer until almost all the liquid has evaporated (approximately 1 hour). Stir occasionally.

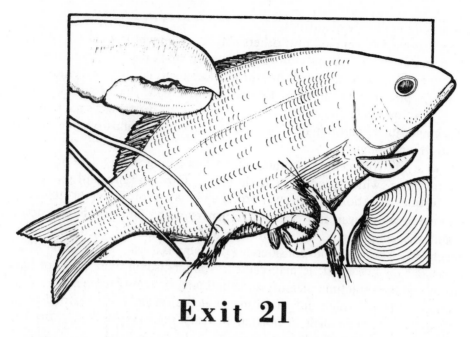

Exit 21
SEAFOOD AND POULTRY

Optional Equipment

Fresh seafood is the most desirable form of animal food you can consume. Fortunately, man has not effectively intervened in nature's production of seafood.

He does not inject fish with growth stimulating hormones, nor feed them rich but unbalanced diets in order to fatten them for the market. In fact, seafood escapes much altering which man perpetuates in the name of "commerce." If you are fortunate enough to have a fisherman in your family, or live near the water, you can probably obtain seafood which has not even been dipped in an antibiotic solution which, unfortunately, is a common practice.

When purchasing fresh fish, look for large, bright, bulging eyes and shiny scales that are tightly attached to the flesh. If you press the fish, the flesh should be firm to the touch. Your nose is another excellent indicator; don't be afraid to believe your senses. If you have any doubts, put the fish in cold water and if it does not float, discard it. A fresh fish will float.

Beware of pre-packaged or stuffed fish and seafoods. They will often contain MSG, eggs and preservatives. Even fresh frozen does not taste nearly as good as fresh, not to mention the difference it means in the quality of the fish. If it is possible, shop for seafood the same day you intend to prepare it. If not, keep it in the coldest part of the refrigerator, but do not freeze.

There are many different types of fish from our oceans and inland waters that you can enjoy, white meat is always preferred. The slower moving varieties of fish are the best ones for you to use, such as flounder, grouper, tilefish, snook, perch or sea bass. In addition, haddock, scrod, cod, whitefish and cobia are among others you may find desirable. If you desire shell fish such as lobster, shrimp, oysters, clams or crabs, have them occasionally but eat them only in moderate quantities.

Some fish may be enjoyed raw, others may be eaten whole and cooked in a variety of ways. The remains of whole fish make an excellent soup stock regardless of whether they are boiled, steamed, fried, poached, baked or stuffed. For a special treat, we enjoy tempura style cookery, which is prepared by dipping the seafood in a light batter and deep-frying in oil. After our meals, to minimize any toxic effects of the meat, we take a small amount of fresh grated radish, ginger juice, and tamari. This also is an excellent sinus opener and one bite will freshen the mouth and tongue.

It is wise to avoid certain combinations when eating seafood. Among them are raw clams and citrus juice, which produce a toxic effect. Carp and mustard greens may also be a source of intestinal irritation in the lower bowel and may result in hemorrhoids. Fresh clams should not be eaten with sugar, nor crabmeat with persimmon. Burdock should never be eaten with trout, and the same applies to mushrooms and short-necked clams. The contents of a lobster stomach, which is sometimes considered a delicacy, is a risky proposition. If at one time the lobster has fed on live coral, it may cause a food poisoning you will not likely forget. It is better to forego the sometime pleasure and eliminate the one time pain.

Whether you are dining out or eating at home, when fresh seafood or shellfish is eaten, always include a grain dish, a portion of leafy green vegetables, a fresh salad with tomatoes, along with your favorite dessert.

MEAT AND POULTRY

Organically fed meats are always preferred. This means no chemicals, no dyes, no hormones added. It should be free from pesticides and antibiotics, etc. Meat should be eaten in moderation and always accompanied with plenty of locally grown fresh vegetables. The vegetables to include should be: leafy greens, a root vegetable, a ground vegetable and a fresh salad. The **BALANCED** ration is: 1 part meat to 3 - 4 parts vegetables.

If you are preparing red meat, use some spices and always salt your meat at the end of cooking. When preparing poultry, use a good quality vegetable oil, corn or sesame oil, and sea salt.

TEMPURA

Tempura is a delightful taste treat which can be enjoyed on occasion as a method of cooking any seafood pieces or vegetable slices. The most commonly prepared seafood is shrimp, but fish can be cut into bite size squares and is equally delicious. Onion rings are the favorite with us, and so are slices of squash, slender spears of broccoli, and even a few wedges of apple. All are dipped in a batter and deep-fried in oil. On most foods, it is best to flour them lightly before dipping in the batter. Use between one and one and a half inches of corn oil, which can be strained and re-used later. After frying is complete, put a slice or two of white potato in the oil as it cools to absorb the odor and this will help to clean the oil. When you are making tempura, be sure the oil is heated to 350 - 360 degrees before adding the food to be fried. The following recipe is one of my favorite batters.

TEMPURA BATTER

1 Cup whole wheat or unbleached white
    flour
1 Cup flat beer
1 Fertilized egg
½ Tsp. Sea salt
Corn oil

Beat the egg and sea salt together. Add the beer and beat together then add the flour and continue mixing until there are no lumps. Let the mixture stand a few minutes and if it is too thin, continue adding a little more flour. If it is too thick, add a little more beer. If you are going to flour your tempura pieces before dipping in the batter, be sure your batter mixture is on the thin side as it will accumulate some flour from the food that is dipped.

SEAFOOD RECIPES

FISH KEBAB

1 Fresh flounder, cut into 2" x 3" pieces
1 TBS. sesame oil
3 TBS. tamari
3 Slivers garlic, minced
2 TBS. parsley, chopped
1 Large onion, cut into 1" x 1" pieces
½ Green pepper, cut into 1" x 1" pieces
1 Fresh squeezed lemon, juiced
1 Cup umeboshi juice or juice of 1 lime

Marinate the fish for 30 minutes in the umeboshi juice, oil, garlic, lemon juice, parsley and tamari. Roll up the fish and skewer it, alternating it with the vegetables, starting with the onion, pepper and fish. Repeat this pattern a few times. Pour a generous amount of marinade over your fish kebab. Place under the broiler for 5 minutes at 400 degrees. Turn over, add the remaining marinade liquid and broil for 5 minutes more. Serve on a bed of brown rice.

SEAFOOD CHOWDER

¼ Cup wakame, soak for 10 minutes,
    chop in small pieces (discard
    water)
1 Dozen clams, cooked and 12 ozs.
    broth reserved
2 Dozen fresh shrimp, peeled and
    deveined
1 Dozen fresh oysters
6 Ozs. crab meat
1 Cup white wine
2 Stalks celery, chopped
2 Carrots, diced
1 Onion, diced
2 Scallions, diced
1 Tsp. Sea salt
1 Tsp. thyme
1 Bay leaf
½ Cup pureed butternut squash or mock
    tomato suace
4 TBS. rice flour
Sesame oil
2 Cup soup stock
2 TBS. tamari

Saute all vegetables in sesame oil for 5 minutes. Add the rice flour and stir until lightly browned and all oil is absorbed. Add wakame, bay leaf, thyme and tamari. Lower the flame, add squash puree and stir. Add soup stock and clam juice, bring to a boil, stirring constantly. Add clams, oysters, shrimp and crab. Lower flame and simmer for 2 minutes. Add sea salt and white wine. Stir and simmer 2 or 3 minutes more. Garnish with parsley and serve.

*PERSONAL NOTES:

FISH CHOWDER

2 Pounds fresh fillet, or 1 lb. of shrimp
    or 1 lb. of lobster
2 Cloves garlic, minced
2 Onions, diced
¼ Cup sesame seeds, toasted and ground
    in a suribachi bowl
2 Carrots, diced
2 Potatoes, diced
½ Tsp. Sea salt
1 Tsp. thyme
1 Tsp. basil
½ Tsp. paprika
½ Tsp. cumin
2 TBS. freshly chopped parsley
1 Cup dry white wine
3 Cups soup stock or water
7 - 8 Ripe whole tomatoes or 2 cups mock
    tomato sauce

In a large pan, saute the garlic, onions and carrots for 5 - 7 minutes. Squeeze the juice out of the tomatoes and chop the skins fine. Add the tomato juice and skins, soup stock and wine to the vegetables. Add all the seasonings. Bring the mixture to a boil, lower the flame and simmer for 1 hour. Cut the fillet into large chunks and add to the pot. Simmer for 5 minutes. Garnish with parsley. Serve.

FRIED TROUT

1 Whole sea trout, cleaned and scaled
1 Cup whole wheat flour
1 TBS. wakame-sesame condiment, (See
    condiment chapter)
Pinch of Sea salt
Thin slices of fresh lemon

Mix flour, salt and wakame together. Rub a few drops of tamari on both sides of the fish and roll the fish in the whole wheat flour mixture. Heat sesame oil in a cast-iron skillet and fry trout until golden brown on both sides, leave skillet uncovered. Garnish with lemon slices.

TOFU AND SHRIMP DELIGHT

1 Pound fresh shrimp, peeled and deveined
1 Square tofu, steamed for 5 minutes,
    squeeze out all excess liquid, cut into
    1" cubes
2 Cloves garlic, minced
2 Medium onions, cut into 8ths
3 Scallions, cut into ¼" diagonals
1 TBS. sesame oil
½ Tsp. freshly grated ginger juice

PREPARE COOKING SAUCE AND SET ASIDE:

1 TBS. arrowroot
¼ Tsp. Sea salt
1 TBS. light miso, diluted in ½ cup water

Mix all the above ingredients together and set aside.

Lightly coat a cast-iron skillet with sesame oil. When the oil is hot, saute the garlic and onions 3 - 4 minutes. Add the ginger juice and shrimp, saute for 2 minutes. Place ingredients in a bowl. Saute the tofu and scallion for 5 - 7 minutes. Add a little more oil if needed. Combine all ingredients with the sauce. Bring to a rapid boil, stirring constantly, until the sauce thickens. Lower the flame and simmer for 2 - 3 minutes more. Serve.

BROILED SOLE

1 Pound of sole, fresh and cleaned

Sauce, mix together in a separate bowl:
3 TBS. tamari
3 TBS. water
1 TBS. freshly grated ginger juice

Place the fish on a lightly oiled baking dish and baste with the sauce. Cook for 4 minutes under the broiler. Remove from the oven, turn the fish over and pour the remaining sauce over the fish. Return to the broiler and cook for 4 minutes. Garnish with parsley and serve.

LOBSTER IN BLACK BEAN SAUCE

1 Small lobster or a 1 pound lobster tail
2 TBS. cooked black beans
3 Cloves garlic, minced
3 Scallions, sliced
Sesame oil
2 Tsp. tamari
2 TBS. sake or white wine
1 Cup soup stock
1 Fertile egg yolk, beaten
2 Tsp. arrowroot, diluted in 3 TBS. cold
        water

Remove the lobster meat from the shell, and cut in half, then into 8 pieces. Rinse and drain the lobster meat. In a separate dish combine the black beans and minced garlic, allow to marinate for 30 minutes. Heat a cast-iron skillet (or use a wok) and add a small amount of sesame oil. Saute the black beans and garlic marinade for 1 minute. Remove from the skillet. Add a little more oil and saute the lobster pieces for 1 minute. Add the black bean mixture to the lobster, saute for an additional 1 minute. Then add the white wine and soup stock, cover and simmer over medium heat for 2 - 3 minutes. Add the tamari, beaten egg yolk and arrowroot mixture, along with the scallions. Saute and mix together for 1 minute. Serve.

SWEET SOUR FISH

1½ Pounds fresh fish fillet
1 Onion, diced
Corn oil for frying
Sweet and sour sauce - See sauce chapter

Saute onions and remove from the skillet. Heat the oil in a skillet. Cut the fish into serving pieces and fry until lightly browned. Place the cooked onions over the fish, pour the sweet and sour sauce over the fish and simmer for 10 minutes. Serve.

BAKED GROUPER

1 Pound fresh grouper fillet
2 Cloves garlic, minced
2 Onions, diced
½ Green pepper, diced
3 Scallions, diced
2 Tomatoes, sliced
1 TBS. tamari
Juice of a fresh lemon
½ Cup of water
Corn oil

Lightly coat a baking dish with oil. Place the grouper fillet in the dish, and set aside. In a separate bowl, mix together all the other ingredients, EXCEPT the tomato slices. Pour the liquid mixture over the fish and allow to marinate for 15 minutes. Top the fish with tomato slices and bake at 300° until meat is white and tender. Serve.

SHRIMP CANTONESE

1 TBS. sesame oil
2 Small slivers of garlic, minced
4 Scallions, sliced thin
1 Pound fresh shrimp, peeled and deveined
3 TBS. tamari
1½ Cups boiling water
1 Tsp. arrowroot
¼ Cup cold water
1 Fertile egg

Heat the sesame oil in cast-iron skillet and add the garlic and onions. Saute lightly, add tamari, boiling water and mix together. Cover and simmer for 5 minutes over a low flame. Add shrimp, simmer together covered for 3 minutes more. Dissolve the arrowroot in the cold water and add slowly to the skillet, stirring until the sauce thickens and is transparent and smooth. Remove from the heat, beat the egg lightly and add to the shrimp mixture while still very hot. Stir once, gently, then serve.

SHRIMP-BROCCOLI CASSEROLE

1 Pound fresh shrimp, (or lobster) cut
    into ½" pieces, cooked
2 Cups broccoli flowerettes
½ Square tofu, boiled for 10 minutes,
    squeeze out excess liquid, crumble
1 TBS. corn oil
1 Clove garlic, minced
¼ Cup rice or oat milk
¼ Cup parmesan cheese
2 TBS. freshly chopped parsley
1 Cup bread crumbs

In a bowl toss the shrimp and broccoli
flowerettes. Put tofu, oil, garlic and milk
in a blender and mix. Combine with the
shrimp and broccoli and mix well. Sprinkle
on bread crumbs and toss lightly. Place
the ingredients into an oiled casserole dish,
sprinkle the parmesan cheese on top. Bake
at 400° for 10 minutes or until brown.
Garnish with chopped parsley.

SHRIMP AND BROCCOLI DELIGHT

1 Pound shrimp, peeled and deveined
2 Large onions, cut lengthwise in 16ths
2 Cups broccoli flowerettes
3 TBS. tamari
2 TBS. sesame oil
2 TBS. arrowroot, diluted in a little water
Sea salt to taste
2 Cups soup stock or fish stock

Lightly oil a cast-iron skillet and saute
onions until clear. Add the remaining
oil and broccoli flowerettes, sauteing for
a few minutes. Add the stock, cover and
simmer for about 10 minutes. Add the
arrowroot mixture slowly, and stir constantly until the sauce becomes clear and
thickened. Add shrimp and tamari and
simmer for 5 minutes or until the shrimp
becomes pink. Salt to taste if needed and
serve.

CHINESE LOBSTER TAIL

1 Lobster tail
½" Piece of ginger root, minced
Sesame oil
4 Ozs. fresh mushrooms
1 TBS. white wine
½ Cup soup stock
1 TBS. barley malt syrup
1/3 Cup almond milk
1 Fertile egg white, beaten
1 Tsp. arrowroot, diluted in 1 TBS.
    cold water

Remove the lobster meat from the shell,
cut in half then into 8 pieces. Rinse and
drain the lobster meat. Heat a cast-iron
skillet (or use a wok) and add 2 TBS. of
sesame oil. Saute the ginger root for 1 minute, add the lobster and saute for 1 minute.
Then add ½ Tsp. sesame oil, mushrooms,
wine, soup stock, barley malt syrup, a
pinch of sea salt, mix together and saute
for 1 minute. Add the almond milk and
egg white, then the arrowroot mixture.
Stir all the ingredients together and simmer
over medium heat for 1- 2 minutes. Serve
over a bed of brown rice.

CRAB MARINADE

1 Pound crab (or shrimp)
2 Stalks of celery, diced fine
1 Cucumber, sliced thin
1 Medium onion, diced fine
Brown rice vinegar dressing, (See dressing
    chapter)
Sea salt to taste

Boil crab in water to cover, cool, shell
and shred the meat. Sprinkle cucumber
with sea salt and let stand for 10 minutes.
Press the excess liquid from the cucumber
with hands or a vegetable press and drain
off. Combine crab meat, onion, celery
and cucumber with the brown rice vinegar
dressing and allow to marinate for 1 hour.
Serve chilled if desired by placing in the
refrigerator for 25 minutes topped with
slices of red radishes.

STEAMED FISH FILLET WITH TARGA SAUCE

1 Pound fresh white meat fish fillet
1¾ Cups of water

TARGA SAUCE:

2 Cloves of garlic, minced
2 Scallions, sliced thin
1 Tsp. freshly grated ginger juice
1 TBS. barley malt syrup
1 Tsp. corn oil

Combine all the ingredients for the sauce and set aside. Place the water in a wok, place the fish on a rack at least 1" above the water. Brush the Targa Sauce all over the fish. Cover and steam for 12 - 15 minutes. Serve.

SASHIMI

1 Pound white fish, bass or tuna,
    cut in 1½" x 2" pieces
½ Cup daikon radish or red radish, sliced
½ Cup fresh chopped parsley
1 Carrot, grated

SAUCE: MIX TOGETHER:

1 Tsp. freshly grated ginger juice
½ Tsp. freshly grated horseradish or wasabe
10 Tbs. tamari

Arrange slices of fresh fish overlapping one another on a platter. Place all other ingredients attractively around the fish with some small dishes served to each person enjoying this treat, so that they can choose their marinade. Usually the tamari forms the basis for the dip and the other flavors are stirred into it with chopsticks or cocktail forks. The raw fish is then selected a piece at a time and soaked in the sauce first on one side, then the other before enjoying.

FISH SAUCES

1. 2 TBS. tamari
   A few drops of fresh grated ginger
2. 2 TBS. tamari
   ½ Tsp. fresh lemon juice
3. 2 TBS. tamari
   1 Tsp. fresh squeezed orange juice
4. 3 Cups soup stock or/water
   4 TBS. tamari
   2 TBS. rice wine
   ¼ Tsp. Sea salt
   2 Scallions, thinly sliced rounds
*   You may add ¼ cup of water to all dips

Bring stock to a boil, add salt and tamari. Allow to come back to a boil again. Pour rice wine into the liquid and remove from the heat immediately so the alcohol will not evaporate. Place the sauce in a bowl and top with scallions. This is a great dip for fish or shrimp tempura.

OYSTER STUFFING

2 Dozen oysters, cooked, reserve ½ cup
   liquid
5 - 7 Scallions, sliced thin
2 Cloves garlic, minced
½ Green pepper, minced
1 Stalk of celery, minced
1½ Cup bread crumbs
¼ Cup freshly chopped parsley
½ Tsp. Sea salt
¼ Tsp. thyme
3 TBS. corn oil

Saute the garlic, scallions, celery, and green pepper. Add the oysters and bread crumbs, and stir together. Add a little liquid and cover. Simmer for 3 minutes. Add the sea salt, parsley and thyme, mix well. Simmer for an additional 2 - 3 minutes. Serve.

FISH STUFFING

¼ Pound, lean white fish fillets, chopped
    (You may use crab)
1 Scallion, minced
1 Tsp. onion, minced
1 Small clove garlic, minced
1 Tsp. tamari
¼ Tsp. sesame oil
¼ Tsp. arrowroot
1/8 Tsp. Sea salt
1 TBS. barley malt syrup
¼ - 1/3 Cup of water

Blend all ingredients together, adding water last. You may use more or less water. Use as stuffing for fresh baked or broiled fish.

FILLET AND VEGETABLES

2- 3 Scallions, chopped
1 5 Oz. fish fillet, cut into small pieces
2 Onions, cut into 8ths
1 Carrot, matchsticked
2 Cups of caulifloweretts, cut small
2 Cups water or vegetable soup stock
2 TBS. arrowroot
¾ TBS. fresh ginger juice
1 Tsp. Sea salt
Corn oil for sauteing

Lightly coat a skillet with corn oil and saute the garlic, onions and scallions, saute for 1 - 2 minutes. Add the caulifloweretts and carrots. Cook for 4 - 5 minutes. Dilute the arrowroot in cool water, add the ginger juice and pour over the vegetables. Bring to a boil, stirring. Lower the flame and simmer for 10 minutes. Add the fish and sea salt. Allow to simmer for 10 minutes more. Serve.

BROILED FISH

1 Broiling fish, fresh, cleaned and scaled
2 TBS. lemon juice
1 Tbs. chopped parsley
1 Clove garlic, minced
1 Small onion, minced
1 TBS. corn oil
1 TBS. tamari
Pinch of Sea salt
Slivered almonds, (Optional)

Combine all ingredients for sauce except the almonds. Lightly oil a baking dish and place the fish in half the sauce to marinate, 5 - 10 minutes, turning once. Place under the broiler and cook for 5 minutes, then pour the remaining sauce over the fish. Add slivered almonds to garnish the top and broil another 2 minutes or until done. Serve.

POULTRY RECIPES

STUFFED BAKED CHICKEN AND VEGETABLES

1 Whole organic chicken
2 Cups of rice stuffing (see Rice stuffing)
2 White potatoes, cubed
2 Carrots, cubed
2 Stalks of celery, cubed
¼ Butternut or acorn squash, cubed
2 Onions, quartered
2 Apples, cubed
1 Cup of water
Sesame oil

Preheat the oven to 350°. Salt the cavity of the chicken and stuff with the rice stuffing. Lightly oil an oblong casserole dish and place the chicken breast side down. Place the vegetables around the chicken. Add the water and cover. Place in the oven and bake for 40 minutes. Uncover and bake an additional 15 - 20 minutes or until done. Check occasionally and add water if necessary. Serve.

CHINESE STYLE CHICKEN

½ Cooked chicken, cut into pieces
1 Onion, chopped
1 Clove garlic, minced
½ Green pepper, chopped
2 Stalks celery, chopped
½ Cup almonds, diced
¼ Cup yellow squash, chopped
½ Pound fresh mushrooms, sliced
½ Cup snow pea pods
1 Cup bean sprouts, mung bean
3 - 4 TBS. tamari
2 TBS. arrowroot or kuzu

Saute all the vegetables in a little sesame oil, saute the almonds and snow pea pods last. Dissolve the arrowroot in ½ - ¾ cups of cool water or vegetable stock. Add the mixture to the vegetables. Add the tamari to the ingredients. Now add enough water to cover the vegetables, mix well. Bring the mixture to a boil, lower the flame, the mixture should thicken, stir well. Add the chicken and sprouts and simmer for a few minutes. Serve over brown rice. The vegetables should be crunchy and not overcooked.

ROAD RUNNER

1 Organic chicken, whole or cut into pieces
1 Cup brown rice
1 Stalk of celery, sliced
1 Carrot, sliced
½ Pound fresh mushrooms, sliced
1 Onion, chopped
1 Clove garlic, minced
1 Cup yellow squash, peeled and chopped
½ Green pepper, chopped
½ Cup broccoli, floweretts
½ Tsp. Sea salt
½ Tsp. coriander
¼ Cup tamari, diluted in 4 cups of water

Place the brown rice, vegetables and water in a large roasting pan or casserole dish. Clean the chicken and remove all the skin. Sprinkle the chicken with the seasonings and salt the cavity. Place the chicken on top of the rice and vegetables. Cover with a lid and place in the oven and bake at 350 degrees for 1 - 1½ hours or until the rice is done.

BROWN RICE AND CHICKEN CASSEROLE

2 Cups brown rice, cooked
2 Cups chicken, cooked and cut into pieces
½ Cup snow pea pods
½ Cup almonds, sliced
4 - 5 Scallions, chopped
½ Green pepper, sliced
½ Cup yellow squash, sliced
1 Stalk celery, chopped
2 Cloves garlic, minced
1 Cup fresh mushrooms, sliced
½ Tsp. freshly grated ginger
2 TBS. arrowroot or kuzu, diluted in
    ¼ cup cold water
½ Cup vegetable soup stock
2 TBS. tamari
Corn oil for sauteing
Grated parmesan cheese

Saute the scallions, garlic, pepper, squash, mushrooms and ginger in a little corn oil. Dissolve the arrowroot in the water and add the tamari. Add this mixture to the sauteed vegetables, bring to a boil, lower flame and add the brown rice, chicken, snow pea pods and almonds. Place the grated cheese on top and simmer for 3 - 5 minutes. Serve.

*PERSONAL NOTES:

CHICKEN VAN

**4 Organically fed chicken breasts,
    boneless**
1½ Cups cooking sherry or red wine
1 Medium onion, chopped fine
1 Carrot, chopped fine
½ Turnip, chopped fine
3 Stalks celery, chopped fine
½ Cup fresh mushrooms, in quarters
2 Cloves garlic, minced
¼ Green pepper (or red), minced
¼ Tsp. thyme
Sesame oil
**Whole wheat flour and unbleached
    white flour**
Tamari to taste

Brown all your finely chopped vegetables in a cast-iron skillet coated with sesame oil. Set aside. Roll the chicken breasts in whole wheat or unbleached white flour. In the same skillet brown the chicken using a little sesame oil. Then set the chicken aside. Brown 2 TBS. of flour and add the wine and all the seasonings. You may add a little water to the sauce. Return the vegetables and chicken to the sauce **except** the mushrooms. Simmer for 40 minutes, then add the mushrooms and tamari to taste. Simmer for 5 - 10 minutes more.

BARBEQUED SHIITAKE MUSHROOMS
(Our BBQ Beef)

Soak the shiitake mushrooms in 2 cups of water for 30 minutes. Destem and discard the soaking water. Place the mushrooms in 2 cups of fresh water and bring to a boil in a saucepan. Lower the flame and simmer, uncovered for 30 minutes. Strain off the liquid and squeeze out any excess liquid. Set the shiitake mushrooms aside.

Make the sauce:

1/3 Cup barley malt syrup
3 TBS. rice vinegar
1 Tsp. stone ground mustard (Hains)
1 TBS. tamari
Pinch of Sea salt

Mix all the ingredients together and blend well. Place the mushrooms in a casserole and pour over the sauce. Marinate the mushrooms for 30 minutes. Then place the casserole in a 300° oven and bake for 20 minutes. Serve.

*PERSONAL NOTES:

Exit 22
SAUCES - SPREADS
SALAD DRESSINGS

Polish, Shine, And Glamorize

All the recipes given for sauces, spreads and dressings are made from natural ingredients. Each creates a flavor enhancing addition to a basic item on your plate. You will want to experiment with many other combinations of your own after you have tried the ones I have given here, and I encourage you to do so. You will notice that some recipes do not contain spices. Spices are not necessary to create delicious recipes. I avoid the over use of spices, using them on a regular basis would cause an overly acidic condition. In moderation, and on occasion, spice usage is fine.

The one piece of equipment we would recommend in preparing these recipes is a simple suribachi bowl with a wooden pestle. They are available in most natural food stores or can be ordered through their suppliers. They are inexpensive, but do a much better job of blending ingredients than electric blenders. Blenders may do the work more efficiently but in most cases the ingredients are soft enough to require little effort and the slower process lends a more tranquil vibrational energy to the food. This in turn creates a more relaxed feeling in the body.

I am so fond of our condiments and dressings that when I dine out, I take them along in small jars and order my salads plain. This gives me the pleasure of the social experience but does not send me home with indigestion from over-rich eating.

SAUCE RECIPES

SWEET AND SOUR SAUCE

1 Clove garlic, minced
1 Small onion, minced
¼ Cup barley malt syrup
¼ Cup umeboshi or rice vinegar
1 TBS. fresh squeezed lemon juice
1 TBS. tamari
1/3 Cup of water

Blend all ingredients together and refrigerate for 1 hour. Serve.

SWEET SAUCE

1½ Cups apple juice
½ Cup raisins
1/3 Cup barley malt syrup
¼ Tsp. dry ginger
2 TBS. fresh mustard
½ Tsp. garlic powder

Bring all the ingredients to a boil in a saucepan, stirring. Lower the flame and simmer for 3 minutes. Serve.

APPLE SAUCE

1 Dozen apples, peeled and cored, cut
    in quarters
Pinch of Sea salt
Dash of cinnamon
¼ Cup raisins
¼ Cup of water

Put the apples, water and raisins in a pressure cooker. Add the sea salt and cinnamon, bring to full pressure over a high heat. Lower the flame and cook for 5 minutes. Allow pressure to return to normal. Uncover and puree with a hand masher. Serve hot or cold.

BECHAMEL SAUCE WITH BROCCOLI

1 Clove garlic, minced
1 Small onion, diced
2 Scallions, sliced thin
1/8 Red pepper, diced
1 Cup broccoli flowerettes
2 TBS. whole wheat flour
1 TBS. almond nut bread
1 TBS. tamari
2 Cups of water

Saute all the vegetables in a cast-iron skillet lightly coated with sesame oil. Blend the flour with nut butter and add it to the water, a little at a time until thoroughly mixed. Pour into the vegetables and bring to a boil. Lower the flame, add tamari and simmer for 10 minutes. Serve the sauce on grain or leafy greens such as kale or collards.

HOT SAUCE

1 Clove garlic, minced
2 Small onions, diced
7 - 8 Umeboshi plums, pitted
3 TBS. corn oil
2 TBS. water
¼ Tsp. chili powder

Blend all the ingredients together, then serve.

WHOLE CRANBERRY SAUCE

5 Cups cranberries, washed and stems
    removed
2 Cups of water
2 Cups barley malt syrup
¼ Tsp. Sea salt
1 Tsp. grated orange peel
1 - 1" stick of cinnamon

Bring the water, syrup, and spices to a boil. Add cranberries and sea salt, continue to boil for 5 minutes, covered. Stir occasionally. Add grated orange peel and simmer for 5 minutes more, uncovered. Meanwhile, chill a bowl, then pour in the mixture and refrigerate until the sauce thickens and becomes firm. Serve.

ONION MUSHROOM SAUCE

1 Pound of mushrooms, sliced and dry
    roasted
2 TBS. tamari
2 TBS. arrowroot, diluted in 2 cups of
    cold water
1 Clove garlic, minced
3 Onions, diced

Lightly coat a cast-iron skillet with oil, saute the garlic, onions and dry mushrooms. Add the diluted arrowroot and bring to a boil, lower the flame and simmer for 5 minutes. Add the tamari and simmer for a few more minutes. Serve.

BUTTERNUT PEANUT SAUCE

1 Cup butternut squash, pureed
2 Heaping TBS. peanut butter
½ Cup of water
¼ Tsp. Sea salt

Place all ingredients in a suribachi bowl and blend together by hand, or place in a blender and mix well. Serve over vegetables.

MUSHROOM SAUCE

2 Cups fresh mushrooms, sliced, dry
    roasted for 20 minutes (set aside)
2 Cloves garlic, minced
1 Onion, minced
2 TBS. tamari
2 Cups of water
5 TBS. rice flour/ or unbleached white
    flour
Sesame oil
Pinch of Sea salt

Lightly coat a cast-iron skillet with sesame oil. Saute garlic, onions and mushrooms until the onions are transparent. Mix sea salt, flour, water together and add to vegetables. Bring to a boil, stirring constantly. Lower flame and cover for 3 minutes. Add tamari and simmer 10 minutes more. Serve.

A SAUCE FOR ALL SEASONS

1 Onion, minced
2 TBS. tahini
1 TBS. sesame oil
2 TBS. of water
2 TBS. tamari
2 TBS. white wine or sake

Lightly coat a cast-iron skillet with sesame oil. Saute the onion until lightly browned. Add enough water to cover onions and bring to a boil. Lower the flame and simmer until tender. Dilute the tahini with 2 TBS. of water and then add to the onions, along with tamari. Cook a few minutes then remove from stove and add the wine. Stir and allow to stand a few minutes more before serving over cooked grain. Serve.

RAINBOW SAUCE

2 TBS. oat flour, or unbleached white
    flour
1 TBS. tahini or nut butter
1 TBS. tamari
2 Cups water
½ Tsp. Sea salt
1 Small onion, chopped
2 Small scallions, chopped
¼ Green or red pepper, chopped
10 Drops fresh grated ginger juice
2 TBS. chopped parsley

Lightly coat a cast-iron skillet with sesame oil and saute onions, scallions and peppers. Combine flour, tahini, sea salt and water and add to the skillet. Bring to a boil and lower the flame, stirring constantly. Add tamari, ginger juice, then cover and simmer for 10 minutes, stirring occasionally. Sprinkle with parsley and pour over grains or vegetables.

CAULIFLOWER SAUCE

1 Small onion, diced
3 Scallions, sliced thin
1/8 Red pepper, diced
3 Shiitake mushrooms, soak for 20 minutes, remove stems and slice
1 Cup cauliflower flowerettes
1 TBS. sesame butter
2 TBS. rice flour
2 Cups of water
2 TBS. tamari

Lightly coat a cast-iron skillet with sesame oil and saute all vegetables. Mix flour and sesame butter in a little water until the lumps are thoroughly dissolved, then add remaining water and stir. Add to the vegetables, bring to a rapid boil, lower flame, stir thoroughly and simmer for 10 minutes. Add tamari, stir and serve.

FISH SAUCE

1 TBS. miso, diluted in ½ cup of water
2 Tsp. tamari
1 TBS. sesame oil
1 Onion, minced
2 Cloves garlic, minced
20 Drops fresh grated ginger or/ lemon
      juice

Mix all ingredients and use as a marinade for fish or baste fish just before removing from oven.

ORANGE PLEDGE

1 Clove garlic, minced
4 - 6 Shiitake mushrooms, soak,
      remove stems and slice
2½ Cups of water
2 TBS. whole wheat flour/ or unbleached
      white flour
2 TBS. tamari
2 TBS. almond nut or sesame butter
      (or tahini)
3 - 4 Strips of orange rind

Lightly coat a cast-iron skillet with sesame oil and saute garlic and mushrooms. Mix the sesame butter and flour in water and pour over the mushrooms. Add tamari and orange rinds. Bring to a boil, lower flame and simmer for 15 minutes. Serve.

TARGA SAUCE

2 Cloves of garlic, minced
2 Scallions, sliced thin
1 Tsp. freshly grated ginger juice
1 TBS. barley malt syrup
1 Tsp. corn oil

Combine all the ingredients for the sauce in a bowl. Allow to set for 1 hour before using. Excellent to use as a marinade for fish.

MOCK TOMATO SAUCE
(A tomato sauce without heartburn)

3 Large onions, diced
3 Carrots, diced
2 Small beets, diced
1 Butternut squash, peeled and cubed
3 Cups of water
1 Turnip, diced
1 TBS. Sea salt
1 Bay leaf

Place all the ingredients in a pressure cooker, bring to high heat, lower the flame and simmer for 12 minutes. Remove from the stove and allow to cool. Using a potato masher, mash and blend all the ingredients together until creamy.

While the other vegetables are cooling, saute in a separate skillet the following ingredients. Coat the skillet with a little sesame oil.

3 Cloves of garlic, minced
3 Stalks of celery, diced
2 Onions, minced
½ Green pepper, diced
1 Lb. fresh mushrooms, sliced
½ Tsp. oregano or Italian seasoning
¼ Cup parmesan cheese
2 TBS. light mellow white miso

Combine all the ingredients in one large pot, add 1 TBS. of sea salt and Italian seasoning to taste and ½ Tsp. oregano. Bring to a medium heat, stir constantly, lower the flame and simmer for 30 minutes, stirring occasionally. At the end of cooking, add 2 **TBS.** of light mellow white miso that has been diluted in ½ cup of water. Allow to cook for 5 minutes more. Add ¼ cup of parmesan cheese and stir. Serve over pasta noodles or use a a pizza sauce.

FRESH SHRIMP SPREAD

½ Pound shrimp, cooked and chopped
4 Ozs. tofu, steam 5 minutes,
    squeeze out excess liquid
1 Tsp. freshly squeezed lemon juice
1 Clove garlic, minced
Dash of paprika

Mix all the ingredients together either in a suribachi bowl or blender. Allow to cool and serve with crackers.

DILL SPREAD

1 Cup of mayonnaise
2 Dill pickles, chopped
½ Small onion, chopped
½ Small clove of garlic, minced
1 Tsp. dill weed

Mix all the ingredients together. Allow to cool and serve with fresh vegetables, crackers or as a condiment with fish.

TOFU SPREAD

1 Square tofu, steam 5 minutes, squeeze
    out excess liquid
¼ Cup fresh squeezed lemon or lime juice
2 Cloves garlic, minced
½ Tsp. Sea salt
¾ Tsp. dried dill weed or chives
1/3 Cup corn oil
¼ Cup water

Place all ingredients in a suribachi bowl or blender and blend till creamy and smooth. Serve.

MISO SESAME SPREAD

5 TBS. sesame butter
1 TBS. miso
2 TBS. chives
A little water

Puree all ingredients until creamy and smooth. Serve.

SAVORY TOFU

1 Square tofu, steam 5 minutes, squeeze
    out excess liquid
1 Onion, minced fine
1 Clove garlic, minced fine
¼ Cup sesame butter or tahini
1 TBS. rice vinegar
¼ Tsp. chives
3 TBS. tamari
½ Tsp. Sea salt
¼ Tsp. sage
¼ Tsp. thyme

Place all ingredients in a suribachi bowl or blender and blend till creamy and smooth. Serve.

** One of the most versatile spreads is miso, used in combination with other natural ingredients. When you have unexpected guests or need to serve something delicious in a hurry, miso will form the basis for the perfect solution.

MISO SPREAD

1 TBS. miso
4 TBS. sesame butter or tahini
3 TBS. of water
1 Tsp. orange peel
¼ Tsp. dried basil

Put tahini in saucepan and toast for 2 - 6 minutes. Add miso diluted in water and mix. Allow to cook for 5 minutes, stirring constantly. Add basil and orange peel. Simmer for 2 minutes more. Serve.

SPICY ONION-MISO

1 TBS. miso
¼ Onion, minced
1 Small clove garlic, minced
2 TBS. parsley, chopped
4 TBS. water

Dilute the miso, add garlic, onions and parsley. Mix well and serve.

CHIPS AND CRACKERS

½ Cup cooked chickpeas
1 Square tofu, steamed 5 minutes
1 TBS. orange juice
1 TBS. grated onion
1 Clove garlic, minced
1 TBS. tahini
3 TBS. chives
1 TBS. parsley
1 Tsp. tamari
¼ Cup of water

Place all ingredients in a blender except chives. Blend and remove, place in a chilled bowl, add chives, chill and serve.

MISO-ALMOND-ONION SPREAD

1 TBS. miso
1 TBS. almond butter
1 TBS. oat flour
1 TBS. minced onions
1 Tsp. tamari
½ Cup water

Lightly coat a cast-iron skillet with sesame oil and saute onions. Combine nut butter, tamari, flour, miso and water and add to the onions. Stir and cook for 5 - 7 minutes over a low flame, stir constantly. Serve.

CRACKERS AND CHIPS

1 Cup cooked aduki beans
1 Small onion, minced
1 TBS. almond /or sesame butter
2 Scallions, chopped
1 TBS. barley malt syrup
1 Tsp. tamari
A little water

Mix all ingredients in a blender until smooth. Use as a dip and serve with your favorite crackers.

IRISH MISO

2 TBS. miso
¼ Fresh green pepper, minced
1 Scallion, sliced
1 TBS. parsley, chopped
½ Cup of water

Saute the pepper until tender. Add scallion the last few minutes of cooking. Dilute the miso in water, combine all ingredients. Mix well and serve.

BEAN PATE

1 Cup cooked and mashed aduki beans
      (or chickpeas or lentils)
2 Slices homemade bread, soaked in
      1 cup water
2 TBS. miso, diluted in 1 cup of water
2 TBS. tahini
1 TBS. almond butter
1 Onion, chopped
2 TBS. parsley
1 Tsp. chives
2 Scallions, diced
1 Tsp. sesame oil
Pinch of coriander /or Italian seasoning
1 Clove garlic, minced
¼ Red pepper, finely chopped
2 - 3 Sprigs of dill

Have all the ingredients arranged on the counter. Put the bread to soak in water. In a saucepan, saute onions and scallions for 2 minutes, then add garlic, pepper and saute for a few minutes more. Add the bean puree and all other ingredients, ending with the bread and water. Mix well and break the bread in small pieces. Cook for 10 minutes, stirring constantly. Pour the mixture into an oiled baking dish or casserole. Bake at 350° for 30 minutes or until top browns slightly. Serve warm or cold on bread or use to stuff celery. Refrigerate the unused portion. It is also delicious served on a bed of lettuce.

ALMOND MISO SPREAD

1 Cup almonds
3 TBS. miso (mugi)
¼ Cup of water

Cut almonds in half lengthwise and roast them in a cast-iron skillet over a medium flame until lightly browned, stirring constantly. Remove from the stove and place slivers in a suribachi bowl. Grind them to a paste then add the miso and a little water. Blend until smooth and creamy. Serve.

LEGUME AND MISO SPREAD

1 Cup cooked lentils
1 TBS. miso, diluted in a little water
2 TBS. minced scallions
2 TBS. minced onions
1 TBS. chives

Put the lentils in a blender and puree. (Use a suribachi bowl if available.) Add the miso and mix together. Add scallions and chives. Combine thoroughly and garnish with chopped parsley. Serve.

SALAD DRESSINGS

AUTOBAHN SALAD DRESSING

1 Small onion, chopped
2 Cloves garlic, minced
3 TBS. Cold Mountain miso (light yellow, red or mellow white)
3 TBS. sesame oil
4 TBS. rice vinegar
2 TBS. barley malt syrup
¼ Tsp. dry mustard
Handful freshly chopped parsley
2" Square tofu
1 Cup of water

Place all ingredients in a blender and blend until smooth. Chill and serve over fresh garden greens.

MISO LEMON

2 TBS. miso, Cold Mountain yellow, red or mellow white
2 TBS. lemon juice
½ Cup of water

Blend all ingredients together in a blender until smooth. Serve.

TAMARI LEMON DRESSING

2 TBS. tamari
½ Cup of water
1 TBS. fresh lemon or orange juice

Mix together and serve.

ALMOND BUTTER SALAD DRESSING

1 Tsp. Cold Mountain miso, red, white or yellow
2 Tsp. nut butter
1 Tsp. grated onion
½ Cup of water

Blend all ingredients together and serve.

UMEBOSHI SALAD DRESSING

2 Umeboshi plums, crushed /or juice of a lemon or lime
1 Clove garlic, finely chopped
Small handful parsley, finely chopped
1 Cup of water

Bring water to a boil with the plum and garlic in it. Simmer for 5 minutes. Add parsley, let cool and serve.

SWEET-SOUR PUMPKIN DRESSING

3 TBS. roasted pumpkin seeds
1 TBS. umeboshi paste /or ume vinegar
2 - 3 TBS. rice syrup
4 - 5 TBS. water

Grind the pumpkin seeds in a suribachi bowl until fine. Add the water and mix. Then add the rice syrup, and the umeboshi vinegar, mix thoroughly. Chill and serve over greens.

CABBAGE SALAD DRESSING

2/3 Cup barley malt syrup /or rice syrup
1/3 Cup rice vinegar or umeboshi vinegar
1 Onion, minced
½ Tsp. Sea salt

Combine barley malt, vinegar, onions and salt in a pot, bring to a boil. Lower the flame and simmer for 2 minutes. Remove and allow to cool. Place in the refrigerator for 1 hour. Serve.

BLUE CHEESE ALA TOFU

1 Cup tofu
3 TBS. sesame oil
1 Tsp. Sea salt
4 TBS. rice vinegar
2 TBS. barley malt syrup
2 Cloves garlic, minced
2 Ozs. blue cheese, crumbled

Add all ingredients in a blender, EXCEPT blue cheese. Blend until creamy. Now add the blue cheese and stir into the mixture. Chill and serve.

CASHEW BUTTER SALAD DRESSING

1 Clove garlic, minced
3 TBS. parsley, minced
Juice from 1 lemon
¼ Tsp. Sea salt /or 1 TBS. tamari
4 TBS. toasted cashew or almond
      butter

Place the nut butter and water in a suribachi bowl, blend. Add all the other ingredients and mix together. Chill and serve.

LUAU DRESSING

½ Cup lemon juice
¼ Cup of water
2 TBS. almond butter or tahini
1 TBS. parsley, chopped fine

Mix all ingredients well and serve over salad for an exotic taste.

TOFU SALAD DRESSING

½ Package tofu, boil 5 minutes, squeeze
      out excess liquid
1 Scallion, diced
1 TBS. tamari

Place the scallion in a suribachi bowl and grind, add the tofu and tamari, mix well. Chill and serve. This is excellent on steamed greens.

MAYONNAISE

1 Yolk of a fertile egg
1 TBS. lemon or lime juice
Pinch of Sea salt
¾ Cup corn oil
½ Tsp. dry mustard

Place egg yolk in a mixing bowl, add salt, lemon juice and a few drops of oil. Beat thoroughly, add a little more juice then a little oil. Carefully alternate the ingredients and beat steadily until the consistency becomes light and creamy. A blender may be used for convenience. You may also add chives or parsley for variation.

ITALIAN SALAD DRESSING

3 Cloves garlic, minced
5 TBS. olive oil
3 Tsp. Sea salt
Juice of 1 orange

Mix all ingredients and pour over crisp greens, such as romaine lettuce and watercress.

SUMMERTIME SALAD DRESSING

1 Onion chopped
2 TBS. fresh orange juice
2 TBS. tamari
1/3 Cup sesame oil
2 TBS. parsley, chopped
A little water for consistency

Put all ingredients in a blender and mix until smooth and creamy. Chill and serve.

MANDARIN DRESSING

4 TBS. sesame oil or corn oil
1 Tsp. Sea salt
2 TBS. fresh squeezed orange juice
1 Tsp. onion, minced
1 Tsp. parsley, finely chopped

Place oil in a bowl and add salt. Mix together and add minced onions and parsley. Allow to set for 15 minutes at room temperature. Gently toss in the salad of your choice.

BROWN RICE VINEGAR DRESSING

1 Clove garlic, minced
1 Small onion, minced
1 TBS. sesame oil
4 TBS. brown rice vinegar
2½ Tbs. tamari
½ Cup of water

Mix all ingredients together and allow to stand 1 hour at room temperature. Serve.

GERMAN DRESSING

4 TBS. corn oil
1 TBS. rice vinegar
1 Tsp. onion, minced
1 Tsp. Sea salt

Mix all ingredients together and allow to set for 10 minutes at room temperature before adding to a crisp salad.

GINGER-TAMARI DRESSING

3 TBS. tamari
1 Tsp. fresh grated ginger juice

Mix together and pour over fresh greens or salads.

TAHINI-RICE VINEGAR DRESSING

2 TBS. miso
1 TBS. tahini
2 TBS. rice vinegar
1/3 Cup of water

Puree all ingredients in a suribachi bowl or blender, and serve.

TAHINI-TOFU DRESSING

2 TBS. tahini
1 Cake tofu
1 Small onion, grated
Juice of a fresh squeezed lemon
½ Cup of water
Pinch of Sea salt

Puree the onion and tofu in a suribachi bowl or blender. Add salt, water, lemon and tahini and blend until smooth and creamy. Chill and serve.

CEASAR SALAD DRESSING

2 Anchovies
2 Cloves garlic, minced
¼ Tsp. dry mustard
1 Yolk of a fertile egg, beat well
1 Tsp. fresh lemon juice
¼ Tsp. Sea salt
2 TBS. corn oil
1 TBS. rice vinegar
1/3 Cup freshly grated parmesan or
    romano cheese

In a wooden bowl, completely mash the anchovies with a fork. Add the dry mustard and garlic and mash into the anchovies. Add the beaten egg yolk and sea salt to the mixture and blend well. Then add the lemon juice and oil and rice vinegar. Blend well, pour over pieces of chilled romaine lettuce and sprinkle with the grated cheese.

CELERY SEED SALAD DRESSING

1 Cup barley or rice syrup
2 Cups corn oil
¾ Cup rice vinegar or umeboshi vinegar
3 TBS. arrowroot
2 Tsp. dry mustard
2 Tsp. Sea salt
½ Cup freshly squeezed lemon juice
2 Tsp. celery seeds
2 Tsp. minced garlic
1 Medium onion, minced
½ Cup tamari
½ Cup water

Dilute the arrowroot in the vinegar. Place in a saucepan and bring to a boil, stirring until the mixture becomes clear and thickens. Allow to cool. Place the remaining ingredients in a blender and blend well. Add the cooled arrowroot mixture and blend. Allow to cool and serve.

ORANGE VINEGRETTE

2 TBS. rice vinegar or umeboshi vinegar
2 TBS. fish stock
2 TBS. barley malt syrup
2 Tsp. tamari
¼ Tsp. Sea salt
3 TBS. grated peeled radish (use red
　　radish or daikon radish)
1 TBS. corn oil
½ Tsp. finely grated orange peel

In a saucepan combine the rice vinegar, fish stock, barley malt syrup, tamari, sea salt and ¼ cup of water. Bring to a boil over a medium flame, lower the flame and allow to simmer for 2 minutes. Remove from the heat and cool in the refrigerator uncovered for about 15 minutes. After the mixture has cooled, place in a blender. Add the grated radish, oil and orange peel. Puree until smooth and creamy. Serve.

LEMON SALAD DRESSING

½ Cup fresh squeezed lemon juice
1 Clove garlic, minced
1 TBS. onion, finely diced
2 TBS. barley malt syrup
1/8 Tsp. paprika
¼ Cup corn oil

Combine all the ingredients in a bowl and mix well. Refrigerate for 1 hour. Before using mix again. Use over salads or vegetables.

EAST INDIAN DRESSING

1 Clove garlic, minced
½ Cup raisins
1/3 Cup rice vinegar
¼ Cup corn oil
2 TBS. lemon juice
3 TBS. barley malt syrup
2 Tsp. curry powder
¼ Tsp. Sea salt

In a saucepan heat the oil. Add the curry powder and garlic and simmer for 1 minute. Then add the barley malt syrup, lemon juice, raisins, rice vinegar and sea salt. Simmer for 5 minutes. Serve.

NISSAN DRESSING

½ Cup sesame oil
¼ Cup rice vinegar
¼ Tsp. Sea salt
1/8 Tsp. paprika
1 TBS. rice syrup
1 TBS. tamari
2 TBS. chopped parsley

Place all the ingredients in a bowl and mix together. Chill for 1 hour before serving.

BUGATTI BONANZA SPREAD

1 Cup garbonzo beans, cooked
2 Onions, diced
1 Clove garlic, minced
1/3 Cup toasted sesame seeds
½ Tsp. Sea salt
½ Tsp. coriander
2 TBS. freshly chopped parsley

Puree the garbonzo beans in a blender, add all the ingredients and mix well. Use as a filling for pita bread. Top with fresh sprouts or cheese and heat in the oven. Serve.

CHICK-A-FU SANDWICH MIX

¾ Cup cooked chickpeas
4 Oz. tofu, steamed for 5 minutes
2 TBS. onions, diced
1 Clove garlic, minced
1 Tsp. dill weed
3 TBS. miso nut butter (see
    spreads this exit)
¼ Cup water
1 Scallion, sliced for garnish
Juice of 1 fresh orange

Place all the ingredients in a blender, Blend until it reaches a smooth consistancy. Place in a bowl and garnish with sliced scallion. Refrigerate 1 hour. Use in sandwiches or as a dip.

SESAME ALMOND SANDWICH

½ Cup cooked pinto beans
2 - 4 Cups toasted almond butter
2 Cups toasted sesame seeds, ground
    into meal
1 Clove garlic, minced
2 Onions, diced
¼ Tsp. Sea salt
2 TBS. tamari
½ Tsp. dill weed

Place the garlic, dill, onions and tamari in a blender and blend together. In a separate bowl blend together the pinto beans, almond butter and sesame meal. Add the liquid mixture and blend together until creamy. Add the sea salt. Allow to sit in the refrigerator for several hours before using. Serve on toast or rice cakes with tomato and lettuce.

HUMMUS

1 Cup cooked garbonzo beans
2 Cloves garlic, minced
1 TBS. onion minced
3 TBS. lemon juice
½ Cup tahini
Sea salt to taste

Place the lemon juice, garlic and onions in a blender, mix together. Add the tahini and beans and blend together until it becomes a puree. Spread this on pita bread, chapati or homemade whole wheat bread. Use stone ground mustard for a condiment and top with sprouts to make a delicious sandwich. The traditional Jewish way to serve hummus is on a flat plate, sprinkled lightly with paprika. Then use pita bread to dip.

Exit 23

CONDIMENTS
THE CROWNING TOUCH

Pinstripping

Even rice, the "BEST" of the grains, needs that final adornment of a condiment on occasion. While the natural sweetness of many foods becomes more appreciated by your increasingly sensitive palate, as the tongue learns again to taste anew, still the light sprinkle of the properly prepared condiment enhances, without overpowering the flavor.

Our everyday seasoning is sesame salt, made from unhulled, unbleached (brown) sesame seeds and then roasted in a cast-iron skillet, and blended in a suribachi bowl by hand with non-iodized sea salt, which has also been dry roasted to release toxic gases.

This condiment is prepared in varying proportions, depending on your own needs and activities, along with the seasonal changes. A good standard is 15 parts of seeds to 1 part of sea salt. For children, proportions should be much weaker, at least 50 - 1. Parents should avoid giving infants condiments in any case, and seaweed powders are most suitable for children after the age of two.

Second cousins to sesame salt are its counterparts, wakame sesame and dulse sesame. Both are useful as an everyday garnish, and when you are in need of additional iron, such as in cases of pregnancy and lactation. Toasted nori makes a wonderful condiment that also supplies iron in high amounts.

The unusual flavors of such toppings as tekka and umeboshi plum are so distinctive as to change the foods to which they are added and to give a completely different taste treat.

SESAME SALT

15 Lbs. unhulled, (unbleached) sesame
    seeds, rinsed and drained
1 Lb. non-iodized Sea salt

Place the sea salt in a clean, dry cast-iron skillet and stir gently over a medium flame. Heat until the grains of salt appear to be crystalline and sparkling, about 5 minutes. Meanwhile, let the rinsed sesame seeds drain in a strainer. Place the salt in a suribachi bowl and grind into powder. Cool the skillet slightly before adding the sesame seeds, then dry-roast them, stirring constantly over a medium flame. You will know if your fire is too high because the seeds will pop like popcorn. In about 10 minutes test the seeds for doneness by squeezing a few between the thumb and little finger. If they are done, you will feel them burst open. Place the seeds in the suribachi bowl with the salt and grind with a wooden pestle until nearly all the seeds are powdered and thoroughly mixed with the sea salt. Store in an air-tight glass jar. Sesame salt is high in iron, calcium and vitamin A & B.

WAKAME-SESAME

1/8 Cup dry wakame
¼ Cup unhulled sesame seeds, rinsed
    and drained

Place the wakame on a cookie sheet (dry) and roast in a 350° oven until it becomes crisp and darkens in color. Remove it and grind it in a suribachi bowl until it becomes a fine powder. Dry-roast the sesame seeds, (as per instructions in the sesame salt) then add the seeds to the powdered wakame, grinding them together with a wooden pestle until the seeds are partly crushed. This may be used on a daily basis in place of sesame salt for variety.

WAKAME FISH POWDER

1/8 Cup wakame, roasted
1 TBS. bonita fish flakes or dried
    shrimp flakes
1 TBS. unhulled sesame seeds, rinsed
    and drained

Roast the wakame as above. Roast the bonita flakes or shrimp flakes separately and then put both in a suribachi bowl. Now roast the sesame seeds, add to the other ingredients in the suribachi bowl, and grind until they are partly crushed.

DULSE-SESAME

1/8 Cup dry dulse, roasted (as above)
½ Cup unhulled sesame seeds, rinsed,
    drained, and roasted

Prepare as you would the wakame-sesame recipe. Add the sesame seeds last and grind until half the seeds are crushed.

CARROT AND TAMARI

½ Cup grated carrots
A few drops of tamari

Grate the carrots and add a few drops of tamari, mix together and serve.

TEKKA
(Used in place of pepper)

¼ Cup of sesame oil
1/3 Cup finely minced burdock root
1/3 Cup finely minced carrot
1/3 Cup finely minced lotus root
½ Tsp. freshly grated ginger root
2/3 Cups hatcho miso

Cut all vegetables as **fine** as possible. Heat a cast-iron skillet and add ½ the oil. Saute the burdock, carrot, lotus root and ginger root. Combine the vegetables and add the remaining oil and the miso. Continue to saute the vegetables for 3 hours or more, stirring them constantly. They will eventually become very dry and crumbly. Since this is a very lengthy process, you may wish to purchase tekka at a natural food store where it is available in a packaged form. It is a good condiment to use for strengthening the blood and it is rich in protein, iron and niacin.

TAMARI

Tamari is generally used as a seasoning. You should avoid pouring it directly over your grains and vegetables. It is very strong and will produce a contracted condition if eaten often. When tamari is used as a side dish, I usually dilute it 50% with water to achieve a pleasant taste. (See also miso, Exit 10)

UMEBOSHI PLUMS

Umeboshi plums are grown in Japan. They are pickled in brine and have a salty flavor. Umeboshi aids in digestion and has many medicinal qualities. They are delicious when rubbed on corn-on-the-cob in place of butter. It can be purchased also in the form of umeboshi paste in the natural food stores.

GINGER-RADISHES

1 TBS. fresh grated daikon radish
A few drops of fresh grated ginger juice
A few drops of tamari
¼ Tsp. grated horseradish

Mix all the ingredients together and serve after a meal to minimize the toxic effects of animal food or for use as a nasal decongestant.

CARROT TOPS (Greens) AND SCALLIONS

Cut off the tops (greens) of approximately 3 carrots. Wash thoroughly to remove all the sand. Dice the tops into small pieces. Dice one small onion. This is optional as you may also prepare this condiment without the onion. Lightly coat a cast-iron skillet with sesame oil and saute the onion and then the carrot tops. Cover the skillet and simmer for 20 minutes. Add ½ TBS. of diluted miso and stir. You may also add a few drops of ginger juice. (About 10 drops.)

NORI CONDIMENT

Nori is used just as is except for toasting it. To do this hold a sheet of nori a few inches above a flame. Wave it back and forth until it starts to crinkle and change color. It will then crumble in your hands or it may be cut into small peices with kitchen scissors.

Place several sheets of nori in about ½ cup of water and simmer in a pot until most of the liquid has evaporated. There should be a thick paste. Add tamari to taste, a few minutes before the condiment is completely cooked.

SHIO KOMBU CONDIMENT

Soak kombu in a bowl until the kombu becomes soft, approximately 1 - 2 hours. Cut into 1" squares and add the pieces to a pot with ½ cup of water and ¼ cup tamari. Bring to a boil and lower flame, simmer until all the liquid evaporates. Place in an airtight glass jar and it will keep several days.

* PERSONAL NOTES

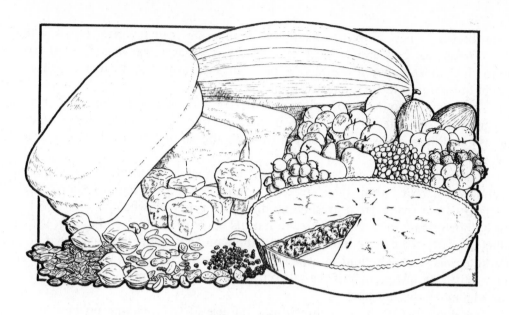

Exit 24
CREATIVE DESSERTS
AND BASIC BREADS

From Model "T" To Thunderbird

It is possible to enjoy an after dinner dessert which is not made with dairy, sugar or any artificial ingredients whatsoever. Recipes which enhance the natural sweetness of fruits, nuts, seeds, and grains can provide a variety of tastes for your pleasure without sacrificing your good health. Unfortunately, you will not find these products at the pastry counters of your local supermarket, since the trend today in breads and desserts is to appeal to the eyes and sensory organs with no consideration for the health of the body as a whole.

Refined sugars, artificial sweeteners and processes which aerate breads and cakes making them soft and fluffy in appearance, but which immediately dissolve in the mouth into a mass of nothingness, create an addictive craving for further consumption of these harmful disaccharide sugars.

If a sweetener is used in our recipes, you will find they are chosen from those poly-saccharide sugars made from grains, such as barley malt syrup, rice syrup (Yinny) and corn syrup. These products can be added to any of the recipes given here if you crave additional sweetness. You can also omit these ingredients, if you prefer.

Amazake, made from sweet rice and fermented in about 8 hours, with koji, (rice kernels which have been inoculated with an enzyme-producing mold) will add enough sweetness to please the most discriminating dessert lover. Do learn to make it, since it is sometimes difficult to find in a natural food store. It is easy to make and stores in the refrigerator. It can be substituted for sugar in many recipes, such as pie fillings, puddings, and other desserts.

You can discover a new source of creativity by adapting your favorite recipes in this fashion.

To replace eggs and milk in desserts, try using agar-agar, kanten and arrowroot or kuzu, to thicken and congeal various recipes. Custards, aspics, and other gelatin-type recipes will adapt quite nicely to these substitutions.

The lighter your use of spices, the better for your body, however, cinnamon and fresh ginger are favorites of ours and, in moderation, do not harm. Keep your recipes as simple as possible and do not use spices to mask the natural flavors, which can be fulfilling enough in themselves.

Our pie crusts are not the flaky, light type that result from the use of animal shortening but, when rolled thin, they are crispy and satisfying. In most desserts, including pie crust, pastry flour made from freshly ground soft types of wheat yields the best results. We have known many people, new to the natural ways of cooking and eating, who exclaimed that they never tasted a better, more flavorful apple pie and could not believe that no sweetener of any kind was used. The hint in achieving sweetness in apples, as well as strawberries, is to use just a little (a few grains) of sea salt on them, and the harmony of opposites creates the illusion of a much sweeter taste.

Cookies that we have made without the use of soda, baking powder, or commercial shortenings, are usually experienced as being more solid than the kind which contain butter, sugar and leavenings but they last longer in the mouth, and, chewed well, they leave no empty feeling. One or two usually satisfy a person who could otherwise sit down and demolish an entire bag of rich pastries.

We have added a few recipes which include baking powder, as well as dry active yeast. It is suggested that you can use the above mentioned ingredients occasionally, if needed, with no harmful side effects.

Nut and grain milks can be made in your own kitchen, to add to dessert recipes of all types, and to enhance custards and puddings. It is so simple to prepare these milks. Just take one cup of whole rolled oats to five cups of water and boil, then simmer until creamy, puree in a blender and strain. Any grain milk is made essentially in the same fashion. Almond milk is made from boiling nuts and pureeing in a blender, and the residue can be used to add variety in other desserts.

When using fruits in desserts, the same principles apply regarding their selection. They should be in season and locally, organically grown. Even when cooking fruit, we choose apples, strawberries, peaches and pears which have come from a climate similar to our own. We avoid tropical fruits, such as pineapples, mangos, bananas and others unless, of course, we are visiting the tropics. Bananas should never be eaten if still green in color. A green color indicates that the banana is still in the starchy stage, which has no food value and is hard to digest. If they are eaten slightly green and not chewed properly, they form gases and putrify, causing you many discomforts. When the bananas are yellow and have brown spots and all the green color is gone especially to the ends, it is then ripe. When the banana is ripe it is easily digestible. Bananas can be mashed up and given to infants 6 months or older and to invalids. Raisins and currants add a lot of life to the taste of many recipes, and other dried fruits can be used with success, especially in winter, when fresh ones may be imported and therefore undesirable.

Our use of nuts does not include exotic varieties but we make extensive use of almonds, walnuts, and filberts and on occasion, peanuts and pecans. Most seeds can be effectively added to dessert recipes, and our favorites include sesame, sunflower, poppy and chia.

The oil I use most frequently in pie crusts is corn oil, cold pressed, of course. It is lighter in texture, however, sesame oil is good for cookies and other recipes, such as apple crisp. We prefer corn oil for bread making, for the same reason. It is wise to keep in mind that quantity changes quality, and this is so with regard to oil, as well as the consumption of desserts and breads in general. Too much use of products which combine oil with flour, no matter how well prepared, will result in intestinal stagnation and possibly constipation, with its related conditions of poor health. Flour, after all, is a secondary grain, and when oil is added to it, digestion is made more difficult. Enjoy your natural desserts, but don't over use them.

BREAD

When I make bread, I prefer flours made from hard, red, winter wheat combined with possibly one or two other grains. You may use any combination you like, but I suggest a limit of three types of flours for best results. Whole wheat is almost always suggested as one of the ingredients, since it is highest in gluten. Other specific qualities may be desired, so I have compiled some comments about the following popular alternate flours:

Brown rice flour: This is an easily blended flour due to its light taste. It is very high in nutrition.

Rye flour: Produces a less elastic, stickier dough, but blends well with whole wheat for a lighter textured bread.

Barley flour: Makes a stickier dough. It is easy to digest and is a good combination with whole wheat.

Corn flour: (or meal): This is best combined with other flours since it tends to create a heavy, grainy loaf. For a corn-bread recipe, this is desired.

Oat flour: This will give a lighter more crumbly texture when added to whole wheat or other flours.

Buckwheat flour: This is a dark, heavy flour and should be used only in combination with lighter flours. It is very contracted and it is best to serve it in the winter months.

Millet flour: This should always be combined with other flours, and comprise no more than a third of the total flour in the recipe.

Soy flour: This will give a sweeter flavor and can comprise up to 1/6th of the amount used in the loaf. It helps a crust to brown and aids in the loaf retaining its freshness.

I suggest you try to master the basic recipes given before you move on to experimenting, however, once you are satisfied with your technique, the above listed flours will provide you with plenty of opportunity to create your own original bread recipes.

Above all things, begin your bread baking with freshly ground flour. Flour is not as complete as whole grains. It begins to oxidize within 18 to 48 hours after it is ground, and loses many important nutrients, as well as its best flavor. If you do not have a stone-grinder, or a hand operated flour mill, you can use an electric grinder or blender, but the best results are obtained with stone grinding.

The next step you will want to learn is to make your own sour-dough starter. Since we try to avoid the **regular use** of yeast, soda, or baking powder in our breads, this is essential if you want a loaf that will rise naturally and be easy to digest. Starter dough is simple to make, but you will find that weather, time of day, and other factors will affect the amount of time required for it to rise.

SOURDOUGH STARTER
(Makes one loaf of bread)

3 Rounded TBS. whole wheat flour
5 TBS. water
Pinch of Sea salt

Place all ingredients in a bowl, then stir until a paste is formed, then cover the bowl with a sheet of paper towel to absorb excess moisture, and place a dish on top of that to keep it warm. Place in a warm spot from one to three days. When it bubbles and rises it is ready and should be used within a day, if possible, as it will continue to ferment and the bubbles will eventually go down and it will become moldy leaving you with a sour-dough effect to your bread but no leavening.

WALNUT BARLEY LOAF

1 Cup walnuts chopped
2 Cup barley malt syrup
1 Cup almond milk
¼ Cup corn oil
1 Unbeaten fertilized egg
2½ Cups unbleached white flour
2 Tsp. baking powder (Rumford)
¼ Tsp. Sea salt
¼ Cup raisins

Combine the barley malt syrup, almond milk, and oil in a saucepan. Heat to lukewarm, stirring until all ingredients dissolve, cool. Add the egg and beat until smooth. Sift the dry ingredients together and add the liquid to the dry ingredients, beat until smooth and blended well. Add the walnuts. Place in loaf pan that has been oiled on the bottom and bake at 325° for 1 hour and 10 minutes. Remove from the pan. Loaf will be golden brown.

AUTOBAHN BREAD
(Makes 3 loaves)

3 TBS. dry active yeast
3 Cups of warm water

Sprinkle the dry yeast into the warm water and stir until dissolved. Place into a large wooden mixing bowl.

2 Tsp. Sea salt
1/3 Cup corn oil
1 Cup barley malt syrup
1 Fertile egg, beaten well

Blend the above ingredients well and add to the yeast mixture in the wooden bowl. Blend together.

7 Cups of whole wheat flour
1 Cup soya flour
5 Cups unbleached white flour

Add to the liquid mixture, 1 cup soya flour, 2 cups unbleached white flour and 2½ cups of whole wheat flour. Blend all together well. Now add the remaining flour and knead the dough until all the flour is blended. (*5 - 6 minutes) Turn the dough out onto a lightly floured board. Knead until smooth and elastic. (*Add additional flour if needed.) Add 3 TBS. of wheat germ or 3 TBS. of caraway seeds. Place into an oiled bowl. Cover the dough with wax paper and then a cotton towel. Place in a warm place and allow to rise until the dough has doubled in size. About 1 - 1½ hours. Turn the dough out onto a lightly floured board, knead again, then divide the dough and place into lightly oiled bread baking pans. Allow to rise again. (About 1 hour). Bake at 325 degrees for 35 - 40 minutes or until done.

BATTER NUT BREAD

2½ Cups whole wheat pastry flour
1½ Cups millet flour
1 Cup brown rice flour
1 Tsp. Sea salt
3 TBS. corn oil
2 Cups of water
1 Cup apple juice
¾ Cup nuts, chopped
½ Cup raisins

Combine flour and salt in a mixing bowl. Blend oil in by rubbing it into the flours with your hands. Stir in the water and apple juice, mix thoroughly. Add the nuts and raisins. Turn mixture into a well-oiled loaf pan and bake at 350° for 1 hour and 15 minutes. Cool on a wire rack before slicing.

————— ALL NATURAL ONION RYE BREAD —————

3 Cups fresh whole wheat flour
3 Cups fresh rye flour
1 Tsp. Sea salt
2 Cups of water
2 Medium onions, sliced in 1/16ths
¼ Cup plus 1 TBS. corn oil
2 TBS. caraway seeds
* Don't forget sour-dough starter

Using a cast-iron skillet, saute onions in 1 TBS. of corn oil until translucent. Add water, cover, and simmer for 15 minutes or longer. While this onion stock is simmering, mix the dry ingredients in a large, wooden bowl. Add the sour-dough starter to the dry ingredients, cutting it into the flours with a pastry blender until the mixture looks crumbly. In another bowl (or a two cup measuring cup) pour ¼ cup of corn oil. Your onion stock should now be ready to use. Drain off the liquid into the oil, making approximately 1¾ cups of liquid or a total of 2 cups with the oil. Use an egg beater or whisk to beat the oil and stock together until the mixture is whitish in color and the oil is blended. Do not wait for the stock to cool, but add it at once to the flours and begin to stir. Using the pastry cutter in the beginning, so your hands will not get sticky, continue to turn and mix the dough. Then flour your hands and knead dough for at least 5 minutes or 100 times. Add the onions which were left from the stock, flour your hands again and knead another 5 minutes. Lightly flour the outside of the dough ball as needed to prevent sticking to the bowl. Proper dough consistency when finished kneading will be like an earlobe. In the last minutes of kneading, add the caraway seeds to the dough. Wet a thin towel and cover the dough, place the bowl in a warm place and let the dough rise a minimum of 8 - 12 hours. (You may prefer to oil your hands instead of using flour when kneading, however, this may increase the oil content of your bread.) After the bread has risen, take a wooden spoon and loosen from sides of bowl, press it down and knead it for an additional 5 minutes or 100 times. Turn it into a lightly oiled loaf pan. Smooth the top and mold gently to conform to the pan. At this point you may choose to let it rise again or bake it immediately. If proceeding to bake, cut a wavy line in the top so the bread will break uniformly when baking. Place it in a 325° oven for a full two hours. Remove from pan, cool on a wire rack and enjoy it. One hint, however, bread should not be eaten warm as it clogs the intestines, nor should it be eaten at the same time as miso soup.

SWEET OATMEAL BREAD

2 TBS. dry active yeast
½ Cup warm bancha tea
1½ Cups hot oat milk
2 TBS. corn meal
½ Cup barley malt syrup
1 Tsp. Sea salt
5 - 5½ Cups unbleached white flour
1 Cup rolled oats

Dissolve the yeast in warm water. In a large bowl, combine, tea, oil, barley malt syrup, and sea salt. Cool to lukewarm and add yeast. Add 2 cups of flour and oats beat vigorously until smooth. Stir in enough additional flour to make a soft dough. Remove the dough from the bowl and place on a floured wooden board and knead the dough until smooth and elastic. Cover the dough and let rest for 20 minutes. Punch the dough down and divide in half and shape into 2 loaves. Place the loaves into oiled loaf pans, cover with oiled waxed paper and plastic wrap and refrigerate for 24 hours. Remove from the refrigerator and uncover. Let stand at room temperature for 10 minutes. Prick any of the gas bubbles and bake at 400° for about 35 minutes. Remove immediately from the pans.

ALMOND NUT LOAF

2 Cups cooked brown rice
1 Cup almonds, chopped
½ Cup whole wheat toasted bread crumbs
1/3 Cup raisins
Almond milk to moisten
2 TBS. onions, diced fine
2 TBS. celery, diced fine
2 TBS. tamari
Pinch of Sea salt

Mix all the ingredients together. If the mixture is too dry, add more almond milk for desired consistancy. Place in a lightly oiled baking dish or casserole. Bake at 325° for 45 minutes. Serve.

WHOLE WHEAT AND RYE BREAD

½ Cup warm water
1 TBS. active dry yeast
4 TBS. barley malt syrup
4½ Cups whole wheat flour
4½ Cups rye flour
3 Cups warm water
2 TBS. corn oil
1 TBS. Sea salt

In a large wooden bowl dissolve 1 TBS. of barley malt syrup, and the yeast, in ½ cup of warm water, let set for 10 minutes. Mix the remaining water with the rest of the barley malt syrup, oil, and sea salt, then add this mixture to the yeast mix. Add the whole wheat and rye flour gradually, (mix together first) and mix well with the yeasted mixture, until the dough comes away from the sides. Remove the dough to a well floured wooden board and let set for 10 minutes. Knead the bread for 10 minutes, adding just enough flour to make a smooth, elastic, non-sticky dough. Place the dough in an oiled bowl and cover with cheesecloth, and let it rise in a warm place for about two hours or until it has doubled in size. Punch the dough down with your hands, and knead it for a few minutes more, then divide it in half and shape into loaves. Place the loaves in oiled pans (bread) approximately 9" x 5" x 3" and let it rise again until doubled in size. Heat the oven to 350 degrees and bake for 45 minutes or until done. Remove from the pan at once and cool before slicing.

CROUTONS

Stale whole wheat bread - homemade
Sesame salt
Tamari
Sesame oil

Cube the bread, spread the cubes out on an oiled cookie sheet. Sprinkle with tamari, toss and then sprinkle with the sesame salt. Bake at 350° until the cubes are browned. It doesn't take long to brown, so watch carefully.

WHOLE WHEAT PRETZELS

2 Cups unbleached white flour
2 Cups whole wheat flour
1 Pkg. dry yeast, dissolved in ½ cup
    warm water
½ Tsp. Sea salt
1 1/3 Cups warm water or bancha tea
1 TBS. corn oil
Coarse Sea salt

Mix the flours together. Mix 1½ cups of the combined flours with the yeast and sea salt. Stir the liquid into the dry ingredients and mix until smooth. Add enough of the remaining flour to make a stiff dough, then knead until smooth. Divide the dough into 12" pieces and roll each into a rope 15" long. Roll in the coarse sea salt and shape into a pretzel. Place the pretzels onto a greased baking sheet and bake at 425° for 20 minutes, or until lightly browned.

ZUCCHINI BREAD

1 Medium zucchini squash, grated
1½ Cups whole wheat flour
1 Fertile egg
½ Tsp. baking powder (Use Rumford
    brand, it contains no aluminum)
1 TBS. active dry yeast, dissolved in warm
    water
¼ Tsp. fresh ginger juice
½ Tsp. Sea salt
¼ - ½ Cup corn oil
1 Cup barley malt syrup
½ Cup walnuts, diced

Beat the egg, barley malt syrup and oil together. Add the sea salt, ginger juice, yeast and baking powder. Then add the grated zucchini and mix in the whole wheat flour and nuts. Place the mixture in an oiled and floured loaf dish or bread dish. Bake at 350° for 1 hour.

WHOLE WHEAT RAISIN BREAD

2 Cups of amazake or bancha tea thickened
    with 4 Tsp. arrowroot
½ Cup of water
¼ Cup of corn oil
1 Cup barley malt or rice syrup
1 Tsp. Sea salt
2 TBS. dry active yeast
3 - 3½ Cups of unbleached white flour
4 Cups whole wheat flour
1 Tsp. cinnamon
1 Cup whole rolled oats
1 Cup raisins

Heat the amazake, (or tea) oil, water and barley malt syrup, till it's lukewarm. Add the yeast and sea salt, stir well. Add 2 cups of white flour and cinnamon in a large wooden bowl. Mix well. Add the liquid and mix thoroughly. Stir in the whole wheat flour, rolled oats and raisins. Add the remaining unbleached white flour and mix all ingredients thoroughly. Turn the dough onto a floured wooden board and knead until smooth. Place the dough in an oiled bowl and cover. Place in a warm place for 30 minutes. Punch down with your hands and divide in half. Form loaves and place the loaves in 9"x5"x3" loaf pans. Let rise again till doubled in size. Bake in a 375° oven for 45 minutes. When done, the loaves will sound hollow, remove immediately from the pans.

BLUEBERRY MUFFINS

1 Pint fresh blueberries
1 Cup whole wheat pastry flour
1 Cup unbleached white flour
3 TBS. corn oil
¼ Tsp. Sea salt
1 Tsp. cinnamon
1 Tsp. vanilla
1 Cup apple juice
½ Cup chopped almonds
¼ Cup barley malt syrup
2 Tsp. baking soda (Rumford brand)

Combine all dry ingredients. Add remaining ingredients except for the blueberries. Mix well. Add blueberries and very gently stir into the batter. Pour into lightly oiled muffin tins and bake at 350° degrees for 40 minutes or until done.

RAISIN NUT MUFFINS

2 Cups whole wheat pastry flour
1 Cup rice flour
1 Cup whole rolled oats
2 Cups apple juice
1 Cup of water
1 Tsp. cinnamon
2 TBS. corn oil
¼ Tsp. Sea salt
1 Cup raisins
½ Cup almonds, chopped
2 Tsp. baking powder (Rumford brand)
¼ Cup rice syrup

Mix all dry ingredients thoroughly. Add remaining ingredients and stir until completely blended. Pour the mixture into oiled muffin tins. Bake at 350° for 1 hour or until done.

CORN BREAD

1 Cup cornmeal
2 TBS. corn oil
1 TBS. unbleached white flour
3 Tsp. baking powder (Use Rumford brand, it contains no aluminum)
3 TBS. barley malt syrup
¼ Tsp. Sea salt
1 Cup oat or rice milk (can substitute bancha tea)
1 Fertile egg, beaten

Preheat the oven to 400 degrees. Place the corn oil in a 9" x 5" baking pan and place in the oven just long enough to heat the pan. Mix together all the dry ingredients in a bowl. Add the milk, barley, malt and egg and beat well. Pour the mixture into the heated pan and bake 25 - 35 minutes.

DAVID'S PITA BREAD

For a delicious sandwich, steamed or toasted, crisp or limp. This recipe will yield 20 - 24 portions.

5 - 6 Cups unbleached white flour or whole wheat pastry flour
3 TBS. barley malt syrup
2 Tsp. Sea salt
1 Pkg. dry active yeast
2 Cups warm water

A. In a large bowl, thoroughly mix two cups flour, barley malt syrup, sea salt and the undissolved yeast. Gradually add water to the dry ingredients and beat for 2 minutes (using a medium speed with an electric mixer). B. Add ¾ cup of flour. Beat at high speed for 2 minutes, scrape the bowl occasionally. Stir in enough flour to make the dough soft. C. Turn the dough out onto a lightly floured board. Knead until smooth and elastic. (About 8 - 10 minutes). Place into a greased bowl, turning to grease the top. D. Cover. Let rise in a warm place, free from drafts, until the dough doubles in size, about 1 hour. E. Punch down the dough. Turn out onto a lightly floured board and cover. Let it rest for 30 minutes. F. Divide the dough into 6 equal pieces. Shape each in a ball. On a lightly floured board, roll each ball evenly into an 8 inch circle. Place on a lightly floured baking sheet. G. Slide the circle directly on the bottom of a pre-heated 450-degree oven or into a pre-heated iron fry pan placed on the lowest rack of a pre-heated 450 degree oven. Bake about 5 minutes. Tops will not be brown. H. Cool on racks. Store in bags, tightly closed. To serve. Toast the top, if desired by running the bread briefly under the broiler and cut each loaf across in quarters. Serve as is, as bread, or fill with an appropriate sandwich spread.

SWEET ROLLS

¾ Cup oat milk
3 Tsp. corn oil
½ Cup rice syrup
½ Cup barley malt syrup
½ Tsp. Sea salt
1/8 Tsp. ginger, fresh or dried
¾ Cup warm water
1 Package yeast, dissolved in warm water
4 Cups unbleached white flour

Heat the oat milk and pour into a mixing bowl. Add the oil, syrups, sea salt, and ginger, stirring to blend. Cool this mixture to lukewarm. Add the yeast, then add 2 cups of flour all at once, beat well. Add another 1½ cups of flour, ½ cup at a time, mixing well after adding each ½ cup. The dough will be soft. Place the dough on a kneading board that has been sprinkled with the remaining flour. Reserve a little flour to sprinkle on the dough while kneading. Knead for about 5 minutes. Cover and let rise in a warm place until the size has doubled. Turn out on the board and pat out to a ½" thickness. Cut into rolls with a small cutter and place on an oiled baking pan and set in a warm place to rise until doubled. Bake at 375° for 25 minutes or until lightly browned. Serve hot.

OATMEAL PIE CRUST

3 Cups rolled oats
1½ Cups whole wheat pastry flour
2 - 3 TBS. corn oil
¼ Tsp. Sea salt
2 Cups of water

Mix all the dry ingredients, then blend in the oil with your hands or a pastry blade. Add the water, this will make a thick batter. This pastry can be used in pie pans, cake pans, cookie sheets, etc. Oil the pans lightly first with corn oil then spread the batter in a thin sheet. Bake at 375° for 10 - 15 minutes. Remove from the oven, then fill with favorite filling and bake again for 25 - 30 minutes.

SWEET DOUGH
Will yield enough for 3 coffee rings or 2 pounds of sweet rolls.

2 Cups of warm bancha tea
2 TBS. dry active yeast
½ Cup corn oil
1 Cup barley malt syrup
2 Tsp. Sea salt
2 Fertile eggs, beaten well
Juice of 1 lemon and grate the rind
8 Cups of whole wheat pastry flour
½ Tsp. ground nutmeg
½ Tsp. cinnamon
½ Cup chopped almonds
½ Cup chopped walnuts
½ Cup raisins
¼ Cup dried apricots, chopped

Sprinkle the yeast into the warm bancha tea, stir until dissolved. Add the oil, barley malt syrup, eggs, sea salt, lemon juice and rind. Blend together well.

Stir in the flour and spices. The dough will appear softer than for bread. Place the dough onto a lightly floured board and knead. Place the dough into a lightly oiled bowl. Oil the top as well. Cover with wax paper and then a towel. Place in a warm place and allow the dough to rise and double in size. (About 1 hour) Punch down and turn out onto a lightly floured board. Shape into a coffee cake or into rolls, twists or rings. Allow to rise again until almost double in size. Bake in a preheated oven at 350 degrees for 20 minutes or until done.

*PERSONAL NOTES:

NEVER FAIL PIE CRUST

1 Cup whole wheat pastry flour
1 Cup unbleached white flour
½ Tsp. Sea salt
2/3 Cup boiling water
¼ Cup corn oil

Mix the sea salt into the flour. Boil the water and add it to the corn oil, beating the oil and water with a hand beater or whisk until it is milky white in color. Now add immediately to the flour and stir clockwise with a fork until the flour is blended. Knead with your hands for 1 minute. Separate the dough into 2 parts and shape into thick patties. Place the patties in the freezer for 20 - 30 minutes. Then roll with a rolling pin to the desired shape crust.

DREAM CAKE
(Dr. Theo's Favorite)

1 Cup unbleached white flour
1 Cup whole wheat flour
3 Tsp. baking powder (option 1 TBS.
    yeast)
2 Cups barley malt syrup
1 Tsp. cinnamon
1 Tsp. Sea salt
½ Cup corn oil
1/3 Cup rice syrup
2 Fertilized eggs
1 Tsp. vanilla
5 Cups peeled apples (or peaches)
1 Tsp. nutmeg
¼ Cup raisins
1 Cup chopped almonds or walnuts,
    toasted

Put all the ingredients, except the nuts, into a large mixing bowl. Beat with a mixer for 3 minutes or until blended well. Stir in the nuts. Pour into an oiled 9" x 13" pan. Bake at 350° for 40 minutes or until the cake tests done. Use the compote topping if desired. This is a favorite with our friends. *Luann makes this same mix and places it into muffin tins for Sunday brunch. Bake only 25 minutes. *Top with the peach or apple compote.

GLAZED APPLESAUCE PIE

1 Prebaked 9" pie crust
10 - 12 Medium apples, peeled, cored,
    and cut in 1/8ths (PLUS 2 - 3 ad-
    ditional apples for the top of pie.)
1/3 Cup barley malt syrup
¼ Cup raisins
1 Tsp. cinnamon
Pinch of nutmeg
1 Tsp. vanilla
¼ Tsp. freshly squeezed lemon juice

Place all the ingredients into a large saucepan. Cook, covered, over a low heat, stirring occasionally, until the apples are soft. Strain off the excess liquid and reserve the liquid for the glaze. Slightly mash the apples so the sauce is chunky not smooth. Place the sauce into the prebaked pie shell. Peel and core 2- 3 additional apples and slice into 1/8th" pieces and arrange the pieces in a circular pattern on top of the sauce. Sprinkle with a **little** sea salt. Place the pie in a pre-heated oven at 425° and bake for 10 minutes /or until the apples on top are soft. Remove from the oven. While the pie is baking prepare your glaze. Cool the reserve liquid, then in a pan add 1 Tsp. arrowroot and ¼ cup of barley malt syrup and heat until the mixture thickens slightly. Brush over the top of the apples and place back into the oven on BROIL. **Watch** carefully, just a few minutes are needed to set the glaze. Remove from oven and cool. Serve.

PECAN PIE

1 Cup pecans, halved
1½ Cup barley malt syrup
4 Fertile eggs, beaten well
2 TBS. whole wheat flour
1 TBS. raw butter
½ Tsp. nutmeg
¼ Tsp. Sea salt

Blend together all the ingredients, EXCEPT the pecans. Blend until frothy. Then stir in the pecans. Pour the mixture into a pie shell. Bake at 350° for 35 - 45 minutes or until done.

CHERYL'S PIE CRUST

1¼ Cups whole wheat pastry flour
1 Cup unbleached white flour
½ - ¾ Tsp. Sea salt
1/3 Cup iced water
3 TBS. barley malt syrup
¼ Lb. fresh raw butter

Combine the flour and sea salt in a mixing bowl. Cut the butter into the flour. Blend the ingredients until mixture is crumbly. Add the barley malt syrup and knead into the dough. Add the ice water and mix together until all the flour has become a doughy consistancy. Turn onto a flour kneading board and knead for 3 - 4 minutes. Divide into two balls and place them into a bowl and into the refrigerator for 15 - 20 minutes. Remove from the refrigerator and using a rolling pin make two pie crusts. Fill the pie with your favorite pie filling, (apple, etc.) Bake at 325° -350° until done.

APPLE PIE WITH CHERYL'S PIE CRUST

6 Medium apples, peeled and sliced
        (Jonathan, Rome, or others are good)
1 TBS. arrowroot
¼ Cup raisins
1 Tsp. cinnamon
Pinch of Sea salt
1 Cup of water

Simmer the raisins in the water for 10 minutes. Cool, then add the arrowroot and bring back to a boil, stirring constantly until thickened. Remove from the heat. Arrange sliced apples on the bottom of the crust, sprinkle half the salt and half the cinnamon in the middle of the apple slices, and the other half on the top of the apples, when all have been arranged in the pie. Spread the thickened raisin mixture over the top of the apples and cover with the top crust. Pinch the edges of the dough to seal, and flute the edges. Bake at 375° for 1 hour, or until done.

APPLE LOAF CAKE

1½ Cups whole wheat pastry flour
½ Tsp. Sea salt
1 Tsp. cinnamon
1 Tsp. baking powder
1 Cup raisins
1 Cup chopped almonds
1 Cup homemade apple sauce
1/3 Cup barley malt syrup
¼ Cup corn oil
1 Fertile egg

Mix the barley malt syrup, egg and oil together, then add the whole wheat flour and cinnamon. Stir in the raisins and nuts and apple sauce. Pour the batter into an oiled 9" x 5" loaf pan. Bake at 350° for 40 minutes or until done.

PUMPKIN PIE

2 Cups pumpkin, fresh, baked and skin
        removed
¼ Cup amazake, (see beverage chapter)
1 Fertile egg
¼ Tsp. Sea salt
½ Tsp. cinnamon
½ Tsp. freshly grated ginger juice
½ Cup half and half (milk and cream)
¼ Tsp. allspice
1/8 Tsp. cloves
½ Cup barley malt syrup
1 Tsp. vanilla
1 TBS. arrowroot
¼ Cup raisins, (Optional)

All ingredients are placed in a deep mixing bowl and blended with a wire whisk or electric mixer until smooth. If the raisins are used, the mixture must be put through a blender to obtain a smooth consistency. Turn out the mixture into a 10" unbaked pie shell, and bake at 350° for at least 1 hour, or until a knife comes out clean when stuck in the center of the pie.

SQUASH PIE

1 Medium buttercup squash, peeled and
    cubed
1 Cup of water
Pinch of Sea salt
½ Tsp. cinnamon
½ Cup barley malt syrup
1 Cup chopped walnuts

Wash the squash and remove the skin, cube in 1½" pieces, place the squash in a pot with a pinch of sea salt and water. Bring to a boil, cover, and reduce the flame. Simmer until the squash is soft. Remove the squash and puree. Place back into the pot and add barley malt syrup and cinnamon. Bring to a boil and then reduce flame and simmer, covered, for 10 minutes. When the squash becomes thick, remove from the heat. Place the filling in a pie crust and sprinkle with the chopped nuts. Bake for 30 minutes at 350° or until the crust browns.

SCOTCH PEACH PIE

8 - 9 Peaches, skinned, remove pit
    and slice
1/3 Cup barley malt syrup
2 TBS. whole wheat pastry flour
2 Tsp. freshly squeezed lemon juice
3 TBS. corn oil
½ Tsp. nutmeg
¼ Tsp. almond extract

Arrange the peaches in a pie shell. Heat the remaining ingredients in a small pot, and simmer for 2 - 3 minutes, stirring constantly. DO NOT boil, pour the mixture over the peaches. Top with a pie crust, pinch the edges together and flute the edges. Slash the top crust to allow steam to escape. Bake at 350° for 40 - 50 minutes or until golden brown.

BARLEY TOFU CREAM PIE

2 Pounds fresh tofu, squeeze out
    excess liquid
½ Cup corn oil
1/3 Cup rice syrup
2/3 Cup barley malt syrup
3 Tsp. arrowroot
¼ Tsp. Sea salt
1 Tsp. cinnamon
2 Tsp. instant grain coffee
½ Cup water, mix in the arrowroot
    and grain coffee

Combine and mix all the ingredients in a bowl or place in a blender. If you use a blender you will have to make this recipe in two parts, as a blender will not hold all the above ingredients. Blend the ingredients until smooth and put into an uncooked pie crust. Bake at 350° for 35 minutes.

OATMEAL COFFEE CAKE

1 Cup rolled oats
2 TBS. corn oil
½ Cup barley malt syrup or/rice syrup
½ Tsp. Sea salt
¾ Cup boiling water
1 Package yeast, dissolved in ½ cup warm
    water
1 Fertilized egg, beaten
2½ Cups unbleached white flour
¾ Cup raisins, plumped in boiling water
    for 15 minutes.

Combine the oats, oil, barley malt, and sea salt in a bowl, stir in the boiling water. Let cool. Add the dissolved yeast, and egg and mix well. Stir in the flour and plumped raisins, (be sure that they are drained) let stand for 15 minutes. Place the dough on a floured kneading board and knead for 5 minutes. Place in an oiled baking pan and cover. Let stand for 1 hour in a warm place. Bake for 30 - 40 minutes in a pre-heated 375ᶜ oven. Top with coffee cake topping while still hot. (See toppings)

PEACH CRISP

6 Large peaches, peeled and sliced
   (You can substitute apples)
1¼ Cups oatmeal
½ Cup whole wheat flour
¼ Cup sesame seeds
½ Cup ground nuts, (almonds, walnuts
   or cashews)
¼ Cup corn oil
½ Tsp. Sea salt
½ Tsp. cinnamon
½ Cup apple juice
½ Cup raisins

Combine and warm the apple juice and raisins in a saucepan. In a separate bowl combine oatmeal, flour, sesame seeds, nuts, oil and sea salt and form a crumbly mixture. Arrange half the peaches in a lightly oiled casserole dish and pour the apple juice and raisin mixture over them. Sprinkle half the crumbly mixture over the peaches. Make a second layer from the remaining peaches and cover with the rest of the crumbly mixture. Bake at 350° for 45 minutes and serve hot/ or you may prefer to have it cool.

FRUIT CAKE

4 Cups whole wheat pastry flour
4 Cups whole rolled oats
3 Cups apple juice
2 Tsp. vanilla
2 Tsp. cinnamon
¼ Cup sesame oil
½ Tsp. Sea salt
1 Cup barley malt syrup
½ Cup raisins
½ Cup chopped almonds
6 Apples, peeled and sliced thin
Water as needed

Combine all dry ingredients in a bowl. Put the raisins in the apple juice along with oil and barley malt syrup. Allow to soak for 10 minutes. Add to the dry ingredients and mix well. Add the apples and mix again. If the mixture is too dry add a little water or apple juice. Place in a lightly oiled baking pan. Bake at 250° for 1 hour.

STRAWBERRY TOFU CHEESECAKE

1 Cup fresh strawberries
2 Squares tofu, steam for 5 minutes,
   drain off excess liquid
½ Cup barley malt syrup
1 TBS. apple juice
½ Tsp. grated lemon rind
1 TBS. almond butter
½ Tsp. vanilla

CRUST:

1/8 Tsp. Sea salt
1 Cup rolled oats
¼ Cup sesame seeds
Sesame oil
Baking dish, well oiled

Preheat oven to 350° . Combine the tofu, barley malt, apple juice, lemon rind, almond butter, vanilla and sea salt, in a blender until creamy. Combine the oats and sesame seeds with a little oil (you may want to add 1 TBS. of barley malt for a sweeter crust), mix well, and press into a well oiled baking dish to form a crust. Place the tofu mixture in the crust, place the sliced strawberries on top. Sprinkle with chopped almonds. Bake at 350° for 30 minutes or until lightly brown. Allow to cool and serve.

OPEN FACE BLUEBERRY PIE

2 Pints fresh blueberries, rinsed
1 Cup barley malt syrup
1 Tsp. vanilla
1 TBS. lemon juice
½ Tsp. Sea salt
2 TBS. arrowroot, diluted in ¼ cup of
   cold water

Place all the ingredients into a sauce pan, EXCEPT the arrowroot mixture. Cook over a medium heat for 20 minutes. Add the arrowroot mixture, a little at a time, stirring constantly. Bring to a boil, turn off the flame and allow to cool. Pour into a 9 inch pie shell and bake at 325° for 30 minutes. Serve cool.

CLEO'S FIESTA CAKE

2 Cups of pinto beans, cooked and mashed
2 Cups raw apples, peeled and diced
¾ Cup rice syrup
¼ Cup corn oil
1 Fertile egg, beaten
1 Cup whole wheat flour (or use
    ½ whole wheat and ½ unbleached
    white)
3 Tsp. baking powder (Rumford brand,
    contains no aluminum)
½ Tsp. Sea salt
1 Tsp. cinnamon
½ Tsp. cloves
½ Tsp. allspice
2 Tsp. vanilla
1 Cup raisins
½ Cup walnuts or almonds, chopped

First cream together the rice syrup and corn oil, then add the beaten egg. Next add the mashed pinto beans and blend. Mix all the dry ingredients together in a separate bowl and add to the creamed mixture. Add the apples, raisins, nuts and vanilla. Pour the cake mixture into a well greased 10" tube pan and bake at 375° for 45 - 50 minutes or until done.

PEACH COBBLER

8 - 10 Peaches, peeled, pitted and sliced
¼ Tsp. Sea salt
¼ Tsp. vanilla
1/3 Tsp. cinnamon
¼ Tsp. allspice
½ Cup barley malt syrup
2 TBS. of arrowroot, diluted in ¼ cup
    of water

Place all ingredients, EXCEPT the arrowroot mixture in a saucepan. Mix together and cook over a medium flame for 5 minutes. Set aside and allow to cool. Add the arrowroot mixture, bring back to a boil, stirring constantly. Remove from the flame when thickened and allow to cool. Place the peach mixture into individual custard dishes.

CARROT CAKE

4 Cups of grated carrots
2 Cups of whole wheat pastry flour
2 Tsp. soya powder
¼ Tsp. Sea salt
¼ Tsp. nutmeg
1 Tsp. cinnamon
1 TBS. active dry yeast (dissolved)
1/3 Cup walnuts, chopped
1/3 Cup raisins
½ Cup bancha tea
1 Fertile egg, separated (save whites)
1/3 Cup corn oil
2 Tsp. vanilla
1 TBS. grated orange peel
½ Cup barley malt syrup

Blend the flour, soya powder, salt, nutmeg, cinnamon, nuts, yeast and raisins together. In a separate bowl, beat the egg yolk, add the oil, tea, vanilla, barley malt syrup and orange peel, mix well. Add the carrots and mix again. Now add all the ingredients together and mix until smooth. Beat the egg white until stiff and fold into the mixture. Pour into an oiled baking dish and bake at 350° for 1 hour or until it tests done.

PEACH COBBLER TOPPING

1½ Cups whole wheat pastry flour
1 Cup unbleached white flour
¼ Tsp. Sea salt
1 Tsp. cinnamon
1/3 Cup chopped almonds
¼ Cup toasted sesame seeds
2/3 Cups barley malt syrup
¼ Cup corn oil

First mix together all the dry ingredients. Add the corn oil and barley malt, mix together until the mixture becomes crumbly. Place the crumb mixture on top of the peaches. Chill and serve.

PEANUT-SESAME BUTTER COOKIES

1½ Cups peanut butter
¼ Cup sesame butter
1 Cup barley malt syrup or/ amazake
2 Cups unbleached white flour
1¼ Cups apple juice
½ Tsp. Sea salt
¼ Tsp. cinnamon

Combine the flour, sea salt, cinnamon and nut butters. Add the barley malt syrup to the flour mixture with the apple juice and mix well. Drop spoonfuls onto a lightly oiled cookie sheet, press flat with a fork. Bake in a pre-heated oven at 325° for 15 - 20 minutes.

PEACH BAVARIAN

6 Fresh ripe peaches, peeled, halved, and pit removed
½ Cup barley malt syrup
1½ Cups multi-grain pancake mix
Dash of Sea salt
1 Cup bancha tea
Corn oil, 1" - 1½" deep heated at 350° in a cast-iron skillet

Place the peaches in a bowl and pour the barley malt syrup over them and allow to stand for 30 minutes. Blend the pancake mix with the tea and sea salt, till smooth. Dip the peaches in the mix and fry in the oil for 2 - 3 minutes. Place on paper towels to remove excess oil. Serve hot.

* Whenever you wish to peel peaches, simple place them into boiling water for approximately 20 - 30 seconds, immediately transfer them to a bowl of ice water. The skins will slip off easily. Always avoid purchasing peaches with wrinkles or browning spots, or green spots, or if they are hard to the touch. Peaches are ready to eat when to the gentle touch they give slightly. Also rely on your sense of smell, the peach is not ripe just because of its red color.

SPICED COFFEE AND NUT COOKIES

(1) Mix the following ingredients separately:

1¾ Cups whole wheat pastry flour
½ Tsp. Sea salt
½ Tsp. allspice
½ Tsp. cloves
½ Tsp. soya powder
1 Tsp. cinnamon
2 TBS. instant grain coffee
* Mix well

(2) Mix the following ingredients separately:

½ Cup raisins
½ Cup chopped almonds or walnuts

(3) Mix the following ingredients separately:

½ Cup corn oil
¾ Cup barley malt syrup
½ Cup amasake or/ oat milk
1 Tsp. vanilla

Now combine all the ingredients in a large bowl and mix well. Lightly oil a cookie sheet or shallow pan and pour the batter out. Bake at 350° for 20 minutes. Allow to cool and cut into squares. Serve.

PEACH OR APPLE COMPOTE

8 Ripe peaches, peeled, quartered, and pit removed/ or apples, peeled
¾ Cup water
1 Cup freshly squeezed orange juice
3 TBS. lemon juice
2/3 Cup barley malt syrup
2 Whole cloves
1 TBS. of kuzu, diluted in a little cold water

Combine all the ingredients in a saucepan and simmer for 10 - 15 minutes or until the peaches are soft. Pour in a chilled bowl and refrigerate. Serve as a topping for Dream Cake or sprinkle with toasted almonds and enjoy as is. You may also use apples in place of peaches.

OATMEAL-RAISIN-NUT COOKIES

3 Cups rolled oats
1½ Cups whole wheat pastry flour
3 TBS. corn oil
1 Cup chopped almonds
1 Cup barley malt syrup
1 Cup apple juice
½ Cup amazake (optional)
¼ Tsp. Sea salt
¼ Tsp. cinnamon
1/3 Cup raisins

Combine all the dry ingredients in a large bowl. Mix apple juice, oil and barley malt syrup together, then add to the dry ingredients. Mix thoroughly and let set for 15 minutes. Drop spoonfuls onto a lightly oiled cookie sheet and bake at 325° for 25 minutes or until done.

BUTTERNUT COOKIES

1½ Cups whole wheat pastry flour or/
    unbleached white flour
1 Cup butternut squash, pureed
2 TBS. cashew or peanut butter
2 Tsp. cinnamon
½ Cup apple juice
½ Tsp. Sea salt
¼ Cup cashews or peanuts, toasted and
    chopped fine
1 Fertilized egg yolk, beaten

In a mixing bowl, combine all dry ingredients and mix thoroughly. Add the cashew butter and squash puree. Add apple juice and mix to form a batter consistency. Drop spoonfuls onto a lightly oiled cookie sheet. Bake at 325° for 30 minutes or until browned.

APPLE DUMPLINGS

Prepare the pie crust recipe (half the recipe
    will make 4 dumplings)
8 Medium apples, peeled and cored
Currants or raisins
Chopped nuts, almonds or walnuts
1 Cup bancha tea
½ Cup barley malt syrup
Pinch of nutmeg
Pinch of cinnamon

Fill the center of the apples with raisins and nuts. Roll the pie crust into a thin rectangle, and cut into 4 squares. Place the apple in the middle of the squares sprinkle with a little sea salt, cinnamon and nutmeg. Bring corners together and pinch firmly together. In a separate pan mix the bancha tea and barley malt syrup adding just a pinch of sea salt, nutmeg and cinnamon. Heat until warm, pour the mixture over the dumplings. Bake at 350° for 35 - 40 minutes or until browned. Baste the dumplings every 5 - 10 minutes with a brush or spoon. Serve warm.

OUR GRANOLA

4 Cups rolled oats
½ Cup coconut, fresh
½ Cup wheat germ
1 Tsp. toasted sesame seeds
1 Tsp. toasted sunflower seeds
1 Cup raisins
½ Cup chopped almonds
1 Tsp. cinnamon
1 Tsp. Sea salt
¾ Cup barley malt syrup
1/3 Cup corn oil

Mix all the ingredients together except the raisins. Spread out evenly onto a cookie sheet and place in the 300° oven for 15 minutes, until the mixture browns evenly. It should be a light golden brown when finished. Remove from the oven add the raisins, mix well and serve.

RICE PUDDING
(Serves 6)

1 Cup brown rice, rinsed (soak for 3 hours before pressure cooking)
2 Cups of water
Pinch of Sea salt

After pre-soaking the brown rice for 3 hours, pressure cook for 1 hour and 20 minutes. Remove from flame and allow to return to normal pressure. Then in a heavy cast-iron saucepan place the following ingredients:

Cooked rice
2 Cups almond milk (See beverage section)
½ Cup raisins
1 Tsp. vanilla
2 Tsp. lemon rind, grated fine
5 TBS. rice syrup
3 TBS. amazake (See beverage section)
¼ Tsp. cinnamon

Bring all the ingredients to a boil, stirring constantly. Lower the flame and cook for 10 minutes. Then remove the lid, lower the flame to simmer and cook an additional 10 minutes. Pour into individual pudding dishes, cool and serve.

STRAWBERRY PUDDING FREEZE

2 Cups of strawberries, mashed
1/3 Cup barley malt syrup
1 Cup cold oat milk or amazake
½ Package of agar-agar
1/3 Cup apple juice

Pour milk in a saucepan, add the agar-agar and apple juice. Simmer for 5 minutes. Add the mashed strawberries and barley malt syrup, mix well and simmer for 5 minutes more. Pour into a shallow dish and allow to cool in the freezer until firm, 4 - 5 hours.

STRAWBERRY APPLE CUSTARD

2 Cups fresh strawberries, washed and sliced
4 Cups of apple juice
1 Cup rice syrup
1/3 Cup tahini
1 Tsp. vanilla
½ Tsp. cinnamon
¼ Tsp. Sea salt
2½ Bars agar-agar, shredded
2 TBS. arrowroot

Before beginning, set aside 2 TBS. of arrowroot and ¼ cup of apple juice, stir together and dissolve. Now place all the ingredients in a saucepan, mixing thoroughly. Allow to stand at room temperature for 20 - 25 minutes. Then place the pan on a burner and bring to a boil. Lower the flame and simmer for 4 minutes. Add the arrowroot mixture and stirring constantly, bring back to a boil. Lower the flame and simmer for 1 minute. Allow to cool then place in a blender and blend until smooth. Pour into custard cups and place in the refrigerator for 1 hour before serving. Top with cinnamon or toasted almonds.

BARLEY, FRUIT AND NUT PUDDING

1 - 1½ Cups barley, cooked
1/3 Cup barley malt syrup
¼ Cup apple juice
2 Apples, peeled and diced
1/3 Cup raisins
1/3 Cup toasted almonds, chopped
¼ Tsp. nutmeg
¼ Tsp. cinnamon
1 Tsp. vanilla

Mix all the ingredients together and place in a lightly oiled casserole dish. Bake at 350 degrees for 30 minutes. Serve warm.

TOFU RICE PUDDING

1 Pound tofu, squeeze out all excess liquid
1 Cup brown rice, cooked
1/3 Cup raisins
1/3 Cup almonds, finely chopped
1/3 Cup fresh strawberries, peaches, or
     apples (Optional)
1/3 Cup barley malt or rice syrup
¼ Cup corn oil
2 TBS. freshly squeezed lemon juice
3 TBS. vanilla
2 Tsp. cinnamon
½ Tsp. nutmeg
¼ Tsp. Sea salt

Place the rice and raisins in a bowl. Blend all the remaining ingredients in a blender, then mix together with the rice and raisins. Place the mixture in a lightly oiled baking dish and bake at 350° for 1 hour.

STRAWBERRY CUSTARD

2 Pints fresh strawberries, cleaned
4 Large apples, peeled and cut in pieces
2 TBS. raisins
½ Package agar-agar
2½ Cups apple juice
1 Tsp. vanilla
2 TBS. almond butter
¼ Tsp. Sea salt
¼ Cup chopped almonds
2 Tsp. arrowroot, diluted in ½ cup cool
     apple juice

Cook the strawberries, apples and raisins in 2 cups of apple juice for 10 minutes over a low flame. Pour into blender and add the nut butter, salt, vanilla and blend. Pour back into the saucepan and add the diluted arrowroot and agar-agar. Bring to a boil, stir constantly, lower flame, simmer 2 minutes. Allow to cool. Place in a shallow dish and put in the freezer for 1¼ hours. Top with almonds and serve.

BARLEY APPLE PUDDING

1 Cup barley flour
1/3 Cup barley malt syrup
1 TBS. dry yeast
½ Tsp. Sea salt
1 TBS. corn oil
½ Cup rice milk
3 Apples, peeled and sliced
¾ Cup fresh squeezed orange juice
1 TBS. corn oil
2 TBS. barley malt syrup
½ Tsp. cinnamon
½ Cup chopped nuts (almonds or walnuts)

Sift together the flour and salt. Cut in the barley malt. Dissolve the yeast in ¼ cup of warm water and allow to sit for 5 minutes. Add the yeast, oil and rice milk to the flour mixture and mix together to make a stiff batter. Allow to set in a warm place for 10 - 15 minutes. Spread the batter into an oiled 9" round cake pan. Arrange the apples on the outer edge, overlapping slices. Fill the center with apple slices. Then mix together the barley malt syrup, cinnamon, nuts and juice. Mix together well. Spread over the apples. Bake at 350° for 1 hour. Serve warm.

CARROT COOKIES

1/3 Cup corn oil
1 Cup barley malt syrup
1 Fertile egg, unbeaten
2 Cups whole wheat flour
½ Tsp. vanilla
2 Tsp. baking powder
Pinch of Sea salt
1 Cup cooked mashed carrots, cooled
½ Tsp. cinnamon

Blend together the oil, barley malt syrup and egg. Add to the ingredients the flour and baking powder and sea salt. Blend in the carrots, vanilla and cinnamon. Mix all the ingredients together well. Place teaspoon size cookies onto a greased or oiled cookie sheet and bake at 350 degrees for 10 - 12 minutes or until done.

RED/WHITE/BLUE

2 Cups freshly sliced strawberries
½ Cup amazake blend with 1/3 cup apple
    juice, until smooth
1½ Cup fresh blueberries

Place 1/3 cup sliced strawberries in a par-
fait glass top with 2 TBS. amazake, and top
with ¼ cup blueberries, chill and serve.

AMAZAKE CHERRY PUDDING

2 Cups amazake
1/3 Cup bing cherries, remove pits, or
    use strawberries
2 TBS. kuzu, diluted in ¼ cup
    apple juice
Toasted chopped almonds, for garnish
2 TBS. rice syrup

Place the amazake and cherries in a saucepan. Warm over a medium heat, gently
stir in the diluted kuzu, bring to a boil,
stirring gently. Remove from the heat
when the mixture has thickened. Pour into
individual serving dishes. Garnish with
chopped toasted almonds, chill and serve.

CHESTNUT FRUIT DELIGHT

1 Cup dried chestnuts, rinse and soak
    in 2 cups of water for 15 minutes
1/3 Cup raisins
1/3 Cup pears or apples, slice and soak
    in 1 cup of water for 5 minutes
2/3 Cup of water
Pinch of Sea salt

Place the chestnuts and pears along with
the soaking water in a pressure cooker.
Add the raisins and the 2/3 cups of water
and a pinch of sea salt. Bring to full pressure. Lower flame and simmer for 45 minutes. Remove from flame and allow pressure to return to normal. Serve hot or
chilled.

TOFU-NUTS & FRUIT

1 Square tofu, boiled for 10 minutes,
    drain and squeeze out excess
    liquid
3 TBS. orange juice or apple juice
¼ Cup toasted chopped nuts
¼ Cup raisins
¼ Cup strawberries, cleaned
¼ Tsp. cinnamon

Gently mix all ingredients together, **except**
the strawberries. Add the berries to the
mixture gently and place in the refrigerator
and cool. Serve.

STRAWBERRIES AND AGAR-AGAR

1 Cup fresh strawberries, cleaned, left
    whole
½ Cup raisins
¼ Cup almonds, toasted
2½ Cups apple juice
½ Tsp. Sea salt
2 Bars agar-agar

Place the strawberries and raisins and 1 cup
of apple juice in a saucepan. Bring to a
boil, lower the flame and simmer for 5
minutes. Dilute the agar-agar in the remaining apple juice and pour into the
saucepan. Add the sea salt and bring to a
rapid boil. Lower the flame and allow to
simmer for 5 minutes and then pour the
mixture into a glass casserole dish. Allow
to cool. Cut into pieces, top with almonds
and serve.

BAKED APPLES

6 Apples, cleaned and cored
½ Cup almond nut butter
1 TBS. tamari
¼ Cup raisins

Mix the nut butter, tamari, and raisin
together. Fill the apples with the mixture.
Place in a baking dish with a little water.
Sprinkle the apples lightly with sea salt
and bake at 350ʳ for 25 minutes.

RICE CRISPIE SNACKS

2 - 2½ Cups of brown rice crispies
3 TBS. of almond, sesame or peanut
    butter
½ Cup almonds or walnuts, chopped
1/3 Cup barley malt or rice syrup
1/3 Cup raisins
Pinch of cinnamon
1 Tsp. vanilla
3 TBS. apple juice

Place the peanut butter, barley malt syrup, apple juice, vanilla and cinnamon in a double boiler, heat until all the ingredients are blended well. Add the nuts and raisins to the mixture, blend together. Take the mixture off the heat and gently mix in the rice crispies. Stir gently until all the crispies are covered. Place the mixture into a lightly oiled pie dish and cool in the refrigerator for 15 - 30 minutes. Cut into squares and serve.

DESSERT TOPPING

2 Cups almonds or cashews
1 TBS. lemon rind
2 TBS. tahini
1½ Cups apple juice
½ Cup raisins
Pinch of Sea salt

Mix all ingredients in a blender. When the mixture is smooth, it is ready to be served on puddings, custards, baked apples, or pies. It may be refrigerated and re-heated for use later.

COFFEE CAKE TOPPING

1 TBS. corn oil
½ Cup barley malt or rice syrup
1 Egg white

Mix the syrup and oil together and stir in the egg white. Spread the mixture over the hot coffee cake. Top with chopped nuts.

FRESH FRUIT GELATIN

1 Cup apples, peeled and sliced
1 Cup pears, peeled and sliced
¼ Cup raisins
Pinch of Sea salt
3 TBS. kuzu, diluted in ¼ cup cold water
2 2/3 Cups of water

Place the water and raisins in a saucepan, add a pinch of sea salt. Bring to a boil, cover and lower the flame. Simmer for 15 minutes. Then add the remaining fruit and simmer for an additional 3 minutes. Add the diluted kuzu, stirring constantly, simmer until a thick clear sauce appears. Pour into individual serving dishes. Allow to cool, refrigerate and serve.

FRESH FRUIT CUP

1 Pint strawberries, rinse, stem and slice
½ Canteloupe, sliced in chunks
1/3 Cup raisins
2 Apples, diced
¼ Cup almonds, diced
2 Oz. brie cheese
Lettuce

Place all the ingredients EXCEPT the cheese and lettuce in a salad bowl, gently mix together. Refrigerate for 30 minutes. Serve on a bed of lettuce with brie cheese.

AGAR-AGAR AND FRUIT

3 Cups of water
2 Bars of agar-agar
2 Cups fresh fruit (in season)
¼ Tsp. Sea salt

Place the water and agar-agar in a pot and bring to a boil. Lower the flame and simmer for 20 minutes, stirring occasionally. Add the fruit and simmer for another 15 minutes. Sprinkle the sea salt on top, pour into a mold and chill.

APPLE BUTTER

1 Dozen apples, peeled, cored and cut
    into quarters
Pinch of Sea salt
1 Tsp. cinnamon
¼ Cup of raisins
¼ Cup of water

Put the apples, sea salt, cinnamon, raisins and water into a pressure cooker. Bring to full pressure, reduce the flame and cook for 5 minutes. Allow pressure to return to normal. Uncover and place into a cast-iron or stainless steel pot. Add to the sauce the following ingredients:

1/3 Cup barley malt syrup
1 Clove
Juice of 1 lemon
Pinch of Sea salt
¼ Tsp. of grated lemon rind

Cook all the ingredients over a low flame for several hours until the sauce becomes brown. Stir often, this will prevent the mixture from sticking. When finished allow to cool and place in an air tight glass jar.

DRIED STEWED FRUIT

1 Cup dried fruit, apples, peaches, pears,
    apricots, prunes, etc.
Water to cover

Place all ingredients in a saucepan. Bring to a boil, lower the flame and simmer until the fruit is tender. Serve hot or cool. Store in a glass container and refrigerate.

PANCAKE OR WAFFLE TOPPING

2 Cups of strawberries, clean and remove
    stems
1/3 Cup barley malt syrup
2 TBS. freshly squeezed orange juice

In a saucepan, combine all the ingredients and heat. Pour over pancakes or waffles, hot.

APPLE-STUFFED ACORN SQUASH

3 Acorn squash, wash and cut in half
3 Tart cooking apples, peeled and diced
¾ Cup barley malt syrup
1 TBS. lemon rind
1 TBS. lemon juice
2 TBS. sesame oil
Sea salt
Cinnamon

Place the acorn squash halves into a baking dish, add ½" of water and bake at 375° until the squash is nearly done. (about 25 minutes). Remove from the oven. Mix the diced apples, barley malt syrup, lemon juice and lemon rind. Mix sesame seeds and oil, with the apples. Use the remainder and lightly brush over the squash. Sprinkle with a dash of sea salt and cinnamon. Fill with apple stuffing and place in the baking dish. Add ½" of boiling water and bake for another 30 minutes.

BANCHA FRUIT POPS

Use any of the following fresh fruits: apples, blackberries, cherries, peaches, strawberries or raspberries. Take equal parts of fresh fruit and bancha tea and blend well in a blender. Place the mixture in popsicle containers or in dixie cups, insert a wooden popsicle stick and place in the freezer. These may be enjoyed after they have frozen, especially nice on a hot summer day.

SWEET TOFU BAR

4 Cakes of freeze dried tofu, (soak for
    20 minutes, squeeze out excess liquid)
5 TBS. barley malt syrup
1 Tsp. vanilla

In a saucepan place the barley malt syrup and vanilla, add the tofu squares. Cook on both sides until the syrup has evaporated. Place on dish and allow to cool.

BOILED APPLES

3 Apples, peeled and sliced
¼ Cup of water
Pinch of Sea salt

Place the apples, water and sea salt in a sauce pan. Bring to a boil, lower heat and cook for 10 minutes or until the apples are done.

SNACKS
The Pit Stop

FRESH FRUIT
Apples
Strawberries
Oranges
Tangerines
Peaches
Pears
Raspberries
Blueberries
Plums
Apricots

DRIED FRUITS
Apples
Apricots
Figs
Pears
Prunes
Raisins

NUTS
Almonds
Cashews
Peanuts
Pecans
Filberts
Macadamia
Walnuts

SEEDS
Sunflower seeds
Sesame seeds
Pumpkin seeds
Squash seeds

MISCELLANEOUS
Apple butter
Rice cakes
Rice crackers
Popcorn
Sesame sticks
Sesame crackers
Herb Crackers
Bancha fruit pops
Peanut butter
Sesame butter
Almond butter
Tahini
Rice syrup (Yinney)
Plum candy
Yinney candies
Amazake
Rice crispie snacks
Homemade cookies
Homemade desserts
Granola
Whole wheat pretzels

Exit 25
BEVERAGES

Thermostatic Control

The beverages that I use most often are those which are non-aromatic, non-stimulating, and contain no sugar, caffein, artificial coloring, preservatives or other additives. Teas which contain dyes or other stimulants, such as caffein, or that are high in tannic acid are to be avoided. These include so called aromatic teas, such as peppermint, camomile, red zinger and ginseng, to mention a few. Kukicha twig tea, sometimes called bancha tea, is a mild **BALANCED** tea.

KUKICHA TWIG TEA (Bancha tea)

Kukicha twig tea is one of the few drinks that I find truly beneficial to the body. This tea is made from the twigs of the plant. I do not use the green leaf tea which contains a high amount of caffein.

Kukicha twig tea does contain a trace of caffein. A valuable aspect of using this tea is its ability to act as a buffer. A buffer's purpose is to neutralize an acid or akaline state. I recommend using kukicha tea 10 - 15 minutes after eating. This will help **BALANCE** an acid or akaline condition, which often results from UNBALANCED eating.

Kukicha tea is easy to prepare and is economical. I recommend using 2 - 3 tablespoons of the twigs to 2 quarts of water. Place the twigs in a stainless steel tea ball or loose in the pot of water. Bring the water to a rapid boil, cover and boil for 3 minutes. Reduce the heat and simmer for 5 minutes. Remove the twigs and store the brewed tea in covered glass containers. This tea can be refrigerated. You can save the twigs and reuse them a second time. When using them for the second time, I add an additional tablespoon to the used portion.

For a delightful treat, try using 80% kukicha tea and 20% fresh squeezed fruit juices. A favorite is apple juice. I also use kukicha tea in place of milk in many of my recipes and to steam or boil vegetables.

Calcium builds bones and good teeth. The National Dairy Council, from kindergarten on, has been telling us that milk provides calcium, and that we must drink milk for health. They advertise the same message on T.V. nowdays, because milk sales are falling sharply. According to a recent Department of Agriculture report, milk has dropped to third place among the most popular commercially produced beverages. Why? People are discovering the **truth**. Cows' milk and goats' milk form hard curds in the stomach which putrify and leave the body susceptible to many diseases.

The St. Petersburg Times published an article titled, " *DRINKING MILK LINKED TO ARTERY HARDENING,"* December 9, 1983, by Dennis C. Milewski, United Press International. It stated in part, "An enzyme in homogenized milk can start hardening of the arteries in infancy and drinking it may even be more dangerous than smoking, researchers warn. They said milk cartons should carry warnings like cigarette packages."

The article continued to state," Dr. Kurt A. Aster and Donald J. Ross, of Fairfield University, released results of **20 years** of **research** at a news conference Wednesday with a blistering attack on the dairy industry, urging changes in milk processing to minimize the presence of the enzyme. Oster and Ross said the risk comes from an enzyme released in homogenized milk and some ice creams, which start arteriosclerosis long before cholesterol and cigarette smoking become factors."

"Ross said the enzyme is responsible for an estimated **500,000 deaths** each year in the United States, and the researchers said it may have caused 'million of deaths' worldwide."

"THEY SUGGESTED drinking milk can be more dangerous than smoking."

Long before milk became "fashionable," in the late 19th century, we had a healthy intake of calcium by eating whole cereal grains and fresh fruit. These still provide the best source of calcium, and **will continue to do so** long after milk and the National Dairy Council falls from grace.

When drinking cows' milk, it is preferred to drink fresh raw milk, instead of pasteurized and homogenized. It is especially appealing to the taste. One should always boil raw milk, have no fear, you will not destroy the nutritional value. Bring it to a boil, lower and simmer for 1 minute. Allow to cool and enjoy the taste of fresh raw milk. This is a much better way to consume milk, and easier to digest, along with destroying undesireable bacteria.

ALMOND MILK

½ **Cup almond or cashews**
1 **Cup apple juice**
2 **TBS. barley malt or rice syrup**
1/8 **Tsp. corn oil**
3 **Cups water**
1 **Apple, peeled and diced**

Place all ingredients into a blender and liquify. Pour into a saucepan and bring to a boil, lower the flame, and simmer for 5 minutes. Allow to cool and refrigerate. You may choose to strain off the liquid and reserve the nut meat. This milk is excellent on breakfast cereals and used in place of cow's milk in dessert, cookie and bread recipes.

OAT MILK

1 **Cup whole oats**
5 **Cups of water**
Pinch of Sea salt

Bring water to a boil, add the oats and sea salt, reduce the flame to low and simmer on low flame until creamy (approximately 1½ hours). Puree after cooling in a blender or put in a cheesecloth and squeeze out the milk. The latter will produce a thinner consistency.

SOYA MILK

1 Pound soybeans, rinsed
4 Quarts spring or well water
1/8 Tsp. Sea salt
Barley malt or rice syrup, to taste

*Although the following instructions for making soy milk may seem lengthy and complicated, it really is very easy and simple to make.

Place the soybeans in a large saucepan, cover with water. Soak them overnight or at least 12 hours. Drain and rinse. Cover with water and bring to a boil, drain and rinse. Again cover with water, bring to a boil, drain and rinse. Repeat this process once again, making a total of three times that the soybeans are boiled and drained. This process will remove the soybean taste completely. Drain the beans and allow them to dry. Then grind the beans in a blender. Place the ground up beans in a cheese cloth and securely tie the top. Place the cheesecloth in a large crock or pail. Pour two quarts of warm water over the soybeans, knead the soybean sack well, washing and squeezing the milk out. Pour the soy milk into a separate pot. Pour two more quarts of water over the soy bean sack and repeat the kneading and squeezing, until the water becomes milky. Combine the second soybean milk with the first. Place the 4 quarts of soybean milk into a large casserole or flat bottomed dish. Bring to a boil, stirring constantly, add the sea salt and boil for 20 minutes. Sweeeten with barley malt or rice syrup to taste. When the soybean milk is cool, place in an air tight glass container and refrigerate.

If you are going to use the soya milk for cooking, it is best to add your sweetener to the cool milk just before cooking. You may add vanilla or almond for additional flavor.

This recipe is well worth your time and effort.

RICE MILK

1 Cup brown rice, rinsed
7 Cups of water
¼ Tsp. Sea salt

Place the rice and water in a pressure cooker. Cover, place a trivet under the cooker and bring to full pressure. Reduce the heat to low and cook for 1 hour and 45 minutes to 2 hours. Remove from the heat and allow pressure to return to normal. Uncover and ladle the mixture onto a piece of cheesecloth in a bowl. Wrap the cheese cloth tightly around the soft grains. Squeeze all the rice liquid through the cloth until only the rice grains remian and no more can be extracted. Put the rice pulp aside for later use in bread or soup making. Use rice milk for babies or for treatment of gastric or intestinal illness. It may be refrigerated and diluted with a little water to obtain the right consistency for bottle-feeding.

OATMEAL WATER

1 Cup oatmeal
1 Quart water

Place 1 Qt. of water in a bowl, add 1 cup of oatmeal, allow to soak overnight or 12 hours. Strain through a piece of cheesecloth or a fine sieve. This can be used in place of water, for thicker and creamier preparation of soup stock, stews, breads, desserts, and is a good substitute for cow's milk.

AMAZAKE

Amazake is a very versatile preparation and the basis for a beverage by the same name, but it can be used in its more solid form in recipes calling for sweetening agents or thickeners such as bread, cakes, cookies, puddings, etc. Because its basis is sweet brown rice, it is naturally nutritious and aids digestion through the addition of koji. Koji is made from steamed rice that has been innoculated with spores of a mold called Aspergillus Oryzae and incubated for several days. The quality of the Koji is also a key ingredient in making good miso. This mold produces enzymes that help break down proteins, carbohydrates, and oils, into more digested nutrients. To make amazake, prepare as follows:

½ Cup koji rice
2 Cups sweet brown rice
4 Cups of water

Rinse and soak the sweet rice overnight. Place in a pressure cooker with the water and bring to full pressure over a high heat. Reduce the heat to low, place on a trivet or dispersing pad and simmer for 30 minutes. Remove rice from pressure cooker and put into a large ceramic or glass bowl. **DO NOT use metal pans.** When cooled, mix in the koji rice which is the special fermenting agent. Cover with a towel and allow to set for 4 - 7 hours. Stir it occasionally with a wooden spoon and keep it in a warm place. After fermentation has taken place, put the rice in a stainless steel or cast-iron pot. Add a small amount of water and bring to a full boil. Remove from the heat as soon as it begins to bubble. If a beverage is desired, put the rice into a blender with enough water or apple juice to create the desired consistency. Add a dash of cinnamon or nutmeg and a few drops of fresh ginger juice. Use it undiluted in recipes which call for sugar. Store the unused portion in the refrigerator, or for longer storage, cook over a low flame until it becomes dark in color. Store in glass jars.

BARLEY TEA

2 - 3 TBS. pearled or unhulled barley, rinsed
1 Quart water

Dry roast pearled barley or unhulled barley in a cast-iron skillet, constantly stirring to prevent burning. Roast until the barley becomes dark brown. This can be stored in an air-tight glass container. Bring to a boil, 1 quart of water, add 2 - 3 TBS. of barley, lower the flame and simmer for 10 minutes. Strain through a strainer. Drink hot or cool. Refrigerate in a glass container. This is a pleasant drink in hot weather.

BROWN RICE TEA

2 TBS. brown rice, rinsed
1 Quart water

Dry roast the rice in a skillet, constantly stirring to prevent burning. Roast the rice until it releases a nutty fragrance and is golden brown. Store the roasted rice in an air tight jar. Place 2 TBS. of rice in a sauce pan with 1 quart of water, bring to a boil, cover, lower the flame and simmer for 5 minutes. Strain the liquid through a strainer. Drink hot or cool. Store in a glass container in the refrigerator.

HOT APPLE DELIGHT

1 Cup of apple juice
2 TBS. barley malt syrup
¼ Tsp. lemon juice
1 Cinnamon stick

Place all the ingredients in a saucepan and heat. Serve with the cinnamon stick. Increase ingredients for more servings.

STRAWBERRY FREEZE

1 Cup strawberries
½ Cup apple juice
½ Cup bancha tea
2 TBS. barley malt syrup or amazake
1/3 Cup crushed ice

Place all ingredients into a blender, cover and blend. Serve.

GRAIN COFFEE

To add variety to your beverage intake, it is possible to purchase some very pleasant tasting grain coffees at the natural food stores. We have found brand names such as Wilson's Heritage, Durham, Bambu and Cafix, but there are undoubtedly others which will serve the purpose or satisfy the need for change. At home, we have experimented with a variety of roasted grain and beans, and are able to produce a product which tasted very good and nearly like coffee. We always try to avoid products which rely on dates, figs and spices, to produce the flavor desired, since we know a delightful flavor can be made from only grains, beans and chicory.

SANDALWOOD GRAIN COFFEE

2 Cups brown rice, rinsed
1½ Cups winter wheat, rinsed
¾ Cups aduki beans, rinsed
1 Cup garbonzo beans (Chick-peas), rinsed
½ Cup chickory root

Dry roast all the ingredients in a cast-iron skillet until they become dark brown in color, stir constantly so the grains will roast evenly. Grind all the grains in a hand-operated mill if possible. Coffee grinders produce a better grind if you have one or you can use one in the coffee section of some supermarkets. To brew: Use a tablespoon of the above ground grains. Bring to a boil in 1 cup of water. Be careful to quickly reduce the flame or the liquid may bubble over the edge of the pan. Simmer it over a low flame for 5 - 10 minutes or until the color has a rich, dark look. Serve with or without the grounds. We prefer to pour it through a strainer, however, the effect of expresso is obtained by leaving the grounds in the drink.

FRESH PEACH SHAKE FREEZE

1 Cup fresh peaches, peeled and sliced
1 Cup crushed ice
¼ Cup amazake
1 TBS. lemon juice
3 TBS. barley malt syrup

Place all ingredients in a blender, cover and blend. Serve.

BANCHA TEA (Kukicha Tea)

3 TBS. bancha twig tea
2 Quarts of water

Place the twigs in a stainless steel tea ball or directly into 2 quarts of water. Bring to a rapid boil, cover and boil for 3 minutes. Reduce the flame and simmer for 5 minutes. Drink hot or refrigerate. Try using 75% bancha tea with 25% apple, orange or strawberry juice.

WATER

When we must make a choice of drinking waters, we always choose well or spring water over tap water, but we prefer tap water to distilled water. Distilled is the most lifeless form of water, even though it is bacteria free. It has lost many important trace minerals. It is desireable to filter out impurities with various charcoal filters, however, we drink so little water by itself that it seems hardly worth recommending. During the warmer seasons, fruit juices are used in moderation. Among these are apple juice, apple cider, as well as fresh squeezed orange juice and grapefruit juice. Lucky are those who live in Florida, California and Arizona.

OTHER BEVERAGES

Occasionally, or at a social gathering, simply for enjoyment, a good quality beer may be used in moderation such as Coors, Guiness Stout, and Rolling Rock. However, it is not adviseable to consume these on a daily basis or in excessive amounts.

All drinks and beverages should be served warm or at room temperature. Cool drinks can be used occasionally in the summer, but should never be served ICE COLD. Ice drinks tend to stop digestion, paralyze the stomach, and can produce head and eye aches, along with other various problems.

Always remember to **chew your food well**. This will help you cut down your liquid consumption.

Exit 26
PICKLING

The Wholesome Additive

Pickles can be a satisfying part of your daily menu and are usually enjoyed at the end of our meal. In general, quickly made pickles are best eaten in hotter weather, and the longer pickling processes enjoyed in the colder months of the year.

Pickles are a wonderful aid to your digestive process. Our intestines are similar to the roots of trees. As they take nourishment from the soil, our intestines take our energy from food. The fermentation process used in pickling requires the presence of some friendly bacteria which converts the vegetables into lactic acid. This beneficial enzyme aids digestion and the intestinal flora allows our intestines to take the proper nourishment.

When the body is not producing a **BALANCED** bacterial culture, one result may be a vitamin deficiency. This can be accompanied by conditions such as body pain, fatigue, loss of memory, shortness of breath and rapid heart beat. To correct these deficiencies and stimulate the intestinal flora, we recommend rice bran pickles.

Salt, pressure and time are the key factors in pickling, and any variables in these three important items will greatly affect the final outcome. It may take some experimenting to determine the correct amount of salt to use. However, if your pickles are too salty, you can soak them in water for a short time before serving. If not enough salt is used, spoilage may occur since not enough water will be drawn out of the vegetables.

Pressure requirements are less exacting. Some recipes do not use any at all. If water is supposed to rise and fails to do so, you have probably not used enough salt. It usually does not take more than 10 hours after the pressure has been added for this to happen. If

283

too much water rises, reduce the amount of weight until the level is just above the pickles and below the plate.

Room temperature and weather also affect pickling. Cooler weather is better for pickling recipes which take longer to ferment. Shorter processes ferment better in slightly warmer situations, for example, dill pickles, which can be made even in summer.

Some ingredients we use in pickling are sea salt, tamari, miso, rice bran, wheat bran, rice flour, rice koji, shiso leaves, garlic, bay leaves, ginger, coriander, cloves, red pepper, dill, lemon and orange rinds, apples and parsley. It is also important that you buy the freshest vegetables possible. The longer the cucumbers are off the vine, the greater the chances they will have hollow centers. Vegetables must be cleaned thoroughly and, in some cases, dried. In our pickle making we use only the finest, natural ingredients we can find, unlike those sold in supermarkets, which frequently contain sugar, vinegar, dyes and preservatives.

We refrain from boiling natural pickles, since the heat will destroy bacteria and enzymes. When we are making dill pickles, we boil water and salt for a brine and refrigerate until cool before pouring over the cucumbers.

Pickles should be checked daily and, if mold appears, remove it immediately. We also suggest that the weights or plates that are placed on top of your ceramic crock-pots or wooden kegs be kept from direct contact with the brine, as this may also cause mold. Always place a piece of cheesecloth under the plate or disc used to hold the vegetables down. Because of the acidity involved in pickle making, be careful to choose stoneware, pottery, or glass, unless you have wood, which is preferred. Utensils for handling the pickles should be wood and storage should be in very clean (sterilized if possible) glass jars.

A fast, simple, and practical vegetable press may be purchased at a natural food store. It's possible to pickle in two days. You can pickle just about any vegetable in this press. Similarly, broccoli and cauliflower take about the same amount of time. Cucumber will pickle in 8 hours. Onions and radishes in a few hours. Lettuce takes about 12 hours. Sprinkle the vegetables lightly with sea salt. You can add bay leaves or dried mustard for flavoring.

PICKLED BROCCOLI AND CAULIFLOWER

Broccoli, stems only, cut in ½" pieces
1 Small head of cauliflower, floweretts
2 Cloves garlic, minced
2 Tsp. grated ginger
2 TBS. Sea salt
2 Bay leaves
Pinch of corinader
1 Clove
¼ Cup of corn oil
2 Quarts of water

Place the vegetable ingredients in bottom of a large Mason jar. Bring water to a boil. Allow to cool. Add remaining ingredients to the water. Mix and pour into the jar. Refrigerate. They will be ready in 7 days.

QUICK UME SAUERKRAUT

1 Medium head of cabbage, cut fine
1 Tsp. Sea salt
2 Umeboshi plums
Pickle press or crock

Mix ingredients together in a kneading motion, place in a pickle press or crock and press the cabbage. After one day remove the liquid and re-press. Store in a cool dark area for 5 days. Remove and store in a sterilized glass container.

HOMEMADE DILL PICKLES

2 Dozen small unwaxed pickling cucumbers
1¾ Quarts of water
1/3 Cup Sea salt
½ Red pepper (green pepper optional)
1 Dozen pearl onions (small)
4 Cloves garlic
2 Bay leaves
4 Sprigs of dill

Wash cucumbers with a vegetable brush, cutting out any soft spots. Slice in 6ths lengthwise and place in a crock pot or earthenware container measuring approximately 12" in diameter and 6" deep. Add pearl onions to sliced cucumbers and arrange in layers. Boil water, add salt and dissolve, then cool the mixture in refrigerator. Add finely diced red pepper, whole garlic cloves and bay leaves to the liquid. Stir and allow to set 10 minutes. Pour over the cucumbers and place dill on top. The liquid **MUST** cover the cucumbers completely. If more liquid is needed, boil additional water and add sea salt. Cover the crock with a cheesecloth, place in a cool, dark place and leave for 4 - 6 days.

When ready, rinse the pickles in brine, remove from the crock and store in a clean, glass jar in the refrigerator. The pickled onions may also be rinsed and stored in a separate jar. Enjoy your preservative-free pickles.

PICKLED DAIKON AND CELERY

4" Piece of daikon radish, sliced thin
1 Stalk of celery, diced
4 TBS. tamari
1 Tsp. fresh grated ginger

Wash the vegetables, place in dish and add tamari and ginger. Allow to stand for 3 - 5 hours.

CORN RELISH

6 - 8 Ears of fresh corn, cooked on the
    cob, cooled, kernels removed
½ Cup rice vinegar
1 Tsp. fresh lemon juice
1 - 1½ Tsp. Sea salt
2 TBS. parsley, chopped
2 TBS. barley malt or rice syrup
1 Tomato, sliced thin and quartered
¼ Tsp. basil
¼ Tsp. cayenne
½ Green pepper, finely chopped
4 Scallions, finely chopped

Combine all ingredients in a bowl and mix well. Refrigerate for 6 hours. Serve. Store in an air tight glass container.

PEACH CATSUP

4 - 4½ Pounds of fresh peaches, peeled,
    pitted and sliced
2 Cups onions, chopped fine
2 Cloves garlic, minced
1½ Cups barley malt syrup

TIE THE FOLLOWING IN A CHEESE-CLOTH:

1 Tsp. whole cloves
1 Tsp. allspice

Coat a large saucepan lightly with oil and saute the garlic and onions. Then add all the other ingredients, the cheesecloth last. Cook over a medium heat for 1 hour, stirring occasionally, until the mixture thickens. Remove the cheesecloth and puree ingredients in a blender. Pour into hot sterilized jars and seal. Store in a cool place. Will yield approximately 4 pints.

HOMEMADE SAUERKRAUT

3 Pounds cabbage (firm heads)
    shred fine 1/10" (remove first few
    leaves, save)
3 Shallots
1 TBS. Sea salt
1 Tsp. brown rice vinegar

Mix the shredded cabbage, sea salt, shallots, and rice vinegar together. Place in crock and cover with a few outside leaves from the cabbage. Now cover with cheesecloth and place a plate on top. Place a stone on the plate to weigh it down. This will cause the brine to come up to the plate. Your cloth will become wet. Check daily, remove any scum that appears and change your cheesecloth. Store in a cool place. Fermentation should take place in three weeks. You may enjoy as is or saute sauerkraut. This is a real treat, and worth the time and effort.

HOMEMADE PICKLES

1 Quart water
1 TBS. Sea salt
1 Bay leaf
3" Piece of kombu
Fresh vegetables (carrots, onions, daikon
    radish, cauliflower, broccoli. Use one
    or any combination)

Boil the water with the sea salt. Allow the salted water to completely cool. Place the kombu in a jar, add the pieces and slices of cleaned fresh vegetables. Pour the cooled salted water over the vegetables. The vegetables must be completely covered. If not, place a jar or cup on top to submerge the vegetables. Cover with a cheesecloth and store in a cool, dark place for 2 - 4 days. Then refrigerate in a sealed glass jar with a little of the brine. Have 1 or 2 pickles after each meal.

HOMEMADE DIJON STYLE MUSTARD

3 Cloves garlic, minced
3 Onions, diced
2 Cups rice vinegar or 1 cup of ume vinegar
    and 1 cup of rice vinegar
1/8 Tsp. cayenne pepper
2 TBS. Sea salt
1 TBS. corn oil
4 TBS. barley malt syrup
1 Cup dry mustard

Place the garlic and onion in a glass jar, add the vinegar. Cover and allow to set for 24 - 30 hours. Strain off the liquid through a cheesecloth, reserve the liquid and throw away any residue in the cheesecloth. Combine in a bowl the cayenne pepper, sea salt, dry mustard and ½ cup of the reserved vinegar. In a cast-iron saucepan or stainless steel saucepan bring the remaining vinegar to a boil, and gradually add the mustard mixture. Simmer over a low heat for 5 minutes, stirring constantly. Allow to cool, covered. When cooled, add the barley malt syrup and corn oil. Use a blender or a hand mixer and beat the mixture for 3 - 4 minutes. Store the mustard in a glass sealed jar. Will yield 3 - 4 cups.

*PERSONAL NOTES:

GLOSSARY

ADUKI or AZUKI BEANS: A small hard red bean imported from Japan and also grown in America.

AGAR-AGAR: A while gelatin made from sea vegetables used in desserts.

ARAME: A thin black sea vegetable, with a mild flavor.

AMAZAKE: A refreshing drink and sweetener used in desserts. Made from sweet brown rice and koji.

ARROWROOT: A starch flour from the root of an American plant. Used in place of corn starch as a thickening agent for making stews, gravies, desserts, etc.

BANCHA TEA aka KUKICHA TEA Comes from the stems and leaves of tea bushes that are at least 3 years old. Aids in digestion and is reported to be a good source of calcium. It contains no chemicals or dyes.

BARLEY MALT SYRUP: A polysaccharide sugar made from whole grain barley. Also made with combinations of corn.

BONITA FLAKES: Shaved from dried bonita fish. Used in soup stocks or noodle dishes.

BROWN RICE: Whole, unpolished rice. Comes in three types: short grain, medium grain and long grain. Brown rice contains a balance of protein, minerals and carbohydrates.

BUCKWHEAT: A staple food in most European countries. This cereal is eaten mainly in the form of kasha, whole groats, or soba noodles.

COUSCOUS: Partially refined cracked wheat.

DAIKON RADISH: A long white radish. May be used fresh, dried or pickled.

DULSE: A reddish-purple sea vegetable, rich in minerals.

GARBONZO BEANS aka: CHICKPEAS A small hard, round tan bean. Should be pre-soaked before using.

GENMAI MISO: Miso made from brown rice, soybeans and sea salt. Used in soups, sauces, seasonings, etc.

GINGER ROOT: A spicey, pungent root used in cooking.

HATCHO MISO: Miso made from soybeans and sea salt and aged at least 3 years. Used in soups, seasonings, sauces, etc.

HIZIKI: A dark brown sea vegetable, when it is dried, turns black. It is strong and wiry.

KANTEN: A jelled dessert that is made with fresh fruit.

KOJI: A grain that is innoculated with bacteria and is used to cause fermentation to occur. Used in making amazake, miso, tamari etc.

KOMBU: A thick, wide dark green sea vegetable which is cultivated deep in the ocean waters. Used in soup stock preparation, combined with vegetable dishes and in preparing beans.

KOME MISO: Miso made from white rice, soybeans and sea salt, rice miso.

KUKICHA: The more mature stems and leaves of the Japanese tea bush.

KUZU: A white starch made from the root of a wild plant called a kuzu plant or in America the plant is called, Cudzu. Used as a thickening agent for making gravies, sauces, desserts, etc.

LOTUS ROOT: Looks similar to a potato, but is the root of a type of water lily. It is brownish with a white hollow center.

MILLET:	A tiny, yellow grain, originally native to China, Asia and Africa. Grown in America. Cooked in soups, in whole form and in combination with beans and vegetables.
MISO:	A fermented soybean paste, used in diluted form in soups, sauces, as a seasoning for vegetables, spreads and salad dressings. There are many varieties using soybeans as the base and combinations of barley and other grains.
MOCHI:	A dumpling made from pounded, cooked sweet brown rice. Used as snack or in soups.
MUGI MISO:	Miso made from soybeans, barley and sea salt. Used in soups, sauces, salad dressings and seasonings.
NIGARI:	Used in making tofu. It is a hard, crystallized salt made from the liquid drippings of dampened sea salt.
NORI:	Purple, thin sheets of dried sea vegetables. Heated over a flame nori turns green and is then used on rice balls, to make sushi or as a condiment.
ORGANIC FOODS:	Foods grown without the use of artificial chemicals or fertilizers, herbicides or pesticides.
OAT MILK:	Creamy liquid made from oats and water. Used in soups and in baking.
POLYSACCHARIDE SUGARS:	Found in large quantities in whole cereal grains and vegetables. A complex sugar that gradually assimilates during the digestive process.
POLYUNSATURATED FATS:	Essential fatty acids found in high concentration in grains, beans, seeds and in smaller quantities in animal foods, especially fish.
RAMEN NOODLES:	Made from buckwheat flour or white flour, these noodles have been fried then dried. They cook very quickly.
REFINED OIL:	Any cooking oil that has been chemically processed to remove or alter the taste, color or odor.
RICE SYRUP:	A polysaccharide sugar made from whole grain brown rice.
SAKE:	A Japanese rice wine. Usually served warm in small cups. Excellent for cooking.
SASHIMI:	Raw, sliced fish. Served with tamari and wasabi.
SATURATED FAT:	Primarily animal fat. This contributes to hardening of the arteries and cholesterol.
SEA SALT:	This salt is obtained from the ocean, not mined from the land. It is sun baked and contains a high amount of trace minerals. It contains no sugar, chemicals or iodine.
SESAME SALT:	A delightful condiment made from roasted sea salt and unhulled sesame seeds, that are ground together in a suribachi bowl. Sesame salt should be stored in an air-tight glass container to retain its freshness.
SHIITAKE MUSHROOMS:	A dried mushroom imported from Japan and also grown in America. The scientific name is Lentinus edodes. Presoak before using.
SHOYU:	Naturally processed tamari soy sauce.
SOBA NOODLES:	Noodles that are made with buckwheat flour or a combination of whole wheat and buckwheat flours.

288

SURIBACHI BOWL:	A specially made serrated, baked clay bowl. Used for grinding and pureeing foods using a wooden pestle.
SUSHI:	Rice rolled with vegetables, fish, or pickles. It is wrapped with nori sea vegetables and cut into rounds.
TAHINI aka SESAME BUTTER:	A product made from hulled sesame seeds formed into a paste. Also known as sesame butter, it is used in sauces, spreads and dressings.
TAMARI:	Naturally made soy sauce, made with or without wheat. The name tamari will distinguish it from the other chemically produced soy sauces.
TEKKA:	A condiment made with Hatcho miso, sesame oil, burdock root, lotus root, carrots and ginger root. A seasoning similar to pepper.
TEMPEH:	A product made from soybeans, vinegar, water, and a special bacteria. Can be used in soups, as a main dish, in sandwiches and casseroles.
TEMPURA:	A dish that is prepared by slicing vegetables, fish and sometimes fruit, then dipping it into a batter and deep frying until golden brown.
TOFU:	A white cake made from soybeans, nigari, and water. Used in soups, for sauces, dressings, sandwich mixes and casseroles.
UDON NOODLES:	Japanese noodles that are made from whole wheat or a combination of whole wheat and unbleached white flour.
UMEBOSHI PASTE:	Japanese plums pickled in salt with beefstake leaves and dried in the sun, then made into a paste. Excellent on corn-on-the-cob.
UMEBOSHI PLUM:	Salt pickled plums that are made from freshly picked still green Ume fruit. They are pickled up to one year by a natural lactic acid bacteria process. They add a delicious flavor to rice balls, vegetables, sauces and salad dressings.
UMEBOSHI VINEGAR:	A red vinegar that is made from freshly picked still green ume fruit, packed in salt and left to pickle for 1 month. Red Shiso leaves are added to give it color and the liquid is drawn off.
UNREFINED OIL:	A vegetable oil that has been pre-pressed and/or solvent extracted to retain the color, aroma, flavor and nutrients.
WAKAME:	A long thin, green sea vegetable. Cut it into tiny pieces and use in soups. Also used in condiments, salads and dressings.
WASABI:	A Japanese hot mustard, green in color. Used especially with Sashimi.
WOK:	A deep, stainless steel frying skillet.
YANNOH:	A grain coffee that is made with five different grain and beans. It is roasted and then ground into a fine powder.
YELLOW MISO:	A miso that has been fermented a short time. It is very mild and excellent for sauces and salad dressings. It is made from koji and sea salt.

BIBLIOGRAPHY

Abehsera, Michel. *Cooking for Life.* Binghamtom, N.Y.: Swan House

Aihara, Cornelia. *The Do of Cooking,* 4 volumes. Orville, California: George Ohsawa Macrobiotic Foundation

Aihara, Hermann. *Milk, A Myth of Civilization.*   George Ohsawa Macrobiotic Foundation; Oroville, California, 1977.

American Cancer Society. *Ca-A Cancer Journal for Clinicians.* Vol. 33, No. 1 Jan/Feb 1983. American Cancer Society, Inc., N.Y.

Balletine, Dr. Rudolph. *Diet and Nutrition.* The Himalayan Institute, 1979. Homesdale, Pa.

Bricklin, Mark. *Natural Healing.* Rodale Press, Inc., 1976. Emmaus, Pa.

Carrel, Alexis. *Man the Unknown.* New York: Harper and Row

Diet, Nutrition, and Cancer: Washington, D.C.: National Academy of Science, 1982.

Dufty, William. *Sugar Blues.* New York: Warner Publications.

East-West Foundation. *Cancer and Diet.* East West Foundation Publ., Brookline, Mass. 1980.

Esko, Edward and Wendy. *Macrobiotic Cooking for Everyone.* Tokyo: Japan Publications, Inc., 1980.

Hippocrates. *Hippocratic Writing.* Edited by G.E.R. Lloyd, Translated by J. Chadwick and W.N. Mann: New York: Penquin Book, 1978.

Jacobson, Michael. *The Changing American Diet.* Washington, D.C.: Center for Science in the Public Interest, 1978.

Kervran, L. *Biological Transmutation.* Condensed and translated by George Oshawa.

Kirkman, Don. *Millions Have Fat Chance For Illness.* Scipps-Howard News Service, Philadelphia Daily News, Thursday, February 14, 1985.

Kirschmann, John D. *Nutrition Almanac.* McGraw-Hill, Paperback Edition, New York, 1979.

Koufas, Theo, Ph.D. *A Guide To Better Own Your Own Health.* Largo, Florida: Nutri-Bio-Genetics, Inc., 1983.

Koufas, Theo, Ph.D. *The Food Connection, A Natural Alternative.* Palm Harbour, Florida. M & M Printing, & Typesetting, Inc., 1983.

Kushi, Aveline. *How to Cook with Miso.* Tokyo, Japan Publications, 1978.

Kushi, Michio. *The Teachings of Michio Kushi,* Volumes I and II. Tokyo, Japan Publications.

Lonsdale, Dr. Derrick. *American Journal of Clinical Nutrition.*

Markoutsas, Elaine. *Building Solid Eating Habits.* The Orlando Sentinel Star, July 23, 1983.

Mendelsohn, Robert S., M.D. *Confessions of a Medical Heretic.* Chicago, Illinois: Warner Books, Inc. 1980.

Muramoto, Noboru. *Healing Ourselves.* New York: Avon, London. Michael Dempsey, Cassell.

National Institute of Health

Needham, Joseph. *Science and Civilization of China.* Volume 5, Part II.

Ohsawa, George. *The Book of Judgement.* Los Angeles, California: Oshawa Foundation.

Ohsawa, George. *Pathological Calcification.* Los Angeles, California: Oshawa Foundation.

Ohsawa, Lima. *The Art of Just Cooking.* Tokyo: Autumn Press.

Peterkin, Nichols and Cromwell. *Nutrition Labeling.* U.S. Department of Agriculture, Bulletin N. 382, 1975. Washington, D.C.

Sattilaro, Anthony, M.D. with Tom Monte. *Recalled by Life.* Boston: Houghton-Mifflin, 1982.

Select Committee on Nutrition and Human Needs. U.S. Senate, *Dietary Goals for the United States.* February 1977.

Silberg, William. *"Teen Emotional Problems Linked to Poor Nutrition."* Sentinel Star, Orlando, Florida.

BIBLIOGRAPHY CONTINUED

Steen and Montagu. *Volume One.* Harper and Row; 1959.

The American Heart Association.

The Bible. King James Version.

The Surgeon General's Report on Health Promotion and Disease Prevention, Healthy People. Washington, D.C. Government Printing Office, 1979.

Thomas, B. Robert. *The Old Farmers Almanac. 'The Egg.'* Dublin, N.H., Yankee Publishing, Inc., 1983.

Toynbee, Arnold. *The Study of Nature.*

United States Congres. *Nutrition Research Alternatives.* Office of Assesment, Washington, D.C.

Williams, Dr. Roger. *Nutrition Against Disease.* Pitman Publishing Co. N.Y. 1980.

INDEX

A

ADUKI BEANS, 179 (See also beans)
    Adukis & Companions, 183
    Adukis, chestnuts & raisins, 183
    Adukis with squash or pumpkin, 182
    Bean burgers, 184
    Bean pate, 244
    Bean salad, 217
    Bronco aduki bean soup, 105
    Bronco beans, 186
    Continental barley soup, 105
    Crackers & chips, 244
    Fruit bean casserole, 183
    Macaroni salad, 168
    Millet & shrimp creole, 133
    Mock meat loaf, 185
    Refried beans, 185
    Sweet baked beans, 186
    Sweet brown rice & adukis, 123
    Triple carb special, 184
    Wheatberries & beans, 143
AGAR-AGAR, (See also sea vegetables)
    Agar-agar & fruit, 274
    Strawberry agar-agar, 274
ALL NATURAL ONION RYE BREAD, 259
ALMONDS, (See also nuts)
    Almond butter salad dressing, 245
    Almond flavored granola, 160
    Almond milk, 278
    Almond miso spread, 245
    Almond nut loaf, 265
    Almond vegetable saute, 209
AMAZAKE, 280 (See also beverages)
    Amazake cherry pudding, 273
APPLE (S),
    Apple butter, 275
    Apple compote, 269
    Apple dumplings, 270
    Apple nut loaf cake, 265
    Apple nut pancakes, 158
    Apple pie, 265
    Apple sauce, 240
    Apple stuffed acorn squash, 275
    Baked apples, 273
    Barley apple pudding, 272
    Boiled apples, 276
    Cleo's fiesta cake, 268
    Dream cake, 264
    Fresh fruit cup, 274
    Fruit cake, 267
    Fruit Ferrari, 168
    Hot apple delight, 281
ARAME, 221 (See also sea vegetables)
    Arame & dried daikon, 224
    Arame, daikon & curry, 223
    Arame, dried daikon, carrots & onions, 224
    Arame & fried tofu, 225
    Arame & herbs, 226
    Arame & lentils, 226
    Arame & lotus root, 223
    Windjammer salad, 216
ARROWROOT, 287
AUTOBAHN BREAD, 258

AUTOBAHN DIET, 81 - 92
    14 day menu, 89 - 92
    Diet, 81 - 86
    Shopping list, 87
AUTOBAHN SALAD, 218
AUTOBAHN SALAD DRESSING, 245
AUTOBAHN MISO SPECIAL, 101

B

BAKED APPLES, 273
BAKED BARLEY PARMESAN, 140
BAKED BROWN RICE, 128
BAKED CORN ON THE COB, 149
BAKED GROUPER, 233
BAKED TOFU, 193
BANCHA TEA, 271 (See also beverages)
    Bancha fruit pops, 275
    Bancha tea, 271, 281
BANDIT SOUP, 104
BARBECUED SHIITAKE MUSHROOMS, 238
BARLEY, 138 - 140
    Baked barley parmesan, 140
    Barley apple pudding, 272
    Barley breakfast cereal, 156
    Barley delight, 139
    Barley eggplant bake, 140
    Barley, fruit & nut pudding, 271
    Barley nut casserole, 139
    Barley tea, 280
    Barley tofu creme pie, 266
    Barley & vegetables, 139
    Berlinetta miso soup, 111
    Brown rice & barley, 121
    Brown rice, barley & companions, 123
    G.T. mushroom barley soup, 110
    Power shift burgers, 139
    Pressurized, 138
    Simmered, 138
    Whole grain soup mix, 108
    Yokohama barley soup, 110
BARLEY MALT SYRUP, 71
BATTER NUT BREAD, 259
BEAN(S), 179 - 186 (See also: aduki, black, garbonzo, green kidney, lentils, lima, navy, pinto, & split peas)
    Adukis, chestnuts & raisins, 183
    Aduki beans with squash, 182
    Adukis & companions, 183
    Arame & lentils, 226
    Bean burgers, 184
    Bean pate, 244
    Bronco beans, 186
    Fruit bean casserole, 183
    Garbonzo bean delight, 186
    Kidney beans & squash, 186
    Lentil bulghur burgers, 184
    Lentil & shrimp gumbo, 182
    Limas & cabbage, 184
    Mock meat loaf, 185
    Pinto beans, 182
    Refried beans, 185
    Sweet baked beans, 186

Triple carb special, 184
    Widetrack lentil, 183
BEAN SALADS,
    Bean salad, 217
    Garbonzo bean salad, 217
    Italian salad, 216
    Kidney bean salad, 169, 218
    Lentil salad, 219
    Three bean salad, 163
BEAN SOUPS, (See also soups)
    Blue flame 6, 112
    Bronco aduki bean soup, 105
    Col. Belanger's fast back soup, 105
    Continental barley soup, 105
    Daytona split pea, 107
    Electra 225, 111
    G.M. navy bean soup, 106
    High cam millet soup, 109
    Koni kidney bean, 107
    Lamborghini lentil soup, 104
    Lancia lima bean soup, 106
    Milan minnestroni soup, 106
    Mosport miso soup, 103
    Rice runner, 111
    Taladega vegetable soup, 111
    Veloce lima bean soup, 112
    Warmup quick miso soup, 104
    Whole grain soup mix, 108
BECHAMEL SAUCE WITH BROCCOLI, 240
BEETS, (See vegetables)
BENZ PATTIES, 167
BERLINETTE MISO SOUP, 111
BEVERAGE(S), 277 - 282
    Amazake, 280
    Almond milk, 278
    Bancha tea, 277, 281
    Barley tea, 280
    Brown rice tea, 280
    Fresh peach shake freeze, 281
    Grain coffee, 281
    Hot apple delight, 281
    Oat milk, 278
    Oatmeal water, 279
    Rice milk, 279
    Sandlewood grain coffee, 281
    Soya milk, 279
    Strawberry freeze, 281
    Water, 282
BLACK BEAN, (See also beans)
    Col. Belanger's fast back soup, 105
BLUEBERRY MUFFINS, 160
BLUE CHEESE ALA TOFU, 246
BLUE BLAME 6 SOUP, 112
B.M.W. SOUP, 114
BOILED APPLES, 276
BOILED BROCCOLI, CARROT SALAD, 216
BOILED SALAD(S), 215
    Boiled broccoli & carrot salad, 216
    The dynaflow, 215
    The power glide, 215
BOILED SQUASH WITH TAMARI, 208
BOK CHOY, (See vegetables)

BONITA FLAKES, 98
BREAD(S), 257 - 263
    All natural onion rye bread, 259
    Almond nut loaf, 260
    Autobahn bread, 258
    Batter nut bread, 259
    Corn bread, 262
    Croutons, 260
    David's pita bread, 262
    Sourdough starter, 258
    Sweet oatmeal bread, 260
    Walnut barley loaf, 258
    Whole wheat raisin bread, 261
    Whole wheat & rye bread, 260
    Zucchini bread, 261
BREAKFAST(S), 153 - 160
    Almond flavored granola, 160
    Apple nut pancakes, 158
    Barley breakfast cereal, 156
    Blueberry muffins, 160
    Buckwheat cream, 157
    Buckwheat pancakes, 159
    Cinnamon, oatmeal & fruit, 154
    Cold cereal, 160
    Cracked wheat & apples, 156
    Cream of oats, 154
    Cream of whole wheat, 155
    Daytona 500 start up cereal, 154
    Grain combo & fruit, 157
    Grand prix cereal, 155
    Heavy duty porridge, 157
    Hot cracked wheat, 156
    Hot cream of wheat & fruit, 156
    Millet & oats, 155
    Oatmeal pancakes, 158
    Omelette, 159
    Quick start breakfast cereal, 154
    Raisin nut muffins, 160
    Rice cream, 155
    Rice cream cereal, 154
    Rice flour waffles, 159
    Squash pancakes, 158
    Three gear cereal, 155
    Watkin's glen special, 154
    Whole grain combination, 157
    Whole wheat pancakes, 158
    Winter porridge, 156
BRIDGESTONE MISO SOUP, 102
BROCCOLI PARMESAN, 206
BROILED SOLE, 232
BRONCO ADUKI BEAN SOUP, 105
BRONCO BEANS, 186
BROWN RICE, 118 - 130
    Baked brown rice, 128
    Brown rice & almonds, 126
    Brown rice barley, 121
    Brown rice, barley & companions, 123
    Brown rice & cheese casserole, 128
    Brown rice & chicken casserole, 237
    Brown rice & corn, 122
    Brown rice delight, 125
    Brown rice, fruit & nut, 126
    Brown rice & garbonzo beans, 122
    Brown rice & kidney beans, 123
    Brown rice & millet, 122

    Brown rice & pinto beans,
    Brown rice & sesame seeds, 124
    Brown rice & shiitake mushrooms, 126
    Brown rice & squash or pumpkin, 125
    Brown rice stuffed peppers, 130
    Brown rice, tamari & bancha tea, 122
    Brown rice tea, 280
    Brown rice & wheatberries, 122
    Cabriolet rice milk, 121
    Casserole Monte Carlo, 127
    Curried eggs & brown rice, 124
    Fiesta rice, 126
    Fried rice, 124
    Grain, fruit & nut casserole, 128
    Grain omelette, 129
    Grain & sunflower bake, 127
    Pressurized, 121
    Pungent heart rice, 129
    Rice 356, 125
    Rice balls, 223
    Rice burgers, 128
    Rice tofu casserole, 127
    Rice milk, 279
    Rice stuffing, 129
    Rice & vegetable casserole, 127
    Simmered, 121
BROWN RICE CEREALS (See breakfasts)
BROWN RICE DESSERTS (See desserts)
BROWN RICE SALAD(S),
    Continental salad, 219
    Greek style salad, 219
    Rice curry salad, 219
BROWN RICE SOUPS,
    Carrera miso soup, 109
    Corvette chicken & rice soup, 116
    LeBarrone miso soup, 110
    Rice runner, 111
    Rocket rice, 109
    Straight 8/vegetable soup, 108
    Taladega vegetable soup, 111
    Whole grain soup mix, 108
    Voyager rice soup, 113
BROWN RICE VINEGAR DRESSING, 247
BUCKWHEAT, 136 - 137
    Benz patties, 137
    Buckwheat cream, 157
    Buckwheat groats, 136
    Buckwheat pancakes, 159
    Buckwheat & vegetables, 137
    Cabbage 6.9, 137
    Heavy duty porridge, 157
    Kasha, 136
BUGATTI BONANZA SPREAD, 164
BULGHUR, 141 - 143
    Bulghur & vegetables, 142
    d'Elegance salad, 142
    Lentil bulghur burgers, 167
    Simmered bulghur, 143
BURDOCK ROOT, (See vegetables)
BURGERS,
    Bean burgers, 184
    Benz patties, 167
    Lentil bulghur burgers, 167
    Millet burgers, 133
    Power shift burgers, 139

    Rice burgers, 128
    Tofu burgers, 190
BUTTERNUT COOKIES, 270
BUTTERNUT PEANUT SAUCE, 240

C

CABBAGE, (See vegetables)
CABBAGE SALAD, 216
CABBAGE SALAD DRESSING, 246
CABRIOLET RICE, 121
CAESER SALAD, 218
CAESER SALAD DRESSING, 247
CAKES, (See also desserts)
    Apple nut loaf, 265
    Carrot cake, 268
    Cleo's fiesta cake, 268
    Dream cake, 264
    Fruit cake, 267
    Oatmeal coffee cake, 266
    Strawberry tofu cheesecake, 267
CALORIES, 76
CANDIED KOMBU, 227
CANDIED SWEET POTATOES, 210
CARRERA MISO SOUP, 109
CARROTS, (See also vegetables)
CARROTS ALA SESAME, 204
CARROT & CABBAGE SAUTE, 205
CARROTS & GREEN BEANS WITH
    TOFU, 205
CARROT & TAMARI, 252
CARROTS & TURNIPS, 205
CARROT CAKE, 268
CARROT COOKIES, 272
CARROT TOPS (GREENS) SCALLIONS,
    253
CASHEW BUTTER SALAD DRESSING,
    246
CASSEROLE(S),
    Baked barley parmesan, 140
    Baked brown rice, 128
    Barley nut casserole, 139
    Brown rice & chicken casserole, 237
    Casserole Monte Carlo, 172
    Corn casserole, 150
    Grain, fruit & nut, 128
    Grain & sunflower bake, 127
    Kasha casserole, 136
    Millet almond casserole, 134
    Millet vegetable casserole, 134
    Rice & vegetable casserole, 127
    Rice & tofu casserole, 127
    Rye casserole, 145
CAULIFLOWER, (See vegetables)
CAULIFLOWER SAUCE, 241
CELERY, (See vegetables)
CELERY 928 SOUP, 114
CELERY SEED SALAD DRESSING, 248
CHAKRAS, 19
CHANGING LANES NATURALLY, 45 - 47
CHART OF RELATIVE BALANCE, 72
CHERYL'S PIE CRUST, 265
CHESTNUT FRUIT DELIGHT, 273

CHICKEN, 226 - 238
    Brown rice & chicken casserole, 237
    Chicken Van, 238
    Corvette chicken & rice soup, 116
    Chinese style chicken, 237
    Road runner, 237
    Stuffed baked chicken & vegetables, 236
CHICK-A-FU SANDWICH MIX, 163
CHILLED BROCCOLI WITH DRESSING, 208
CHINESE LOBSTER TAIL, 234
CHINESE MILLET, 132
CHINESE STYLE CHICKEN, 237
CHIPS & CRACKERS, 244
CHINESE STYLE CHICKEN, 237
CHIPS & CRACKERS, 244
CHOW MEIN, 178
CLAMS, (See also seafood)
    Marquis clam chowder, 115
    Seafood chowder, 232
    Spaghetti & clam sauce, 177
CINNAMON, OATMEAL & FRUIT, 154
CLEO'S FIESTA CAKE, 268
COFFEE CAKE TOPPING, 274
COLD CEREAL, 160
COL. BELANGER'S FAST BACK SOUP, 105
CONDIMENTS, 251 - 253
    Carrot & tamari, 232
    Carrot tops & scallions, 253
    Dulse & sesame, 252
    Ginger-radish, 253
    Nori, 253
    Nori condiment, 253
    Sesame salt, 251
    Shio kombu condiment, 253
    Tamari, 252
    Tekka, 252
    Umeboshi plum, 252
    Wakame fish powder, 252
    Wakame sesame, 252
CONTINENTAL BARLEY SOUP, 105
CONTINENTAL BROWN RICE SALAD, 219
CONTRACTION/EXPANSION, 35 - 40
COOKIES, (See also desserts)
    Butternut cookies, 270
    Carrot cookies, 272
    Oatmeal raisin cookies, 270
    Peanut sesame cookies, 269
    Rice crispie snacks, 274
    Spiced coffee & nut cookies, 269
CORN, 148 - 151
    Baked corn on the cob, 149
    Brown rice & corn, 151
    Brown rice delight, 125
    Corn on the cob, 151
    Corn bread, 262
    Corn casserole, 150
    Corn chowder, 150
    Cornmeal (Polenta), 150
    Cornmeal cereal, 149
    Corn relish, 285

Pressurized corn, 151
RPM corn, 150
Tabouly-Bo, 151
CORVETTE CHICKEN AND RICE SOUP, 116
COUPE SOUP, 108
COUSCOUS, 142
    Couscous & cousins, 143
    Pressurized, 142
    Steamed, 142
CRAB,
    B.M.W. soup, 114
    Crab marinade, 234
    Fish stuffing, 236
    Salad granada, 217
CRACKED WHEAT, 141- 143 (See also breakfast)
    Cracked wheat with apples, 156
    Hot cracked wheat, 156
CRACKERS & CHIPS, 244
CREAM OF OATS, 154
CREAM OF WHOLE WHEAT, 155
CREAMED CARROTS & ONIONS, 205
CRANBERRY SAUCE, 240
CROUTONS, 260
CUCUMBER-WAKAME SALAD, 217
CURRIED EGGS WITH BROWN RICE, 124
CUSTARDS, (See desserts)

D

DAIKON, (See vegetables & sea vegetables)
DAIKON AND CARROT, 213
DAIKON, GREENS & KOMBU, 213
DAVID'S PITA BREAD, 262
DAYTONA 500 START UP, 154
DAYTONA SPLIT PEA SOUP, 107
DEGENERATIVE DISEASES, 29
D'ELEGANCE SALAD, 142
DELOREAN MISO SOUP, 102
DENTAL DISEASE, 30
DESSERT(S), 255 - 276
    Cakes,
        Apple nut loaf, 265
        Carrot cake, 268
        Cleo's fiesta cake, 268
        Dream cake, 264
        Fruit cake, 267
        Oatmeal coffee cake, 266
        Strawberry tofu cheesecake, 267
    Cookies,
        Butternut cookies, 270
        Carrot cookies, 272
        Oatmeal raisin cookies, 270
        Peanut sesame butter cookies, 269
        Rice crispie snacks, 274
        Spiced coffee & nut cookies, 269

Fruit,
    Apple butter, 275
    Apple compote, 269
    Apple crisp, 267
    Apple dumpling, 270
    Applesauce, 240
    Apple stuffed acorn squash, 275
    Baked apples, 273
    Boiled apples, 276
    Chestnut fruit delight, 273
    Dried stewed fruit, 275
    Fresh fruit cup, 274
    Peach bavarian, 269
    Peach compote, 269
    Peach cobbler, 268
    Peach crisp, 267
    Peach topping, 268
    Red/white/blue, 273
    Tofu, nut & fruit, 273
Custards & puddings,
    Agar-agar & fruit, 274
    Amazake cherry pudding, 273
    Barley apple pudding, 272
    Barley, fruit & nut pudding, 271
    Fresh fruit gelatin, 274
    Rice pudding, 271
    Strawberry & agar-agar, 273
    Strawberry apple custard, 271
    Strawberry custard, 272
    Strawberry pudding freeze, 271
    Tofu rice pudding, 272
Granola,
    Almond flavored granola, 160
    Our granola, 270
Pie(s),
    Apple pie, 265
    Barley tofu pie, 266
    Blueberry pie, 267
    Glazed applesauce pie, 264
    Pecan pie, 264
    Pumpkin pie, 265
    Scotch peach pie, 266
    Squash pie, 266
Pie crust(s),
    Cheryl's butter crust, 265
    Never fail pie crust, 264
    Oatmeal pie crust, 263
Rolls,
    Sweet dough, 263
    Sweet rolls, 263
Toppings,
    Coffee cake topping, 274
    Desserts topping, 274
    Peach compote, 269
    Pancake or waffle topping, 275
DIABETES, 30
DIETARY GOALS FOR THE U.S., 29 - 31
DILL SPREAD, 243
DREAM CAKE, 264
DRIED DAIKON, (See vegetables & sea vegetables)
DRIED STEWED FRUIT, 275
DULSE, (See also sea vegetables)
DULSE - SESAME, 252

DULSE & VEGETABLES, 227
DUNLOP CHEESE SOUP, 115
DUNLOP RYE, 145
DYNAFLOW-BOILED SALAD, 215

E

EAST INDIAN DRESSING, 248
EAST INDIAN VEGETABLES, 210
EBONY MISO BAKE, 208
EGGS, 161
    Curried eggs & brown rice, 124
    Grain omelette, 129
    Nissan tamari soup, 103
EGGPLANT, (See vegetables)
ELECTRA 225 SOUP, 111
ENDIVE, (See vegetables)
ESCORT MISO SOUP, 103
EXPANSION/CONTRACTION, 35 - 40

F

FAT, 97 - 98
FERRARI & FRIENDS, 112
FETTUCCINE ALA VEGETABLES, 177
FIESTA RICE, 126
FILLET & VEGETABLES, 236
FILTER MISO SOUP, 101
FISH, (See also seafood),
    Baked grouper, 233
    Broiled fish, 232
    Broiled sole, 232
    Fillet & vegetables, 236
    Fish chowder, 232
    Fish kebab, 231
    Fish sauce, 235
    Fish stuffing, 236
    Fried trout, 232
    Sashimi, 235
    Steamed fish fillet with targa sauce, 235
    Sweet sour fish, 233
FLAKES OF VEGETABLES, 146
FIVE LITER MISO SOUP, 101
FRAZER MISO, 103
FRESH FRUIT CUP, 274
FRESH FRUIT GELATIN, 274
FRESH PEACH SHAKE FREEZE, 281
FRESH SHRIMP SPREAD, 243
FRIED RICE, 124
FRIED SPICY TOFU, 193
FRIED BEAN CASSEROLE, 183
FRUIT CAKE, 267
FRUIT FERRARI, 168
FOOD CONTROLS THOUGHT, 18
FUEL INJECTED POWER VEGETABLES, 206

G

GARBONZO BEANS, (aka chickpeas)
    Bean salad, 217
    Brown rice & garbonzo beans, 122
    Bugatti bonanza spread, 164
    Chick-a-fu-sandwich mix, 163
    Chips & crackers, 244
    Couscous & cousins, 143
    Garbonzo bean delight, 186
    Garbonzo salad, 217
    Hummus, 164
    Italian salad, 216
    Milan minestroni soup, 106
    Taladega vegetable soup, 111
    Three bean salad, 169, 217
GENMAI MISO, 96 (See also miso)
GERMAN DRESSING, 247
GINGER-RADISH, 253
GINGER-TAMARI DRESSING, 247
GLAZED APPLESAUCE PIE, 264
GLAZED CARROTS, 204
GLAZED ONIONS, 211
GRAINS, 117 - 151 (See also barley, brown
    rice, buckwheat, bulghur, corn,
    cracked wheat, millet, oatmeal, rye,
    wheatberries, whole wheat)
GRAIN COFFEE, 281
GRAIN COMBO & FRUIT CEREAL, 157
GRAIN, FRUIT & NUT CASSEROLE, 128
GRAIN & SUNFLOWER BAKE, 127
GRAIN OMELETTE, 129
GRAND PRIX, 155
GRANOLA,
    Almond flavored granola, 160
    Our granola, 270
GREEK SALAD, 169, 219
GREEN BEANS, (See also beans, soups &
    vegetables)
GREEN BEANS & ALMONDS, 213
G.M. NAVY BEAN SOUP, 106
G.T. MUSHROOM BARLEY SOUP, 110

H

HATCHO MISO, 96 (See also miso)
HEART DISEASE, 29 (See also degener-
    ative diseases)
HEAVY DUTY PORRIDGE, 157
HEEL & TOE MISO SOUP, 101
HI BOOST MILLET, 134
HI TURBO MILLET, 135
HIGH CAM MILLET SOUP, 109
HIGH RISK FOODS, 41 - 43
HIPPOCRATIC OATH, 17
HIZIKI, 221 (See also sea vegetables)
    Hiziki & beans, 223
    Hiziki & sesame seeds, 224
    Hiziki & vegetables, 224
HOMEMADE DIJON STYLE MUSTARD,
    286
HOMEMADE DILL PICKLES, 285
HOMEMADE PICKLES, 286
HOMEMADE SAUERKRAUT, 286
HOMEMADE WHOLE WHEAT NOODLES,
    176
HOT APPLE DELIGHT, 281
HOT CRACKED WHEAT, 156
HOT CREAM OF WHEAT & FRUIT,
    156
HOT OPEN FACED SANDWICH, 164
HOT SAUCE, 240
HOT TURNIPS, 212

HUMMUS, 164
HYPERTENSION, 30

I - J

IRISH MISO, 244
ITALIAN SALAD, 216
ITALIAN SALAD DRESSING, 246
ITALIAN STYLE GREEN BEANS, 208

K

KALE KLUTCH, 209
KALE SALAD, 216
KASHA, 136 (See buckwheat)
KASHA CASSEROLE, 136
KIDNEY BEANS, (See also beans)
    Brown rice & kidney beans, 123
    Kidney beans & squash, 186
    Kidney bean salad, 169, 218
    Koni kidney bean soup, 107
    Rye casserole, 145
KOMBU (See also sea vegetables)
    Beans, 179
    Candied kombu, 227
    Dried daikon & kombu, 224
    Land & sea, 226
    Soup stock, 98
    Vegetables wrapped in kombu, 225
KOME MISO, 96 (See also miso)
KUKICHA TEA, 271 (See also beverages)

L

LAMBORGHINI LENTIL SOUP, 104
LANCIA LIMA BEAN SOUP, 106
LAND AND SEA, 226
LUAU DRESSING, 246
LAYERED BROWN RICE & CHEESE
    CASSEROLE, 128
LAYERED VEGETABLES, 210
LEBARONE MISO SOUP, 110
LEEKS & MISO, 211
LEGUME & MISO, 245
LEMON SALAD DRESSING, 248
LENTILS (See also beans)
    Arame & lentils, 226
    Blue flame 6 soup, 112
    Electra 225 soup, 111
    Lamborghini lentil soup, 104
    Legume & miso spread, 245
    Lentil bulghur burgers, 167
    Lentil salad, 219
    Lentil shrimp gumbo, 182
    Millet burgers, 133
    Millet maserati, 132
    Millet, V-12, 134
    Rye casserole, 145
    Rye & lentil delight, 145
    Widetrack lentil, 183
    Whole grain soup mix, 108

LIMA BEANS, (See also beans)
    Lancia lima bean soup, 106
    Limas & cabbage, 184
    Veloce lima bean soup, 112
LINOLEIC ACID, 95 - 96
LOBSTER, (See also seafood)
    B.M.W. soup, 114
    Chinese lobster tail, 234
    Lobster in black bean sauce, 233
    Salad granada, 168, 217
LOW RISK FOODS, 41 - 43
LUNCHEON SUGGESTIONS, 163 - 173
    Bean burgers, 166
    Benz patties, 167
    Brown rice stuffed peppers, 172
    Bugatti bonanza spread, 164
    Casserole monte carlo, 172
    Chick-a-fu, 163
    Col. Belanger's fast back soup, 105
    Continental brown rice, 168
    Corvette chicken rice soup, 170
    d'Elegance salad, 170
    Electra 225, 171
    Fresh shrimp spread, 166
    Fruit ferrari, 168
    G.T. mushroom barley soup, 171
    Greek salad, 169
    High cam millet soup, 170
    Hot open faced sandwich, 164
    Hummus, 164
    Kidney bean salad, 169
    Lentil bulghur burgers, 167
    Macaroni salad, 168
    Marquis clam chowder, 171
    Milan minestroni soup, 172
    Millet burgers, 167
    Millet delight, 164
    Nissan dressing, 169
    Noodles & broth, 172
    Onion delight, 173
    Potato stew, 173
    Power shift burgers, 168
    Rice burgers, 167
    Rice curry salad, 169
    Rocket rice soup, 170
    Salad granada, 168
    Sauteed onions & tempeh, 166
    Savory tofu, 165
    Sesame almond sandwich mix, 163
    Supra vegetable soup, 171
    Tabouly-bo, 173
    Three bean salad, 169
    Tofu burgers, 165
    Tofu eggsalad, 164
    Tofu sandwich mix, 165
    Tofu sloppy joes, 165
    Tofu spread, 165

M

MACARONI, (whole wheat)
    Ferrari & friends, 112
    Kasha casserole, 136
    Macaroni salad, 168, 216
    Milan minestroni soup, 106

MANDARIN DRESSING, 247
MASHED SWEET POTATO & SQUASH, 207
MAYONNAISE, 246
MARQUIS CLAM CHOWDER, 115
MAZDA CARROT SOUP, 114
MENU PLANNING
    AUTOBAHN DIET, menu, 14 days, 89 - 92
    Holiday menus, 66
    14 day family menu, 59 - 65
MILAN MINESTRONI SOUP, 106
MILK, (See also beverages)
    Almond milk, 278
    Oat milk, 278
    Rice milk, 279
    Soya milk, 279
MILLET, 131 - 135
    Brown rice & millet, 122
    Chinese millet, 132
    Hi-boost millet, 134
    High cam millet, 109
    Hi turbo millet, 135
    Millet almond casserole, 134
    Millet burgers, 133
    Millet & cauliflower, 132
    Millet delight, 131
    Millet hushpuppies, 133
    Millet maserati, 132
    Millet & oats, 155
    Millet on the green, 133
    Millet-shrimp creole, 133
    Millet stew, 132
    Millet V-12, 134
    Millet vegetable casserole, 134
    Mustang millet soup, 109
    Pressurized, 131
    Quick start breakfast cereal, 154
    Simmered, 131
    Straight 8 vegetable soup, 108
    Tuned oatmeal, 146
MINERALS, 23 - 26
    Food list, 73
MISO, 95 - 96
    Dressings, (See dressings)
    Genmai, 96
    Hatcho, 96
    Kome, 96
    Mugi, 96
    Sauces, (See sauces)
    Soups, 99
MISO SPREAD, 243
MOCHI, 130
MOCK MEAT LOAF, 185
MOCK TOMATO SAUCE, 185
MOON ROOF BEETS, 212
MOSPORT MISO SOUP, 103
MOUNTAIN ARK TRADING CO., 50 - 51
MUFFINS,
    Blueberry muffins, 160, 261
    Raisin nut, 160, 262
MUSHROOMS, (See vegetables)
MUSHROOM SAUCE, 241
MUSTANG MILLET SOUP, 109
MUSTARD,
    Homemade dijon mustard, 286

N

911 MISO SOUP, 103
NAVY BEANS, (See also beans)
    G.M. navy bean soup, 106
    Blue flame 6 soup, 112
NEVER FAIL PIE CRUST, 264
NISSAN DRESSING, 248
NISSAN TAMARI SOUP, 103
NOODLES, 175 - 178
    Chow mein, 178
    Fettuccine ala vegetables, 177
    Homemade whole wheat noodles, 176
    Noodles & broth, 177
    Noodles & leeks, 177
    Noodles & mushrooms, 178
    Noodles & shrimp bake, 178
    Ramen noodles & vegetables, 178
    Spaghetti & clam sauce, 177
NORI, 221 (See also sea vegetables)
    Nori condiment, 225
    Nori, fried tofu & sesame seeds, 226
    Rice balls, 223
NUTS,
    Almonds,
        Almond flavored granola, 160
        Almond milk, 278
        Almond vegetable saute, 209
        Apple nut pancakes, 158
        Barley nut casserole, 139
        Breads, (See breads)
        Brown rice & almonds, 126
        Cereals, (See breakfasts)
        Desserts, (See desserts)
        Grain fruit & nut casserole, 128
        Hi-turbo millet, 135
        Millet almond casserole, 134
        Green beans & almonds, 213
        Our granola, 270
        Tofu, nut & fruit, 273
    Cashews,
        Chinese millet, 132
        Cold cereal, 160
    Chestnuts,
        Adukis, chestnuts & raisins, 183
    Walnuts,
        Cereal, (See breakfasts)
        Desserts, (See desserts)
        Grain, fruit & nut casserole, 157
        Raisin nut muffins, 160
    Sauces, (See sauces)
    Spreads, (See spreads)
NUT BUTTER, (See sauces, spreads & dressings)

O

OATS, 146 - 147
    Cereal, 153 (See breakfasts)
    Cinnamon, oatmeal & fruit, 154
    Cold cereal, 160
    Cream of oats, 154
    Flakes of vegetables, 146
    Millet & oats, 155

OATS (continued)
Oatmeal, 146
Oatmeal coffee cake, 266
Oat milk, 278
Oatmeal pancakes, 158
Oatmeal raisin nut cookies, 270
Oatmeal water, 279
Steel cut oats, 147
Tuned oatmeal, 146
Watkin's glen special, 154
Desserts, (See desserts)
OBESITY, 30, 75
ONIONS, (See vegetables)
ONION DELIGHT, 206
ONION MUSHROOM SAUCE, 240
ONO CHEESE, 192
OPEN FACED BLUEBERRY PIE, 267
ORANGE-GREEN & WHITE, 211
ORANGE PLEDGE, 242
ORANGE VINEGRETTE, 248
ORIENTAL VEGETABLES, 210
OUR GRANOLA, 270
OVEREATING, 75 - 92
OYSTERS, (See also seafood)
Oyster bugaeti, 114
Oyster stuffing, 235

P

PANATERA TOFU, 192
PANCAKES,
Apple nut pancakes, 158
Buckwheat pancakes, 159
Oatmeal pancakes, 158
Squash pancakes, 158
Whole wheat pancakes, 157
PANCAKE OR WAFFLE TOPPING, 159
PASSPORT TO HEALTH, 68
PARSNIPS & BARLEY MALT, 213
PARSNIPS WITH BLACK EYED PEAS, 209
PEACH BAVARIAN, 269
PEACH OR APPLE COMPOTE, 269
PEACH CATSUP, 285
PEACH COBBLER, 268
PEANUT-SESAME BUTTER COOKIES, 269
PECAN PIE, 264
PEPPERS, (See vegetables)
PICKLED BROCCOLI & CAULIFLOWER, 284
PICKLED DAIKON & CELERY, 285
PICKLES, 283 - 286
PICKLING, 283 - 286
Corn relish, 285
Homemade dijon mustard, 286
Homemade dill pickles, 285
Homemade sauerkraut, 286
Peach catsup, 285
Pickled broccoli & cauliflower, 284
Pickled daikon & celery, 285
Quick ume sauerkraut, 284
PIES,
Apple, 265
Barley tofu creme, 266
Glazed applesauce, 264

Pecan, 264
Pumpkin, 265
Scotch peach, 266
Squash, 266
PIE CRUSTS,
Cheryl's butter crust, 265
Never fail crust, 264
Oatmeal crust, 263
PINTO BEANS, 182 (See also beans)
Bean burgers, 184
Bronco beans, 186
Brown rice & pinto beans, 127
Cleo's fiesta cake, 268
Hiziki & beans, 223
Mock meat loaf, 185
Pinto beans, 182
Refried beans, 185
Sesame almond sandwich mix, 163, 249
POTATO(ES), (See vegetables)
POTATO STEW, 206
POWER GLIDE-BOILED SALAD, 215
POWER SHIFT BURGERS, 139
PRESSURE COOKING,
Grains, 121, 131, 138, 151
Vegetables, 202
PRESSURE COOKED SQUASH OR PUMPKIN, 207
PRESSURIZED BARLEY, 138
PRESSURIZED BROWN RICE, 138
PRESSURIZED CORN, 151
PRESSURIZED MILLET, 131
PRETZELS, whole wheat, 261
PRUNES,
Dried stewed fruit, 275
Hi-turbo millet, 135
PUDDINGS, (See desserts)
PUMPKIN OR ACORN SQUASH WITH MISO, 212
PUMPKIN PIE, 265
PUNGENT HEARTY RICE, 129

Q

QUICK START BREAKFAST CEREAL, 154
QUICK UME SAUERKRAUT, 284

R

RALLY GREEN MISO SOUP, 103
RAINBOW SAUCE, 241
RAISIN NUT MUFFINS, 160
RAMEN NOODLES & VEGETABLES, 178
RECARO MUSHROOM SOUP, 113
RED/WHITE/BLUE, 273
REFINED FOOD SUBSTITUTION LIST, 71
REFRIED BEANS, 185
RICE, (See brown rice)
RICE BALLS, 223
RICE BURGERS, 128
RICE CREAM CEREAL, 154
RICE CREAM, 155
RICE CRISPIE SNACKS, 274

RICE CURRY SALAD, 219
RICE FLOUR WAFFLES, 159
RICE MILK, 279
RICE PUDDING, 271
RICE RUNNER SOUP, 111
RICE STUFFING, 129
RICE TOFU CASSEROLE, 127
RICE AND VEGETABLE CASSEROLE, 127
ROAD MAP(S), 53 - 74
Stage 1, The starter wheel, 55
Stage 2, The wheel, 56
Stage 3, Balance wheel, 51 - 57
Stage 4, The turbine wheel, 58
ROAD RUNNER, 237
ROCKET RICE SOUP, 109
ROLLS ROYCE PEPPERS, 211
RYE, 144 - 145 (See also grains)
All natural onion rye bread, 259
Dunlop rye, 145
Rye casserole, 145
Rye & lentil delight, 145
Rye (simmered), 145

S

SALAD(S), 215 - 219
Autobahn salad, 218
Bean salad, 217
Boiled broccoli & carrot salad, 216
Cabbage salad, 216
Ceasar salad, 218
Continental Brown rice, 219
Cucumber wakame salad, 217
d'Elegance, 218
Fruit ferrari, 218
Garbonzo salad, 217
Greek salad, 219
Italian salad, 216
Kale salad, 216
Kidney bean salad, 169, 218
Lentil salad, 219
Macaroni salad, 168, 216
Rice curry salad, 219
Salad granada, 217
The dynaflow, boiled salad, 215
The power glide, boiled salad, 215
Three bean salad, 217
Windjammer, 216
SALAD DRESSING(S), 217, 245 - 249
Almond butter, 245
Autobahn, 245
Blue cheese ala tofu, 246
Brown rice dressing, 247
Cabbage salad dressing, 246
Cashew dressing, 246
Ceasar dressing, 247
Celery seed dressing, 248
East Indian dressing, 248
German dressing, 247
Ginger-tamari dressing, 247
Italian dressing, 246
Luau dressing, 246
Lemon dressing, 248
Mandarain dressing, 247
Mayonnaise, 246

SALAD DRESSING(S)(continued)
    Miso lemon dressing, 245
    Nissan dressing, 248
    Orange vinergette, 248
    Sweet sour pumpkin seed, 245
    Summertime dressing, 246
    Tahini rice vinegar dressing, 247
    Tahini-tofu dressing, 247
    Tamari lemon, 245
    Tofu salad dressing, 246
    Umeboshi dressing, 245
SALT, 43 - 44
SANDALWOOD GRAIN COFFEE, 281
SANDWICH MIXES, 239 - 249
    (See also burgers)
    Bugatti bonanza spread, 164, 249
    Chick-a-fu, 163, 249
    Hot open faced, 164
    Hummus, 164, 249
    Savory tofu, 165
    Sesame almond, 249
    Tofu eggsalad, 192
    Tofu sandwich mix, 165
    Tofu sloppy joes, 190
SASHIMI, 235
SAUCE(S), 239 - 249
    Applesauce, 240
    A sauce for all seasons, 241
    Bechamel sauce with broccoli, 240
    Butternut peanut sauce, 240
    Cauliflower sauce, 241
    Cranberry sauce, 240
    Fish sauce, 235, 242
    Hot sauce, 240
    Mock tomato sauce, 185, 242
    Mushroom sauce, 241
    Onion-mushroom sauce, 240
    Orange pledge, 242
    Rainbow sauce, 241
    Sweet sauce, 239
    Sweet & sour sauce, 239
    Targa sauce, 242
SAUTEED MUSTARD GREENS, DAIKON
    & CARROTS, 214
SAUTEED ONIONS, CARROTS &
    CABBAGE, 205
SAUTEED ONIONS & TEMPEH, 196
SAUTEED SPOUTS, 188
SAVORY TOFU, 165
SCOTCH PEACH PIE, 266
SEAFOOD, 229 - 238 (See also clams,
    crab, fish, oyster, lobster & shrimp)
    B.M.W. soup, 114
    Baked grouper, 233
    Broiled fish, 236
    Broiled sole, 232
    Chinese lobster tail, 234
    Crab marinade, 234
    Fish chowder, 232
    Fish kebab, 231
    Fish sauces, 235
    Fish stuffing, 236
    Fillet & vegetables, 236
    Fresh shrimp spread, 243
    Fried trout, 232

Lentil shrimp gumbo, 182
Lobster in black bean sauce, 233
Marquis clam chowder, 115
Millet shrimp creole, 133
Noodle & shrimp bake, 178
Oyster bugatti, 114
Oyster stuffing, 235
Rice 356, 125
Salad granada, 217
Sashimi, 235
Seafood chowder, 231
Shrimp broccoli casserole, 234
Shrimp broccoli delight, 234
Shrimp cantonese, 233
Spaghetti & clam sauce, 177
Steamed fish, 235
Stuffed tofu ala crab, 193
Sweet & sour fish, 233
Tofu shrimp delight, 232
SEA VEGETABLES, 221 - 227 (See also
    arame, dulse, hiziki, kombu, nori &
    wakame)
    Arame, daikon, curry, 223
    Arame & dried daikon, 224
    Arame, dried daikon, carrots & onions,
    224
    Arame & fried tofu, 225
    Arame & herbs, 226
    Arame & lentils, 226
    Arame & lotus root, 223
    Candied kombu, 227
    Daikon greens & kombu, 213
    Dried daikon & kombu, 224
    Dulse & vegetables, 227
    Hiziki & beans, 223
    Hiziki & sesame seeds, 224
    Hiziki & vegetables, 224
    Land & sea, 226
    Nori, fried tofu & sesame seeds, 226
    Rice balls, 223
    Trible crab special, 184
    Vegetables wrapped in kombu, 225
    Wakame onion, 225
    Wakame, onions, & carrots, 225
    Windjammer salad, 216
SESAME SALT, 251
SESAME ALMOND SANDWICH MIX,
    163, 249
SEVEN MILE POSTS, 49 - 50
SHIITAKE MUSHROOMS,
    BBQ shiitake mushrooms, 238
    Brown rice & shiitake mushrooms, 126
    Continental barley soup, 105
    Fuel injected power vegetables, 206
    Five liter soup, 101
    Heel & toe miso soup, 101
    Noodles & mushrooms, 178
    Orange pledge, 242
    Shiitake mushrooms, onions, & snow peas,
    211
    Wendy's penicillin soup, 104
SHIO KOMBU CONDIMENT, 253
SHOYU, 95
SHRIMP, (See also seafood)
    Fresh shrimp spread, 243

Lentil shrimp gumbo, 182
Millet & shrimp creole, 133
Noodle & shrimp bake, 178
Rice 356, 125
Salad granada, 217
Shrimp broccoli delight, 234
Shrimp broccoli casserole, 234
Shrimp cantonese, 233
Tofu shrimp delight, 232
SIMPLE SUMMER SQUASH, 208
SOUP(S), 99 - 116
    With beans,
        Blue flame 6, 112
        Bronco aduki, 105
        Col. Belanger's fast back, 105
        Continental barley, 105
        Daytona split pea, 107
        G.M. navy bean, 106
        High cam millet, 109
        Koni kidney bean, 107
        Lamborghini lentil 104
        Lancia lima, 106
        Milan minestroni, 106
        Mosport miso, 103
        Rice runner, 111
        Taladega, 111
        Veloce lima, 112
        Warm up quick miso, 104
    Creamed,
        Celery 928, 114
        Dunlop cheese, 115
        Mazda carrot, 114
        Recaro mushroom, 113
    With grains,
        Berlinetta miso, 111
        Blue flame 6, 112
        Carrera miso, 109
        Continental barley, 105
        Corvette chicken & rice, 116
        Coupe soup, 108
        Electra 225, 111
        Ferrari & friends, 112
        G.T. mushroom barley, 110
        High cam millet, 109
        Le Barone miso, 110
        Mustang millet, 109
        Rice runner, 111
        Rocket rice, 109
        Straight 8/vegetable, 108
        Supra vegetables, 110
        Taladega vegetable, 111
        Veloce lima, 112
        Voyager rice, 113
        Whole grain soup mix, 108
        Yokohama barley, 110
    With seafood,
        B.M.W. soup, 114
        Fish chowder, 232
        Marquis clam chowder, 115
        Oyster bugatti, 114
        Seafood chowder, 232

SOUP(S)(continued)
    With vegetables & miso,
        911 miso, 103
           Autobahn miso special, 101
           Bandit miso, 104
           Bridgestone miso, 102
           DeLorean miso, 102
           Escort miso, 103
           Filter miso, 101
           Five liter miso, 101
           Frazier miso, 103
           Heel & toe miso, 101
           Mosport miso, 103
           Nissan tamari, 103
           Rally green miso, 103
           Targa miso, 102
           Toll booth miso, 102
           Turnpike miso, 100
           Unleaded miso, 101
           Warm up miso, 104
           Wendy's penicillin, 104
SOUP STOCK, 98
SOURDOUGH STARTER, 258
SOY SAUCE, 95
SOYA MILK, 279
SOYBEANS,
    Miso, 95 - 96
    Shoyu, 95
    Tamari, 95
    Tempeh, 196
    Tofu, 189 - 196
SPAGHETTI & CLAM SAUCE, 177
SPICED COFFEE & NUT COOKIES, 269
SPICY ONIONS & MISO, 243
SPICED TOFU, 191
SPLIT PEA,
    Daytona split pea soup, 107
SPREADS, 242 - 245
    Almond miso spread, 245
    Bean pate, 244
    Chips & crackers, 244
    Crackers & chips, 244
    Dill spread, 243
    Fresh shrimp spread, 243
    Irish miso, 244
    Legume & miso spread, 245
    Miso, almond, onion spread, 244
    Miso sesame spread, 243
    Miso spread, 243
    Savory tofu, 243
    Spicy onion miso, 243
    Tofu spread, 243
SPROUTS & SPROUTING, 187 - 188
    Sauteed sprouts, 188
    Sprouts & cabbage, 188
SQUASH, (See vegetables)
SQUASH & CHEESE BAKE, 207
SQUASH ITALIANO, 209
SQUASH PANCAKES, 158
SQUASH PIE, 266
STARTER LIST OF NATURAL FOODS,67
STEAMED CARROTS, CAULIFLOWER &
    BROCCOLI, 210
STEAMED FISH FILLET, 235
STEAMED GREENS, 212

STEAMED SQUASH, 208
STEEL CUT OATS, 147
STIR FRY BROCCOLI, 207
STRAIGHT 8 VEGETABLE SOUP, 108
STRAWBERRIES & AGAR-AGAR, 273
STRAWBERRY APPLE CUSTARD, 271
STRAWBERRY CUSTARD, 272
STRAWBERRY PUDDING FREEZE, 271
STRAWBERRY TOFU CHEESECAKE, 267
STROGANOFF TOFU, 191
STUFFED BAKED CHICKEN, 236
STUFFED TOFU ALA CRAB OR FISH,
    193
STUFFING,
    Fish stuffing, 236
    Rice stuffing, 129
SUGAR(S),
    Barley malt syrup, 71, 87, 255
    Di- saccharide, 29, 49, 54, 57, 83, 255
    Poly-saccharide, 29,49, 54-57, 83,
        255
    Rice syrup, 71, 87, 255
SUMMERTIME SALAD DRESSING, 246
SUPRA VEGETABLE SOUP, 110
SWEET & SOUP CARROTS, 204
SWEET & SOUR SAUCE, 239
SWEET & SOUR VEGIES, 204
SWEET BROWN RICE,
    Mochi, 130
    Sweet brown rice & aduki beans, 123
    Three gear cereal, 155
SWEET BAKED BEANS, 186
SWEET DOUGH, 263
SWEET OATMEAL BREAD, 260
SWEET ROLLS, 263
SWEET SAUCE, 239
SWEET-SOUR FISH, 233
SWEET-SOUR PUMPKIN DRESSING, 245

T

TABOULY-BO, 173
TALADEGA VEGETABLE SOUP, 111
TAHINI RICE VINEGAR DRESSING, 247
TAMARI, 95 - 96
    (See also miso, condiments, soups,
    vegetables)
TAMARI LEMON DRESSING, 245
TARGA MISO SOUP, 102
TARGA SAUCE, 242
TEKKA, 252
TEMPEH, 196
    Sauteed tempeh & onions, 196
    Tempeh alfetta, 196
    Tempeh scramble, 196
    Tempeh stew, 196
TEMPURA, 230
    Batter, 231
    Tempura vegetables, 231
    Tofu tempura, 191
THREE BEAN SALAD, 217
THREE GEAR CEREAL, 155
TOFU, 189 - 196
    911 miso soup, 103
    Arame & fried tofu, 225

B.M.W. soup, 114
Baked tofu, 193
Carrots & green beans with tofu, 205
Chow mein, 178
Fried spicy, 193
Nori, fried tofu & sesame seeds,226
Onio cheese, 192
Pantera tofu, 192
R.P.M. corn, 150
Rice tofu casserole, 127
Rice & vegetable casserole, 127
Savory tofu, 165
Spiced tofu, 191
Stroganoff tofu, 191
Stuffed tofu, ala crab or fish, 193
Tofu & sauce, 191
Tofu burgers, 190
Tofu eggsalad, 192
Tofu elan, 194
Tofu, nuts & fruit, 273
Tofu rice pudding, 272
Tofu salad dressing, 194
Tofu sandwich mix, 165
Tofu shrimp delight, 192
Tofu sloppy joes, 190
Tofu spread, 165
Tofu strawberry cheesecake, 267
Tofu tempura, 191
Tofu vegetable cheese bake, 212
Turnpike miso soup, 100
TOLL BOOTH MISO SOUP, 102
TRIPLE CRAB SPECIAL, 184
TUNED OATMEAL, 146
TURNPIKE MISO SOUP, 100

U

UMEBOSHI,
    Umeboshi paste, 252
    Umeboshi plums, 287
    Umeboshi salad dressing, 245
UNLEADED MISO SOUP, 101
UTENSILS, 69 - 70

V

VEGETABLES, 197 - 214
    Cooking, 200 - 202
        Baking, 201
        Boiling, 200
        Cutting, 199 - 200
        Pressure cooking, 202
        Sauteeing, 200
        Steaming, 201
        Tempura, 201
    Beets,
        Moonroof beets, 212
        Mock tomato sauce, 185
    BOK CHOY,
        Oriental vegetables, 210
        Stir fried Chinese style, 211
    Broccoli,
        Bechamel sauce, 240
        Boiled broccoli & carrot salad,
        216

VEGETABLES/Broccoli (continued)
    Broccoli parmesan, 206
    Chilled broccoli with dressing, 208
    East Indian vegetables, 210
    Pickles, 283
    Shrimp & broccoli casserole, 234
    Shrimp & broccoli delight, 234
    Steamed carrot, cauliflower & broccoli, 210
    Stir fried broccoli, 207
Burdock root,
    Fuel injected power vegetables, 206
Cabbage,
    Berlinetta miso soup, 111
    Cabbage dressing, 246
    Cabbage salad, 216
    Carrot & cabbage saute, 205
    Kale salad, 216
    Limas & cabbage, 184
    Mosport miso soup, 103
    Rolls royce peppers, 211
    Sauteed onions, carrots & cabbage, 205
    Sweet & sour vegies, 204
    Targa miso soup, 102
    Turnpike miso soup, 100
    Waterless cooked layered vegetables, 213
Carrots,
    Almond vegetable saute, 209
    Boiled broccoli & carrot salad, 216
    Boiled salad, 215
    Carrot ala sesame, 204
    Carrot & cabbage saute, 205
    Carrots & green beans with tofu, 205
    Carrots & tamari, 252
    Carrots & turnips, 205
    Creamed carrots & onions, 205
    Daikon & carrots, 213
    Fuel injected power vegetables, 206
    Glazed carrots, 204
    Mazda carrot soup, 114
    Layered vegetables, 210
    Orange, green & white, 211
    Sauteed onions, carrots & cabbage, 205
    Steamed carrots, cauliflower & broccoli, 210
    Sweet & sour carrots, 204
    Vegetable stew, 207
    Waterless cooked layered vegetables, 213
Cauliflower, (See also casseroles)
    Almond vegetables saute, 209
    Cauliflower sauce, 241
    East Indian vegetables, 210
    Millet & cauliflower, 132
    Steamed carrots, cauliflower & broccoli, 210
    Vegetable stew, 207

Celery,
    928 soup, 114
Daikon radish,
    Arame & dried daikon, 224
    Arame dried daikon, carrots & onions, 224
    Boiled salad, 215
    Daikon & carrots, 213
    Daikon, greens & kombu, 213
    Filter miso soup, 101
    Fuel injected power vegetables, 206
    Heel & toe miso soup, 101
    Sauteed mustard greens & daikon, 214
    Waterless cooked layered vegetables, 213
    Wendy's penicillin soup, 104
Eggplant,
    Ebony miso, 208
    Barley eggplant bake, 140
Geeen beans, (See also beans)
    Almond vegetable saute, 209
    Bean salad, 217
    Carrots, green beans with tofu, 205
    Green bean & almonds, 213
    Italian style green beans, 208
    High cam millet soup, 109
    Layered vegetables, 210
    Mosport miso soup, 103
    Three bean salad, 217
    Vegetable stew, 207
    Warm up quick miso soup, 104
Greens,
    Boiled salad, 215
    Daikon, greens & kombu, 213
    Endive, 214
    Kale klutch, 209
    Kale salad, 216
    Sauteed mustard greens, daikon & carrots, 214
    Steamed greens, 212
Leeks,
    Leeks & miso, 211
    Noodles & leeks, 177
Mushrooms, 202
    Autobahn miso soup, 101
    Brown rice delight, 125
    Buckwheat & vegetables, 137
    Chinese millet, 132
    Fettuccine ala vegetables, 177
    G.T. mushroom barley soup, 110
    Grain omelette, 129
    Layered brown rice, cheese casserole, 128
    Millet vegetable casserole, 134
    Mushroom sauce, 241
    Onion mushroom sauce, 240
    Recaro mushroom soup, 113
    Rice & vegetable casserole, 127
    Shiitake mushroom, (See shiitake)
    Tofu stroganoff, 191

Onions,
    All natural onion rye bread, 259
    Bandit miso soup, 104
    Creamed carrots & onions, 205
    East Indian vegetables, 210
    Glazed onions, 211
    Layered vegetables, 210
    Nissan tamari soup, 103
    Onion delight, 206
    Onion mushroom sauce, 240
    Orange, green & white, 211
    Oriental vegetables, 210
    Potato stew, 206
    Sauted onions, carrots & cabbage, 205
    Spicy onion miso, 243
    Vegetable stew, 207
    Waterless cooked layered vegetables, 213
Parsnips,
    Parsnips & barley malt, 213
    Parsnips & black eyed peas, 209
    Sweet & sour vegies, 210
Peppers,
    Brown rice stuffed peppers, 130
    Rolls royce peppers, 211
    Sweet & sour carrots, 204
Potatoes,
    Dunlop cheese soup, 115
    Land & sea, 226
    Layered vegetables, 210
    Millet stew, 132
    Potato stew, 206
    Three bean salad, 217
Pumpkin,
    Pressured cooked pumpkin, 207
    Pumpkin or acorn squash with miso, 212
    Pumpkin pie, 265
Squash,
    Acorn squash with miso, 212
    Aduki beans with squash, 182
    Apple stuffed acorn squash, 275
    Boiled squash & tamari, 208
    Brown rice & squash, 125
    Butternut peanut sauce, 240
    Fuel injected power vegetables, 206
    Kidney beans & squash, 186
    Layered vegetables, 210
    Mashed sweet potatoes & squash, 207
    Mock tomato sauce, 185
    Oriental vegetables, 210
    Pressured cooked squash, 207
    Simple summer squash, 208
    Squash & cheese bake, 207
    Squash Italiano, 209
    Squash pancakes, 158
    Squash pie, 266
    Steamed squash, 208
    Tofu vegetable cheese bake, 212
    Triple carb special, 184
    Vegetable stew, 207
    Waterless cooked layered vegetables, 213

301

VEGETABLES (continued)
    Snow peas,
        Shiitake mushrooms, onions &
            snow peas, 211
    Sweet Potatoes,
        Candied sweet potatoes, 210
        Mashed sweet potatoes & squash,
            207
        Victory special, 209
    Tomato Sauce,
        Mock, 185
    Turnips,
        Hot turnips, 212
        Carrots & turnips, 205
    Zucchini,
        Layered vegetables, 210
        Milan minestroni soup, 106
        Zucchini bread, 261
VEGETABLE STEW, 207
VEGETABLES WRAPPED IN KOMBU, 225
VELOCE LIMA BEAN SOUP, 112
VICTORY SPECIAL, 209
VITAMINS, 23 - 27
VOYAGER RICE SOUP, 123

W

WAFFLES,
    Rice flour waffles, 159
    Topping, 275
WAKAME, 221 (See also sea vegetables)
    Cucumber wakame salad, 217
    Soup, 100 (see also soups)
    Soup stock, 99
    Wakame fish powder, 252
    Wakame-onion, 225
    Wakame, onion & carrots, 225
    Wakame sesame, 252
WALNUT BARLEY LOAF, 258
WARM UP QUICK MISO SOUP, 104
WATKIN'S GLEN SPECIAL, 154
WELCOME CENTER, 11
WENDY'S PENICILLIN SOUP, 104
WHEATBERRIES, 141
    Brown rice & wheatberries, 122
    Rice curry salad, 219
    Wheatberries & beans, 143
    Whole wheatberries, 142
WHOLE CRANBERRY SAUCE, 240
WHOLE GRAIN COMBINATIONS, 157
WHOLE GRAIN SOUP MIX, 108
WHOLE WHEAT, 141 - 143 (See also bread
    & desserts)
    Cracked whole wheat & apples, 156
    Cream of whole wheat, 155
    Homemade whole wheat noodles, 176
    Hot cracked wheat, 156
    Macaroni salad, 216
    Milan minestroni soup, 106
    Noodles, 175 - 178
    Veloce lima bean soup, 112
    Whole wheat pancakes, 158
    Whole wheat pretzels, 261
    Whole wheat & rye, 260
    Whole wheat raisin bread, 261

WIDETRACK LENTIL, 183
WINDJAMMER SALAD, 216
WINTER PORRIDGE, 156

XYZ

YANG, 36
YIN, 36
YOKOHAMA BARLEY SOUP, 110
ZUCCHINI, (See vegetables)
ZUCCHINI BREAD, 261